Silver Burdett Ginn Science

DiscoveryWorks

Welcome

to Silver Burdett Ginn **Science DiscoveryWorks** – a science program that engages students in active investigations of scientific concepts. **Science DiscoveryWorks** reflects our belief that the best science education for students is one that gradually introduces them to the knowledge, methods, skills, and attitudes of scientists, while simultaneously recognizing and respecting the educational and developmental needs of all students.

Silver Burdett Ginn

Parsippany, NJ   Needham, MA

Atlanta, GA   Irving, TX   Deerfield, IL   Upland, CA

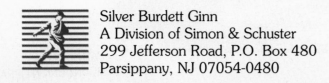

Silver Burdett Ginn
A Division of Simon & Schuster
299 Jefferson Road, P.O. Box 480
Parsippany, NJ 07054-0480

Acknowledgements appear on pages A66, B114, C98, D82, E98, F130, and G66, which constitute extensions of this copyright page.

Grade 6 Unified Teaching Guide   ISBN 0-382-41677-5   ISBN 0-382-31985-0

Modular Teaching Guides
Unit A: Cells and Microbes   ISBN 0-382-41678-3   ISBN 0-382-33483-3
Unit B: The Changing Earth   ISBN 0-382-41679-1   ISBN 0-382-33484-1
Unit C: The Nature of Matter   ISBN 0-382-41680-5   ISBN 0-382-33486-8
Unit D: Continuity of Life   ISBN 0-382-41681-3   ISBN 0-382-33487-6
Unit E: Oceanography   ISBN 0-382-41682-1   ISBN 0-382-33488-4
Unit F: Forces and Motion   ISBN 0-382-41683-X   ISBN 0-382-33489-2
Unit G: Growing Up Healthy   ISBN 0-382-41684-8   ISBN 0-382-33490-6

6 7 8 9 10 11 12 W 05 04 03 02 01 00 99 98

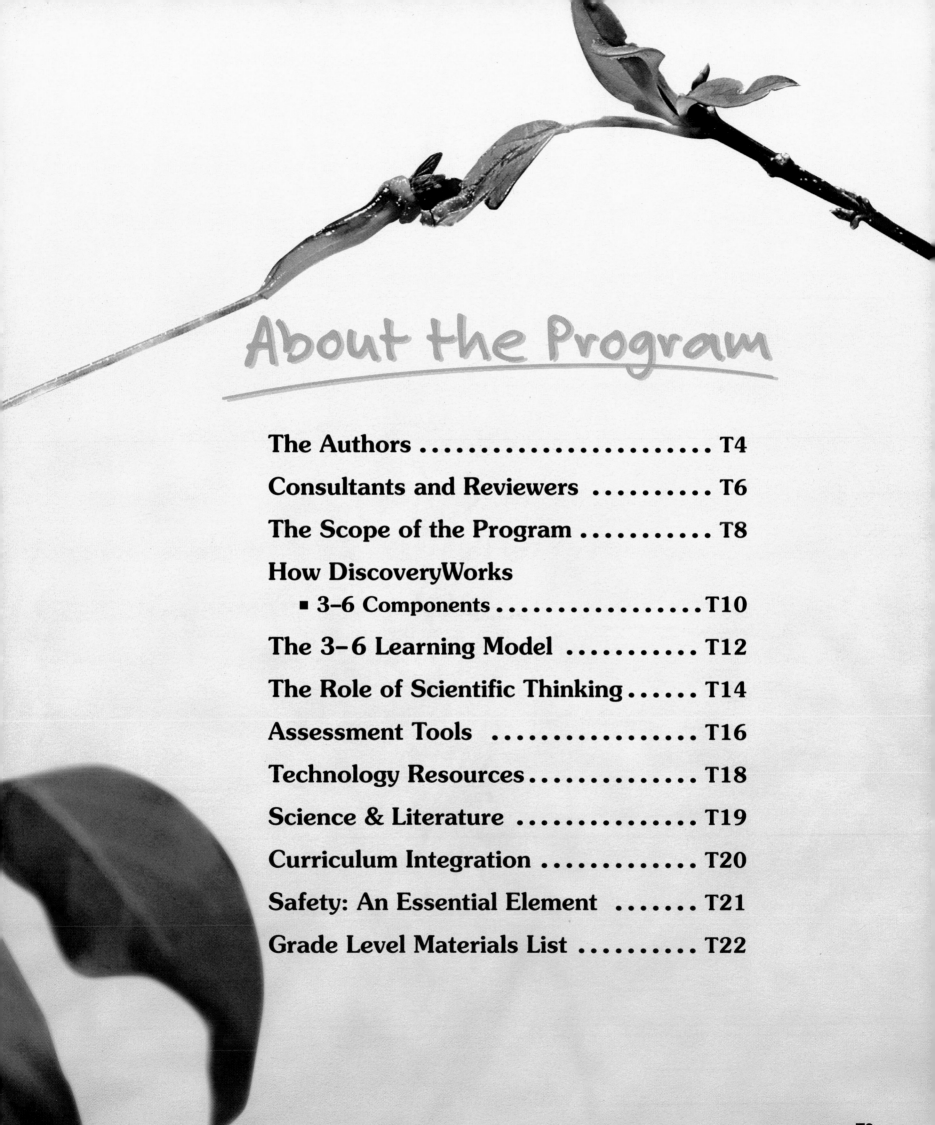

About the Program

THE AUTHORS

Coming from Diverse Backgrounds, Meeting on Common Ground

Mr. William Badders

Science Resource Teacher, Cleveland Public Schools, Cleveland, OH

A 1992 Presidential Awards Winner, Mr. Badders teaches science to students in grades K through 6. He is a member of the Working Group on Science Assessment Standards, a subcommittee of the National Research Council's National Committee on Science Education Standards and Assessment. He specializes in the biological and physical sciences.

Dr. Victoria Fu

Professor of Child Development, Virginia Polytechnic Institute and State University, Blacksburg, VA

Dr. Fu has over twenty years of experience in teaching child development. She has been involved, on the national level, in developing guidelines for appropriate practices, curriculum, and assessment in early childhood programs. She is currently researching and writing papers on how young children construct knowledge.

Dr. Lowell Bethel

Professor of Science Education, The University of Texas at Austin, Austin, TX

Dr. Bethel recently served as Program Director for Teacher Enhancement at the National Science Foundation. He specializes in the biological and physical sciences, urban and multicultural education, constructivism, and the development of learning and teaching models.

Mr. Donald Peck

Director, The Center for Elementary Science, Fairleigh Dickinson University, Madison, NJ

Mr. Peck's extensive experience in science education includes conducting over 500 hands-on science workshops for elementary school teachers. He specializes in the physical and earth sciences.

Dr. Carolyn Sumners

Director of Astronomy & Physics, Houston Museum of Natural Science, Houston, TX

Dr. Sumners directs the museum's Burke Baker Planetarium, the Challenger Learning Center, and the rooftop Brown Observatory and astronomy lab. Her experience includes extensive involvement in the creation and dissemination of science materials and the design and operation of the nation's first Challenger Learning Center. She has a strong background in physics and astronomy.

Ms. Catherine Valentino

Senior Vice President for Curriculum Development, Voyager Expanded Learning, West Kingston, RI

Ms. Valentino has experience as a classroom teacher, as a curriculum coordinator, and as a director of elementary and secondary education. In her current position, she is specializing in developing materials for after-school programs. She has a background in the biological sciences, particularly in the science of the human body.

CONSULTING AUTHOR

Mr. R. Mike Mullane

Astronaut, retired
Albuquerque, NM

As one of the first mission specialist astronauts, Mr. Mullane logged 356 hours aboard the space shuttles. Now retired from NASA, Mr. Mullane works to bring the experience of spaceflight to "Earthbound" students and adults. He has a strong background in engineering and in the physical sciences.

We believe . . .

As individuals we come from a variety of backgrounds, but, as educators, we meet on common ground. We share a vision of effective science education for all children. Our vision is based on these principles.

Our Principles

- Students learn science concepts most effectively when they explore concrete examples of these concepts. We provide students with many opportunities to construct their own knowledge of science through hands-on activities that are pertinent to the concerns of their daily lives.

- In a world that is growing increasingly dependent on the contributions of science, scientific literacy is an important educational goal for all students. To enable you to help your students achieve this goal, we provide resources that help you respond to the needs of individual students and to the cultural diversity of students.

- Science education is enhanced when based upon reliable educational standards that guide student attainment, curriculum content, and teaching practices. **Science DiscoveryWorks** is based on the *Benchmarks for Science Literacy* prepared by Project 2061, a long-term educational reform project of the American Association for the Advancement of Science, and the *National Science Education Standards* prepared by the National Research Council.

- Students should learn about the big ideas or common themes of science as identified by Project 2061. Four common themes—systems, models, constancy and change, and scale—are used throughout **Science DiscoveryWorks**.

The Authors

CONSULTANTS & REVIEWERS

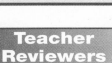

Teacher Reviewers

Lisa Acy
Louis Agassiz Elementary Sch.
Cleveland, OH

Judith Ball
Coordinator for
Math/Science/Health
School District U46
Elgin, IL

Karen R. Bishop
Ferron Elementary School
Ferron, UT

Jean Blackshear
Fred A. Toomer Elementary Sch.
Atlanta, GA

Bonnie Bohrer
Brookview Elementary School
Brook Park, OH

Robert L. Burtch
1990 Presidential Award Winner
Batavia Middle School
Batavia, IL

Martha Christine
Calypso Elementary School
Bethlehem, PA

Mary Eve Corrigan
The Columbus Academy
Gahanna, OH

John S. Detrick
Emeritus Dept. Chair of
Mathematics and Holder of the
McElroy Chair of Mathematics
The Columbus Academy
Gahanna, OH

Robert C. Dixon
National Center to Improve the
Tools of Educators (NCITE)
University of Oregon, College
of Education
Eugene, OR

Denise Pitts-Downing
James Elverson Middle School
Philadelphia, PA

Michaeline A. Dudas
Science and Math Instructional
Support/Consultant
Northbrook, IL

William Dudrow
The Columbus Academy
Gahanna, OH

Barbara Elliott
1990 Presidential Award Winner
Ray E. Kilmer Elementary School
Colorado Springs, CO

Fred Fabry
Retired teacher of Geology
and Biology
Deerfield High School
Deerfield, IL

Rhea Foster
Anderson Park Elementary Sch.
Atlanta, GA

Linda Froschauer
1993 Presidential Award Winner
Weston Middle School
Weston, CT

Joanne Gallagher
Tamarac Middle School
Melrose, NY

Marlene Gregor
Elem. Science Consultant
Bloomington, IL

William L. Handy, Jr.
Parkland School District
Orefield, PA

Beverly Hanrahan
Franconia Elementary School
Souderton, PA

Renee Harris
Northwestern Lehigh Mid. Sch.
New Tripoli, PA

Rhonda Hicks
James Elverson Middle School
Philadelphia, PA

**Sr. Marie Patrice
Hoare, S.L.**
Loretto Middle School
El Paso, TX

**Lester Y. Ichinose,
Ph.D.**
Evanston, IL

Mace A. Ishida, Ph.D.
Diversity and Ed. Consultant
Blacklick, OH

Kristine D. Jackson
Belleville, IL

Pearline A. James
W. F. Slaton Elementary School
Atlanta, GA

Evette Jones
Grover Cleveland Elementary
Philadelphia, PA

Charlene Kalinski
L. L. Hotchkiss Elementary Sch.
Dallas, TX

**Sr. Sharon Kassing,
S.L.**
St. Pius Catholic School
Kirkwood, MO

John Kibler
InterAmerica Intercultural
Training Institute
Des Plaines, IL

Sharon Lempner
R. G. Jones School
Cleveland, OH

Barbara Leonard
1992 Presidential Award Winner
Heritage Elementary School
Pueblo, CO

Gus Liss
Young Elementary School
Burlington Township, NJ

Jo Ann Liss
Intervale School
Parsippany, NJ

Marlenn Maicki
1990 Presidential Award Winner
Detroit Country Day School
Bloomfield Hills, MI

Lynn Malok
Spring Garden Elementary Sch.
Bethlehem, PA

Barbara Mecker
Rockwood South Middle Sch.
St. Louis, MO

Leonardo Melton
Fred A. Toomer Elementary Sch.
Atlanta, GA

Bonnie Meyer
Tremont Elementary School
Cleveland, OH

Dr. Suzanne Moore
L. L. Hotchkiss Elementary Sch.
Dallas, TX

Kathy Morton
Christ the King School
Atlanta, GA

**Dr. Ngoc-Diep T.
Nguyen**
Director, Bilingual and
Multicultural Program
Schaumburg, IL

Michael O'Shea
R. G. Jones School
Cleveland, OH

Wendy Peterson
Harvey Rice Elementary School
Cleveland, OH

Alexandra Pond
Science Coordinator
North Shore School
Chicago, IL

Erika Silverman
Public School 41
Bronx, NY

Christine Spinner
Parma, OH

Jean Ann Strillacci
Kennedy Elementary School
Succasunna, NJ

Laura Swanson
WATTS Intermediate School
Burlington City, NJ

Arthur F. Tobia
Public School 41
Bronx, NY

Nancy Vibeto
1993 Presidential Award Winner
Jim Hill Middle School
Minot, ND

Sandra Wilson
McKinley Elementary School
Abington, PA

Bonita Wylie
Excelsior Middle School
Shorewood, MN

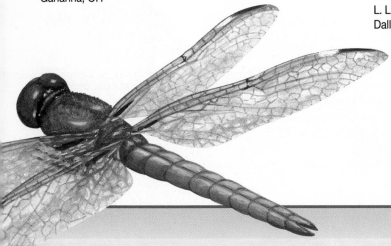

THE SCOPE OF THE PROGRAM
An Overview of Concepts and Themes

	KINDERGARTEN	GRADE 1	GRADE 2
Life Science 	**UNIT A Characteristics of Living Things** Classification of objects as living or non-living; basic needs and stages of growth of living things **Themes:** *Systems, Constancy and Change*	**UNIT A Kinds of Living Things** The similarities and differences between plants and animals; classifying plants and animals according to one characteristic **Theme:** *Systems*	**UNIT A Interactions of Living Things** The needs of living things; plant and animal adaptations to various habitats; the effect of living things, including people, and natural forces on environments **Themes:** *Constancy and Change, Models* 
Physical Science 	**UNIT B Exploring With the Senses** Using the senses to observe the physical characteristics of objects; grouping objects by their physical characteristics **Theme:** *Systems* **UNIT D Pushes and Pulls** Different ways things move; pushes and pulls; surfaces; directional motion **Themes:** *Systems, Models*	**UNIT C Magnets** The properties of magnets; magnetic force; magnetic fields; temporary magnets; magnets and compasses **Themes:** *Systems, Scale* 	**UNIT B Light and Color** Characteristics of light, such as light sources, how light affects vision, and the way light travels; how shadows are formed and changed; the spectrum and color mixing **Theme:** *Systems* **UNIT D Solids, Liquids, and Gases** Properties of solids, liquids, and gases; the changing of materials from one state to another **Theme:** *Constancy and Change*
Earth Science 	**UNIT C Looking at the Sky** Daytime sky and the Sun; differences between the daytime and nighttime sky; the Moon and the stars **Themes:** *Constancy and Change, Scale*	**UNIT B Weather and Seasons** Factors that affect the weather; seasonal weather changes; how people, plants, and animals respond to weather conditions **Theme:** *Constancy and Change* **UNIT D Earth's Land and Water** Properties of soil and rocks; how water and soil mix; how water flows; recycling through composting **Themes:** *Systems, Models*	**UNIT C Earth Through Time** Characteristics of different dinosaurs; how fossil imprints and fossil remains provide clues about Earth's history **Themes:** *Models, Scale, Constancy and Change* 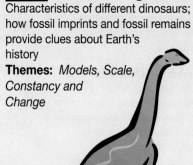
The Human Body	**UNIT E Body Parts** Identification of internal and external body parts; the functions and importance of individual body parts, including the hands, bones, muscles, heart, stomach, and brain **Themes:** *Systems, Models*	**UNIT A Keeping Fit and Healthy** The importance of good nutrition, exercise, sleep, and proper hygiene; the food pyramid and a healthful diet **Themes:** *Systems, Constancy and Change*	**UNIT E What Makes Me Sick** How germs cause illness; how illnesses spread; prevention of illnesses and injuries; how to stay healthy **Themes:** *Systems, Scale*

GRADE 3

UNIT A Life Cycles
Stages in the life cycles of animals and plants; changes in animals and plants as they mature; ways that animals and plants survive
Theme: *Models*

UNIT E Roles of Living Things
The needs of living things in relation to their environments; how living things adapt to their environments, change them, and respond to them
Theme: *Constancy and Change*

UNIT C Forms of Energy
The forms of energy and their effect on matter; how heat energy moves, changes matter, and is measured; the benefits and drawbacks of different energy sources
Theme: *Systems*

UNIT B Sun, Moon, and Earth
The physical features of the Sun and Moon; the rotation and revolution of Earth and the Moon; Earth's seasonal changes; eclipses
Theme: *Scale*

UNIT D Earth's Water
Characteristics of Earth's water, including sources of fresh water and the water cycle; water distribution, pollution, and conservation
Theme: *Systems*

UNIT F What's for Lunch?
Nutrients and the types and amounts of food in a healthful diet; sanitary food storage and preparation; care of teeth and gums; digestion
Theme: *Systems*

GRADE 4

UNIT C Animals
Basic needs of animals; adaptations that help animals meet their needs; classification of living things; characteristics of different animal groups
Theme: *Systems*

UNIT B Properties of Matter
Physical properties; states; effects of heat loss or gain and of physical and chemical changes
Theme: *Scale*

UNIT D Magnetism and Electricity
Properties of magnets; forms of electrical energy; electric circuits; sources of electric current; how electric current is changed into useful energy
Theme: *Models*

UNIT A Earth's Land Resources
How moving water, wind, and ice shape the land; natural resources and conservation efforts; consequences of producing and disposing of trash
Theme: *Constancy and Change*

UNIT E Weather and Climate
Earth's atmosphere; effects of changes in the air on weather; weather patterns and predictions; seasonal weather changes and climate
Theme: *Constancy and Change*

UNIT F The Body's Delivery Systems
Organs and functions of the respiratory, circulatory, and excretory systems; health measures that prevent or fight disease; harmful effects of nicotine, alcohol, and other drugs
Theme: *Systems*

GRADE 5

UNIT A Plants
Parts of flowering plants; plant cells; plant processes; classifying plants; structural adaptations
Theme: *Systems*

UNIT D Populations and Ecosystems
Dynamic interactions of living and nonliving things in an ecosystem; how energy and matter flow through an ecosystem; biomes; biodiversity
Themes: *Systems*

UNIT C Energy, Work, and Machines
Properties of energy, including its forms, ability to change form, and effects; friction; simple machines
Theme: *Systems*

UNIT F Light and Sound
Properties of light; lenses and their uses; color; properties of sound; the sense of hearing; controlling, recording, and transmitting sound
Theme: *Models*

UNIT B The Solar System and Beyond
The night sky; how astronomers learn about space; the solar system; stars and galaxies; survival in space
Theme: *Scale*

UNIT E The Solid Earth
Properties and uses of minerals and rocks; the rock cycle; Earth's structure; fossils as clues to the age of rocks; the formation of mountains; faults
Theme: *Constancy and Change*

UNIT G Movement and Control
Organs and functions of the skeletal and muscular systems; avoiding bone and muscle injuries; organs and functions of the nervous system; harmful effects of tobacco, alcohol, and other drugs
Theme: *Systems*

GRADE 6

UNIT A Cells and Microbes
Structure and life processes of cells, including mitosis; protists and fungi; bacteria and viruses
Theme: *Models*

UNIT D Continuity of Life
Asexual reproduction; sexual reproduction, including meiosis; inherited and acquired traits; evolution, including evidence for evolution and evolutionary processes
Themes: *Constancy and Change*

UNIT C The Nature of Matter
Physical/chemical properties; elements, compounds, mixtures; physical and chemical changes; acids and bases; atomic structure
Theme: *Scale*

UNIT F Forces and Motion
Characteristics of motion; gravity; measuring changes in motion; friction; action/reaction forces; how forces affect the motion of objects
Theme: *Scale*

UNIT B The Changing Earth
Theory of plate tectonics; the movement of continents; the formation of mountains; earthquakes and volcanoes
Theme: *Models*

UNIT E Oceanography
Contents and properties of ocean water; features and exploration of the ocean floor; currents, waves, and tides; resources from the ocean; ocean pollution
Theme: *Systems*

UNIT G Growing Up Healthy
Human reproduction; the endocrine system and the human life cycle; defenses of the immune system; illness and immune system disorders; reducing health risk factors
Theme: *Systems*

How Discovery Works

Silver Burdett Ginn Science

in Grades 3-6

The Teaching Guide and Activities and Resources in the Student Edition, together with the supporting Equipment Kits, present strong science content in an exciting and innovative format. Additional materials, including CD-ROM technology, support and expand the concepts in each investigation.

Trade Book Library

Trade Books in each grade-level library provide in-depth science content, biographies of famous scientists, and science-related fiction. Trade Books can be used to introduce each unit and reinforce investigation concepts.

Teaching Guide

The *Teaching Guide* is a road-map for moving through the activities and resources.

Science Notebook

The *Science Notebook* includes space for students to record their observations and conclusions as they work through Activities, Investigate Further Extensions, and Unit Project Links. Used as the basis for a Portfolio, students can use the notebook to generate ideas about concepts and reassess their learning.

Educational Technology

SCIENCE PROCESSOR: An Interactive CD-ROM contains investigations that can be used in place of or as extensions of print materials. Tools such as Grapher and Spreadsheet allow for easy data interpretation. VIDEOTAPES and VIDEODISCS complement specific units.

Assessment

Portfolio and performance based assessment opportunities are embedded throughout the investigations.

Additional Resources

A wide range of resources provides additional opportunities for teaching and learning through different modalities.

Choose from these resources:

Equipment Kits

Color Transparency Packages

Teacher Resource Book

- Home-School Connections
- Activity Support Masters
- Unit Project Support Masters
- Standardized Tests

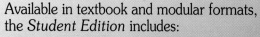

Student Edition

Available in textbook and modular formats, the *Student Edition* includes:

Activities - provide students with opportunities for hands-on explorations

Resources - present science content in several engaging formats

Assessment Guide

This guide offers a wealth of assessment choices including objective tests, performance tests, and strategies for compiling and assessing portfolios. The guide contains:

- Checklists for Observation and Interview
- Investigation Reviews
- Chapter Tests
- Unit Written and Performance Tests

3-6 Components

Student Editions
- **Grade Level Book**
- **Module Books for each unit**

Teaching Guide

Science Notebook

Science Notebook, Teacher Edition

Assessment Guide

Standardized Tests

Teacher Resource Book
- **Home-School Connections**
- **Activity Support Masters**
- **Unit Project Support Masters**

Color Transparency Package

Trade Books
- **Grade Level Libraries**
- **Individual Copies**

Technology Packages
- **Science Processor: An Interactive CD-ROM**
- **Problem-Solving Videodiscs**
- **Books on Tape**
- **Best of the Net CD-ROM**

Professional Handbook

Equipment Kits
- **Grade Level Kits**
- **Module Kits**
- **Consumable Kits**

A Learning Model for
Silver Burdett Ginn Science
DiscoveryWorks

*Flexibility is an important feature of the **Science DiscoveryWorks** program. Although the Teaching Guide suggests ways in which you can use the program compo-nents to organize and guide each lesson, you can adapt these suggestions or develop your own teaching strategies. The model shown here is one way of teaching a unit.*

Get Ready to Investigate!
Using the Unit Opener

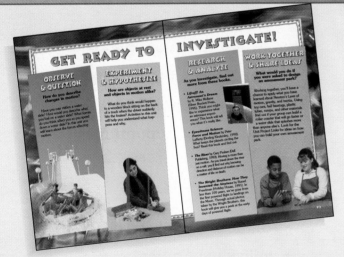

Use the unit opener to engage students' interest in the topic to be studied. Using the four column headings, have students specu-late about what they might discover as they explore the unit.

- Trade Book: Point out the trade book selections, and suggest that students select one they are interested in exploring.
- Unit Project: Introduce the idea of the unit project. Have stu-dents record their initial impressions about the project topic in their *Science Notebooks*.

Teaching Each Chapter

Setting the Stage:
Using the Chapter Opener

- Do a warm-up activity (suggested in the *Teaching Guide*) that relates to the chapter concept.

- Use the photo and introductory copy to begin a discussion of the chapter topics.

- Have students record their initial thoughts on the chapter topic in their *Science Notebooks*.

Note the availability of Home-School Connections (found in the *Teacher Resource Book*) and Technology opportunities for use at appropriate times in the chapter.

Investigate

Investigations form the heart of the **Science DiscoveryWorks** program. Investigations are made up of two types of student pages—**Activities and Resources**.

Activate Prior Knowledge

Use the suggested baseline assessment in the *Teaching Guide* to determine what students already know. Then revisit these assessments at the end of each Investigation to allow students to look back at what they've learned.

Provide Hands-on Experiences with Activities

Doing hands-on activities first provides students with concrete experiences that make subsequent readings more meaningful. These experiences will help form the basis of conceptual development.

- Choose one or more Activities for each Investigation. Have students record their observations, data, and responses in their *Science Notebooks*.

- Go beyond the basic Activity using suggestions found in Investigate Further boxes.

- Have students use the *Science Processor CD-ROM* to make spreadsheets and graphs and to record their observations using Painter and Writer tools.

Develop Depth of Understanding with Resources

Resources are content-rich articles that provide students with information that helps them synthesize the inferences they made while carrying out hands-on activities.

- As extensions, use the Science in Literature selections on the student pages, or the Integrating the Curriculum and the Investigate Further suggestions in the *Teaching Guide*.

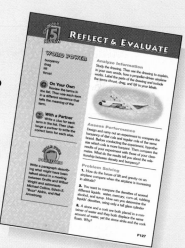

- Continue developing the unit project by using the Unit Project Links and the associated *Science Notebook* pages.

Close the Investigation

- Bring the Investigation to a close by having students write the answers to the *Think It Write It* questions in their *Science Notebooks*.

- Supplement the Investigation assessment with the Investigation Review found in the *Assessment Guide*.

Reflect and Evaluate

- Use the chapter review found on the **Reflect and Evaluate** page to help students link concepts developed in each investigation. Have students reflect on their understandings by writing in their *Science Notebooks*.

- A formal assessment of chapter concepts is available on the Chapter Test in the *Assessment Guide*.

Investigate Further! Unit Wrap-up

After completing the chapters, re-emphasize the big idea of the unit using one or more suggestions from **Investigate Further!**

- For students who have completed the unit project, a Big Event for wrapping up the project is suggested.

- Ideas for further research and experiments related to unit topics are also suggested.

- As a final assessment, use the Unit Test and/or the Unit Performance Test found in the *Assessment Guide*.

The Role of
SCIENTIFIC THINKING

The scientific way of thinking is neither mysterious nor exclusive. The skills involved can be learned by everyone, and once acquired they can serve a lifetime, regardless of one's occupation and personal circumstances.

Benchmarks for Science Literacy

Developing scientific thinking in students is an important part of science education. To learn how to think scientifically, students need frequent opportunities to develop the science process skills, critical thinking skills, and scientific reasoning skills that support scientific inquiry.

In **Science DiscoveryWorks**, students develop process skills as they actively investigate concepts and evaluate the results of their investigations. They develop critical thinking skills and scientific reasoning skills as they respond to thought-provoking questions that conclude every activity and lesson or investigation. In the *Teaching Guide*, questions that promote scientific reasoning skills are identified by this symbol.

The common themes or big ideas that run through science, as well as many other disciplines, are another important aspect of scientific thinking. Common themes are identified for every unit of **Science DiscoveryWorks**, and the connections between the themes and the concepts within a unit are explained in the *Teaching Guide*.

Science Process Skills

Skill	Description
Observing	Determining the properties of an object or event by using the senses
Classifying	Grouping objects or events according to their properties
Measuring/Using Numbers	Skills include: • describing quantitatively using appropriate units of measurement • estimating • recording quantitative data • space or time relationships
Communicating	Using written and spoken words, graphs, tables, diagrams, and other information presentations, including those that are technology based
Inferring	Drawing a conclusion about a specific event based on observations and data; may include cause-and-effect relationships
Predicting	Anticipating consequences of a new or changed situation using past experiences and observation
Collecting, Recording, and Interpreting Data	Manipulating data, either collected by self or by others, in order to make meaningful information and then finding patterns in that information that lead to making inferences, predictions, and hypotheses
Identifying and Controlling Variables	Identifying the variables in a situation; selecting variables to be manipulated and held constant
Defining Operationally	Defining terms within the context of one's own experiences; stating a definition in terms of "what you do" and "what you observe"
Making Hypotheses	Proposing an explanation based on observations
Experimenting	Investigating, manipulating materials, and testing hypotheses to determine a result
Making and Using Models	Representing the "real world" using a physical or mental model in order to understand the larger process or phenomenon

Critical Thinking Skills

Skill	Description
Analyzing	Studying something to identify constituent elements or relationships among elements
Synthesizing	Using deductive reasoning to pull together key elements
Evaluating	Reviewing and responding critically to materials, procedures, or ideas, and judging them by purposes, standards, or other criteria
Applying	Using ideas, processes, or skills in new situations
Generating Ideas	Expressing thoughts that reveal originality, speculation, imagination, a personal perspective, flexibility in thinking, invention, or creativity
Expressing Ideas	Presenting ideas clearly and in logical order, while using language that is appropriate for the audience and occasion
Solving Problems	Using critical thinking skills to find solutions to a problem

Scientific Reasoning Skills

Scientific Reasoning Skill	Description
Longing to Know and Understand	The desire to probe, find information, and seek explanations
Questioning of Scientific Assumptions	The tendency to hold open for further verification presented assumptions, encounters, and ideas
Search for Data and Its Meaning	The propensity to collect information and to analyze it in context
Demand for Verification	The inclination to repeat and replicate findings and studies
Respect for Logic	The inclination to move from assumptions to testing and data collection to conclusions
Consideration of Premises	The tendency to put into context the reason for a particular point of view
Consideration of Consequences	The tendency to put into perspective the results of a particular point of view
Respect for Historical Contributions	The inclination to understand and learn from earlier ideas, studies, and events.

Common Themes*

Theme	Description
Systems	A system is a collection of things that influence one another and appear to be a unified whole. Examples of systems include body systems, the system created as matter and energy interact, and interactions of living and non-living components of ecosystems.
Scale	Ideas concerning the differences in magnitude of variables, such as size, distance, weight, and temperature, including the idea that the properties of something change at different rates as scale changes. Examples of scale include the study of parts of a system, the effects of changing variables in equations, and comparisons of size and distance within systems.
Constancy and Change	The ways in which anything in nature remains the same or changes, as well as the rate at which change occurs. Examples include predator-prey relationships, the idea of conservation of matter and energy, and the continuous cycling of matter and energy in nature.
Models	A model is a physical, mathematical, or conceptual likeness of a thing or process that helps to explain how it works. Models are used to think about processes that happen too slowly, too quickly, or on too large or small a scale to be directly observed. Examples include models of atoms and computer simulations.

*Adapted from _Benchmarks for Science Literacy_ (Oxford University Press, 1993).

ASSESSMENT TOOLS

The key to evaluating the success of any science program lies in assessment methods that help you and your students measure progress toward instructional goals.

A varied assessment program can
- help you determine which students need more help and where classroom instruction needs to be expanded.

- help you judge how well students understand, communicate, and apply what they have learned.
- provide students with strategies for monitoring their own progress and ways to demonstrate their talents and abilities.

Science DiscoveryWorks provides the following comprehensive assessment package.

The *Science DiscoveryWorks* Assessment Package

Learner Objectives	Assessments Available in *Science DiscoveryWorks*	Sources in *Science DiscoveryWorks*
Mastery of content	Observation	TG, AG
	Written Reviews and Tests	SE, TG, AG
	Portfolios	SE, TG, AG
Development of process skills and critical thinking skills	Observation	TG, AG
	Performance Assessment	SE, TG, AG
	Portfolios	SE, TG, AG
	Student Self-Assessment	AG
Development of scientific reasoning skills	Observation	TG, AG
Evaluation of individual or group progress	Portfolios	SE, TG, AG
	Student Self-Assessment	AG
	Group Self-Assessment	AG
Effectiveness of instruction	Written Reviews and Tests	SE, TG, AG
	Portfolios	SE, TG, AG
	Performance Assessment	SE, TG, AG

KEY: SE-*Student Edition*; TG-*Teaching Guide*; AG-*Assessment Guide*

PERFORMANCE ASSESSMENT

Purpose: Performance Assessment helps you evaluate the skills and concepts developed through hands-on activities. In the *Assessment Guide*:

- **Performance Assessment** pages present a formal task for each unit that demonstrates students' ability to apply process skills.
- **Administering the Assessment** provides teacher instructions.
- **Performance Assessment Scoring Rubric** provides a way to evaluate student performance in relation to stated goals.

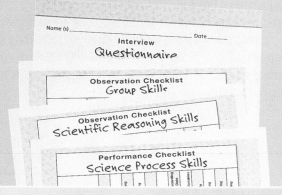

OBSERVATION AND INTERVIEW

Purpose: Observation and Interview allow you to document the day-to-day development of student understanding using the following checklists in the *Assessment Guide*:

- **Observation Checklist: Group Skills**
- **Interview Questionnaire**
- **Observation Checklist: Scientific Reasoning Skills**
- **Performance Checklist: Science Process Skills**

SELF-ASSESSMENT

Purpose: Self-assessment helps students analyze their own performance. In the *Assessment Guide*:

- **Self-Assessment: Student Checklist** helps students evaluate their own performance by rating themselves on set criteria.
- **Self-Assessment: Group Checklist** helps students analyze their group skills.

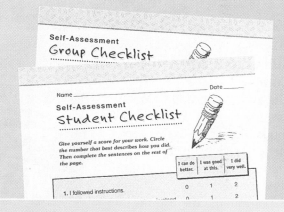

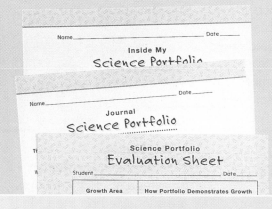

PORTFOLIO ASSESSMENT

Purpose: Portfolio assessment provides a way of demonstrating a student's growth and progress over time. In the *Assessment Guide*:

- **Inside My Science Portfolio** provides criteria for students to use in selecting work for their portfolios.
- **Journal: Science Portfolio** provides students the opportunity to reflect on and write about their individual portfolio selections.
- **Science Portfolio Evaluation Sheet** provides a method for you to record *how* included materials demonstrate growth.

WRITTEN REVIEWS AND TESTS

Purpose: Written reviews and tests measure students' understanding and retention of concepts at the end of investigations, chapters, and units. In the *Assessment Guide*:

- **Investigation Reviews** focus on material covered in each investigation.
- **Chapter Tests** evaluate students' understanding of chapter concepts and vocabulary.
- **Unit Tests** measure students' understanding and retention of concepts developed over an entire unit.

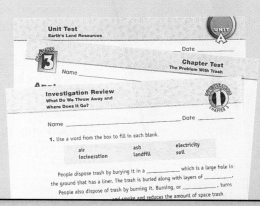

TECHNOLOGY RESOURCES
Extending Our Reach

Science DiscoveryWorks offers a wide variety of technology resources that provide alternative ways of presenting and developing science concepts. These resources also provide students with opportunities to use technological tools and to develop understanding of how technology contributes to advances in science.

The *Teaching Guide* for each unit of **Science DiscoveryWorks** offers strategies for using the technology resources in lessons or investigations. Suggestions include using technology to introduce a concept, as a stimulus for group discussion, as the basis for an activity or project, and to reinforce a concept.

Technology Resources for Grades K–2

Audiotapes and Compact Discs

The audiotapes and CDs feature a variety of delightful songs that relate to many of the lesson concepts. Students reinforce important concepts as they sing along or pantomime the actions in the songs. One audiotape or CD is available for each grade.

Videotapes

Videotapes present unit concepts in fresh and visually appealing ways; they are both entertaining and educational. Titles include: *Arthur's Eyes, What Good Are Rocks?,* and *Keep the Lights Burning, Abbie.* One videotape is available for each unit; grade level libraries are available.

Technology Resources for Grades 3–6

Science Processor, an Interactive CD-ROM

The CD-ROM software provides an interactive, child-centered learning approach. The CD-ROM provides Investigations that replace or enhance Investigations in the student book, a Science Workshop in which students can explore and create in an open environment, and a customized encyclopedia. On-screen tools include a Spreadsheet, a Grapher, a Writer, a Painter, a Calculator, and a Timer.

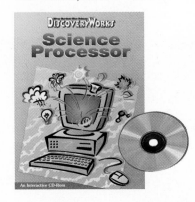

Problem-Solving Videodiscs

The videodiscs use exciting full-motion video, animated diagrams, graphics, and still images to create a captivating learning environment for your students. Each grade-level videodisc contains problems keyed to specific units.

Videotapes

Videotapes that enhance or extend science concepts are suggested on the Using the Power of Technology pages that precede each unit. The videotapes are available from many sources; look for the * to determine which can be ordered from Silver Burdett Ginn.

SCIENCE & LITERATURE
Partners in Learning

In **Science DiscoveryWorks**, literature is used to enhance students' understanding of science concepts. **Science DiscoveryWorks** offers collections of grade-level fiction and non-fiction books that engage students in friendly encounters with the science concepts in each unit of study.

The literary elements of the trade books — imaginative stories, interesting facts, delightful characters, appealing illustrations — have the effect of personalizing science concepts for students. They help connect students' everyday lives to science and heighten their sense of wonder about the natural world.

Trade Books for Grades K–2

A total of ten trade books, two per unit, is available for each grade. The *Teaching Guides* contain suggestions for integrating the trade books into every lesson. Suggestions include using the trade books to:

- introduce a unit or a lesson concept;

- make a baseline assessment of students' understanding;

- deepen understanding of concepts explored in activities or through the Poster Book;

- stimulate group discussions;

- guide students' independent explorations in the Science Center; and

- prompt student writing about science.

The *Teaching Guide* also lists other trade books for teachers and for children.

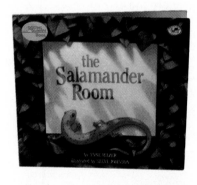
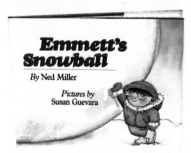

Trade Book Libraries for Grades 3–6

A Trade Book Library, containing a book for each unit, is available for each grade. Highlighted in the Science in Literature features throughout the student editions, the unit trade books provide real-world connections through fictional stories, biographies, and informational genres. The student edition also suggests additional books of interest for each unit that can be used to supplement the Trade Book Library.

CURRICULUM INTEGRATION
Forming Real Connections

In the **Science DiscoveryWorks** program meaningful connections are made between science and other areas of the curriculum. Science becomes more important to students when they become aware of how fundamental it is to every aspect of their lives. Examples of the types of connections made between science and other areas of the curriculum are shown in the model below.

THE SCIENCES

- Exploring how the areas of Life, Earth, and Physical science are related

LITERATURE

- Using science concepts to explain natural events that occur in a story
- Predicting future events in a story by applying knowledge of science concepts
- Using literature to compare the technology and technological practices of the past and the present

MATH

- Using computational and estimation skills in science activities
- Using different units of measurement and measurement tools
- Collecting scientific data and displaying it in graphs

LANGUAGE ARTS

- Writing and illustrating stories and poems
- Exploring the properties of objects that play an important role in a story
- Building vocabulary through an exploration of science terms and related words

CONNECTING SCIENCE TO

CULTURAL CONNECTIONS

- Exploring the natural environments of distant places and the ways in which people have adapted to them
- Exploring the plants and animals of distant places through the literature of other cultures
- Studying the ways in which people from diverse backgrounds have contributed to science

SOCIAL STUDIES

- Studying the ways in which scientific ideas develop over time
- Exploring the influence of social forces on science
- Exploring how geography and natural resources affect the development of science ideas and practices

TECHNOLOGY & SOCIETY

- Exploring the benefits, risks, and limitations of technology
- Relating science concepts to the use of tools and inventions
- Exploring the relationship between science and technology
- Studying the impact of science on society

THE ARTS

- Using music and dance to express science concepts
- Drawing pictures of natural objects and events

SAFETY
An Essential Element

In order for students to develop respect for safety, they need to understand exactly what is meant by safe and unsafe behavior and what the rationale is behind safety rules. Through your teaching as well as your example, students can develop the "safe science" attitudes and skills that are essential both in school and at home.

General Safety Guidelines

- Post an easy-to-read list of safety rules in a prominent place in the classroom. Review it with students on a regular basis.

- Become familiar with the safety procedures that are necessary for each activity before introducing it to your students.

- Discuss specific safety precautions with students before beginning every hands-on science activity.

- Always act as an exemplary model of safe behavior.

- Have students wear protective aprons, goggles, and gloves whenever these items will prevent injury.

- Keep safety equipment, such as fire blankets and fire extinguishers, readily accessible and know how to use it.

- Prepare students for emergencies by having them practice leaving the classroom quickly and safely.

- Show students how to obtain help in an emergency by using the telephone, an intercom, or other available means of communication.

- Never leave students unattended while they are involved in science activities.

- Provide ample space for science activities that require students to move about and handle materials.

- Keep your classroom and all science materials in proper condition. Check their condition regularly.

- Tell students to report all injuries to you immediately.

For more detailed information on safety, you may wish to order the NSTA publication *Safety in the Elementary Science Classroom* (1993). Write or call the National Science Teachers Association, NSTA Publication Sales, 1840 Wilson Boulevard, Arlington, VA 22201-3000; telephone: (703) 243-7100 or (800) 722-6782.

MATERIALS LIST

Following is a complete list of materials needed for all activities included in the Grade 6 student book. Quantities are for a class of 30 students working in groups of 5. Quantities are also listed for those materials included in the Grade Level Deluxe Kit. **Additional kit options are available. Contact your sales representative for details.**

Consumable Materials

Materials	Class Quantity Needed	Grade Level Deluxe Kit Quantity	Activity Page
aluminum foil	1 roll	1 roll	C32, C44, C88, F70
amoebas, culture of (coupon)	1 jar	1 coupon (25)	A31
antacid tablet (seltzer tablets)	6	3 pkg (6)	C86
apples	12		G31
aquarium gravel (sand)	1 lb	2 pkg (2 lb)	C44
bags, brown paper	6	1 pkg (6)	C18
bags, sealable plastic	36	1 pkg (50)	A14, A40, C8, C22
bags, thin plastic garbage	6	1 pkg (6)	F44
baking soda	1 lb	1 lb	C64, C66, C88
balloons, long	6	1 pkg (6)	F114
balloons, small	12	2 pkg (12)	C64, F116
borax	30 oz	3 pkg (30 oz)	C90
bottles, soda with caps (plastic, 1-L)	12		A56, E31
bottles, soda with caps (plastic, 2-L)	6		E14
bread	18 slices		A40
calcium chloride	60 g (teacher only)	1 pkg (500g)	C67
candles	6	6	C33, C66
cardboard	18 sheets	4 pkg (24)	B42, E62, E68, E78
clay, powdered (sediments)	1 lb	1 pkg (1 lb)	E31
boxes, cardboard (assorted)	24		B72
boxes, cardboard small	6	6	F72
chalk, railroad	6 pieces	2 sets (6)	F12
cooking oil (corn oil)	1 bottle	1 bottle	E88, E90
copper foil	6 pieces	6 sheets	C44
copper wire	1 roll	1 roll (100 ft)	C32
cornstarch	1 lb	1 lb	C47, C88
cotton balls	1 box	1 pkg (100)	C6, C8, E90
cups, paper	54	15 pkg (90)	D32, D38, D54, E12, E31
eggs, raw	6		F122
Elodea (coupon)	6 plants	1 coupon (24)	E22
feathers	6	1 pkg (80)	E8
flour	900 g	1 pkg (2 lb)	E12
food coloring, blue and red	12 bottles		B36, C18, C47, C54, C55, C90, E54
food coloring, 4 colors	6 bottles	2 pkg (8)	E54
food lables	variety		G58
gelatin	6 pkg	3 pkg (6)	B62
gloves, plastic	30 pairs	1 pkg (50 pairs)	A40, G38
glue, white	6 bottles		B6, C90, E76, E78
gravel, sand #30 (sediments)	1 lb	1 pkg (2 lb)	E31
index cards	6		F37
iodine solution	1 bottle	100 mL	A6, A14
iodine, tincture of	1 bottle	100 mL	C88
juice, red cabbage	1 head		C78
labels	30	1 pkg (100)	G38
lemon juice	1 bottle		C78, C80
lens paper	1 pkg		D8
lime, powdered	1 pkg	1 pkg (1/2 lb)	C78
litmus paper, blue and red	18 pieces each	2 pkg (200)	C80
magnesium sulfate (Epsom salt)	65 g (teacher only)	1 pkg (500 g)	C67
markers, black, permanent	6	6	A40, C52, D32, D38, D40, E14, E68, E76, E78, G8, G18, G38
markers, water-based	6	6	B24, B68, C46
matches, fireplace	18		C66, C86
milk cartons (0.24 L)	6		B36
milk, powdered	pkg (teacher only)	1 pkg (8 oz)	C88
mineral oil	1 bottle	1 bottle (16 oz)	C54
modeling clay (cream-colored)	2 lb	12 lb	D54
modeling clay (4 different colors)	12 lb	13 lb	B23, B72, C9, D54, D64, E14, E16, F90, F120
newsprint	6 large sheets		G18
oats, quick (oatmeal)	1 box	1 pkg (18 oz)	B94
onion	1		A6

Materials	Class Quantity Needed	Grade Level Deluxe Kit Quantity	Activity Page
paper, construction (black and colored)	as needed		C33, C86, C88, E78
paper, construction, white	12	2 pkg (12)	D18, D20, D38
paper, butcher	6 sheets		F62
paper, filter	12 sheets	1 pkg (100)	C18, C46
paper, graph	60 sheets		D72, E30, F6
paper, shelf	1 roll	1 roll	B68
paper, tracing	6 sheets	1 pkg (40)	B16
peanuts	240		D72
pencils, colored (or markers)	6 sets		D18, D20, E76, E78, F6, F62
pepper	1 container		E52
petroleum jelly	1 jar	1 jar	D54
pineapple juice	1 can		C78
plaster of Paris	3 lb	4 pkg (4 lb)	C88, D54
posterboard	12 sheets		E76, E78
potato	3		D32
ribbon	1 spool		E64
rubber bands	1 pkg	1 pkg (1 oz)	B54, C46, F116
salt	1 box	3 pkg (78 oz)	A6, C88, E14, E54, F122
sand	12 lb	6 pkg (12 lb)	B62, B72, C6, C16, C44
sandpaper, coarse	24 sheets	9 sheets	B54, F70
sand, coarse #60 (sediments)	1 lb	2 pkg (2 lb)	E31
sand, fine (sediments)	1 lb	2 pkg (2 lb)	E31
shoeboxes with lids	6	6	B23, B24
soap, liquid (detergent)	1 bottle	1 bottle (12 oz)	C78
soil	8 lb	5 pkg (20 qt)	D32
starch	1 bottle	1 bottle (16 oz)	A14
straws	150	3 pkg (50)	B24, E14, E52, E54, E90, F114
straws, plastic (flexible)	6	1 pkg (50)	F116
string (twine)	2 rolls	1 roll (430 ft)	B36, B68, E42, E64, E68, F18, F20, F44, F114, F116
sugar	1 lb	5 lb	C16, C33, C44, C88
sugar cubes	30 cubes	1 lb	C52
tape, duct	1 roll	1 roll	B36
tape, masking	6 rolls		B68, B72, D32, E64, G8
tape, removable	1 roll	1 roll	D18
tape, transparent	6 rolls		B23, B24, C18, E68, E78, F44, F114, F116
toothpicks	1 box	1 box	C55, C88
universal indicator solution	1 bottle (teacher only)	1 bottle (25 mL)	G38
vinegar, white	1 bottle	1 qt	C64, C66, C78, C88, G38
wax paper	1 roll	1 roll	C18, C55, F70
window cleaner	1 bottle (teacher only)		C80
yarn, 2 colors	1 skein each color	2 skeins	D18
yeast culture	1 pkg	1 pkg	D8

Nonconsumable Materials

Materials	Class Quantity Needed	Grade Level Deluxe Kit Quantity	Activity Page
action figures, small (paratrooper, plastic)	7		F44
aquariums (container, GL)	6	6	B36, F120, F122
balance and masses	1	1	C6, C8, C9, C22, E12, F30
balls, golf	6	1 pkg (6)	F62
balls, rubber	6	12	F36
balls, table tennis	6		F36
basin (or sink)	1		E16
basketballs	6		F88, F90
beakers, large	12	12	A14, E77
beakers, small	6	6	C16
boards, wooden (long)	6		F64, F70, F72
boards, wooden (short)	6	1 pkg (6)	F64, F70, F72
bottles, clear (with screw-on lid)	6		C54
bottles, glass (narrow-necked)	6		C64
bottles, spray	6	6	A40
bowls, clear plastic, small	6	6	D72
bowls, large (clear plastic, 48 oz)	12	12	B62, C90
boxes (about same size as toy truck)	6	6	F72
buckets or trash cans, large	6		E12
calculators	6		B100, E40, E42, G30
cans, film with lid (containers)	18		C6
coat hangers, wire	6		C18
compasses, drawing	6	6	B70
containers, plastic (large)	6		E22
containers, plastic (small)	18	18	C80, C90, E88, E90
containers, round	6	1 pkg (6)	E6

Material			Location
corks	12	1 pkg (120)	A56
cups, measuring	6		B94, C8, C9, E12
cups, plastic	6	1 pkg (25)	E54
dishes, shallow	24		C24, C33, C47, C66
dishes, small	24		C24
disks, 2 each of 4 different colors (chips)	48	4 pkg (400)	D38, D40
disks, secchi	6	6	E12
dowels	4 pkg	4 pkg (24)	B72
droppers	18	12	A6, A30, A31, C24, C47, C54, C78, C88, D8, E6, G38
fabric scraps	variety		E90
feathers	6	1 pkg (80)	E88
fossils	12	2 pkg (12)	D52
funnels	6	12	C64, E22, E31
game pieces	12		G8
glass squares	6		C33
goggles	30	6	as needed
hand lenses (magnifier, round)	6	6	A40, C18, C33, C44, C86, C88, D52, E6, E88
hot plate	1	1	B94
jars, large plastic, with lids (32 oz)	6	6	E54
jars, small plastic (8 oz)	36	18	C16, C22, C44, C47, C52, C66, C86, D54, G38
jars, wide-mouth (12 oz)	6		C46, C47
knives, plastic	6	1 pkg (6)	C47
lamps	1	1	E77
map of the world	1 (shared)		B6
map pins, red	1 pkg	1 pkg (100)	B84
map pins, yellow	1 pkg	1 pkg (100)	B84
marbles, large	12	2 pkg (12)	F80, F82
marbles, small	400	3 pkg (300)	C16, C47, F12, F80, F82, F120
mesh bags	6		F30, F36
metal washers	12	2 pkg (12)	F18, F20
metersticks	6	6	E12, E40, E42, E64
microscope slides and cover slips	1 box	1 pkg (72)	A6, A30, A31, A40, D8, E6
microscopes	6	6	A6, A8, A20, A30, A31, A32, A40, D6, D8, E6
mirror	6	6	D30
objects of different sizes and masses	variety		F30
oven mitts (pot holders)	6		B94, C33
pans, large aluminum	6	6	B72, E52, E62
pans, large shallow	6	2 pkg (12)	C18
paper clips	30	1 box	F106
ring stands	12		F18, F20
rulers, metric	6	1 pkg (6)	as needed
sandpaper (as long as 5 toy cars)	6 pieces	9	F70
scissors	30		as needed
shells (seashells)	6	1 pkg (6)	D54
slides (prepared; frog blood)	6	6	A8
slides (prepared; human cheek cells)	6	6	A8
slides (prepared; onion root tip)	6	6	A20
slides (prepared; spirogyra)	6	6	A32
slides (prepared; hydra with bud)	6	6	D8
slides (prepared; paramecium whole and dividing)	3 of each	3 sets (9)	D6
sponges, cellulose (latex)	12	12	B44
spoons, large (mixing, plastic)	6	1	B94, F122
spoons, measuring	6	6	C64, C66, E14, E31, E54
spoons, metal	6		C33
spoons, plastic	15	2 pkg (12)	as needed
spring scales	6	6	F30, F36, F42
spring toys	15	6	E42, E64
stirrers	6	1 pkg (6)	C24, C52
tape measures, metric	15	6	E40, F70, F90, F114
test tubes	6	2 pkg (12)	C86, E22
test tube stoppers (stopper, rubber, solid, #0)	12	12	C67
thermometers	12	2 pkg (12)	C22, E14
timers (stopwatch, digital)	15	6	A31, B72, C22, C24, C52, E40, E42, F12, F44
tongs	6	6	C33
towels (at least as long as 5 toy cars)	6		F70
toy cars	6	6	F70
toy trucks	12	12	F54
toy cars with a pull-back friction engine	6	6	F96
tweezers (forceps)	6	6	A6, A40
vegetable peelers (peeler, potato)	6	6	G31
vials	36	24	C78, C80, C88
watering can	1		D32
wood, blocks (3 in. × 3.5 in. × 1.5 in.)	6	6	B62
wood, blocks (3 in. × 4 in. × 1 in.)	12	12	B54
wood, blocks (cube)	6	6	F54, F56, F64

UNIT B
Changing Earth

Overview The Changing Earth examines ways in which Earth changes over time. The theory of plate tectonics helps explain many phenomena, including the shapes and positions of continents, earthquakes and volcanoes, and the location of mountain ranges. Through activities and resources, students make models of Earth's crust and discover how mountains form, how earthquakes occur, and how volcanoes erupt.

Theme Scientists use models to help make sense of seemingly unrelated phenomena. They also use models to make predictions about future events. In The Changing Earth, students will learn about the theory of plate tectonics and how this theory helps scientists understand and explain how Earth changes. Students make models to understand plate movement, sea-floor spreading, earthquakes, and volcanoes.

THE BIG IDEA

Earth's surface—its crust and upper mantle—is broken into great slabs of rock, or tectonic plates, that are constantly moving.

Tracing Major Concepts

The position of Earth's continents has changed as the continents have ridden upon moving plates; earthquakes, volcanoes, and new crust are most common at the edges of these plates.

Subconcepts

- Evidence supports the theory that all the continents were once one large landmass, which gradually separated into several continents.

- Earth's crust and upper mantle are composed of plates that fit together; most strong earthquakes and volcanoes occur at the edges of these plates.

- The sea floor spreads away from cracks in the crust, and magma rises up to form new crust; sea-floor spreading is evidence for the theory of plate tectonics.

The theory of plate tectonics states that the flow of molten rock in the mantle moves tectonic plates; moving tectonic plates can form mountains.

Subconcepts

- The theory of plate tectonics proposes that the tectonic plates are moved by convection currents in Earth's mantle.

- The interaction of moving tectonic plates can cause various kinds of mountains to form.

Earthquakes, which often occur at the margins of tectonic plates, can be described by their energy waves and can be located and measured.

Subconcepts

- Earthquakes are sudden releases of energy stored in rock; most earthquakes occur near the margins of moving tectonic plates.

- Earthquakes produce three kinds of energy waves, each resulting in a characteristic ground motion.

- Earthquakes can be located and measured with seismographs; information about earthquakes can help in warning of tsunamis.

Volcanic eruptions are often associated with plate margins but can also occur in the middle of plates; eruptions can be predicted and measured.

Subconcepts

- Most volcanoes occur where one tectonic plate descends below another; some volcanic activity occurs along spreading plate boundaries.

- Volcanic eruptions are often preceded by changes that can be detected by various instruments; eruptions produce local and worldwide effects.

- Hot spots may produce volcanic islands in the middle of plates; volcanoes also can occur at the margins of rifting continental plates.

CONTENTS

The Changing Earth

CHAPTER 1 Cracked Crust

CHAPTER 2 Tectonic Plates and Mountains

The National Science Education Standards and Project 2061 Benchmarks* are the framework around which _Silver Burdett Ginn Science DiscoveryWorks_ is built.

- The solid earth is layered with a lithosphere; hot, convecting mantle; and dense, metallic core. (p. 159) _Ch. 1, Inv. 2 and 3; Ch. 2, Inv. 1_

- Lithospheric plates on the scales of continents and oceans constantly move at rates of centimeters per year in response to movements in the mantle. Major geological events, such as earthquakes, volcanic eruptions, and mountain building, result from these plate motions. (p. 160) _Entire Unit_

- Land forms are the result of a combination of constructive and destructive forces. Constructive forces include crystal deformation, volcanic eruption, and deposition of sediment, while destructive forces include weathering and erosion (p. 160) _Ch. 2, 3, and 4_

- Some changes in the solid earth can be described as the "rock cycle." Old rocks at the earth's surface weather, forming sediments that are buried, then compacted, heated, and often

recrystallized into new rock. Eventually, those new rocks may be brought to the surface by the forces that drive plate motions, and the rock cycle continues. (p. 160) _Ch. 1_

- The earth processes we see today, including erosion, movement of lithospheric plates, and changes in atmospheric composition, are similar to those that occurred in the past. Earth history is also influenced by occasional catastrophes, such as the impact of an asteroid or comet. (p. 160) _Entire Unit_

- Gravity is the force that keeps planets in orbit around the sun and governs the rest of the motion in the solar system. Gravity alone holds us to the earth's surface and explains the phenomena of the tides. (p. 160) _Ch. 2, Inv. 1; Ch. 4, Inv. 1_

- The sun is the major source of energy for phenomena on the earth's surface, such as growth of plants, winds, ocean currents, and the water cycle. Seasons result from variations in the amount of the sun's energy hitting the surface, due to the tilt of the earth's rotation on its axis and the length of the day. (p. 161) _Ch. 1, Inv. 1_

- Internal and external processes of the earth system cause natural hazards, events that change or destroy human and wildlife habitats, damage property, and harm or kill humans. Natural hazards include earthquakes, landslides, wildfires, volcanic eruptions, floods, storms, and even possible impacts of asteroids. (p. 168) _Ch. 3 and 4_

- Students should understand the risks associated with natural hazards (fires, floods, tornadoes, hurricanes, earthquakes, and volcanic eruptions), with chemical hazards (pollutants in air, water, soil, and food), with biological hazards (pollen, viruses, bacterial, and parasites), social hazards (occupational safety and transportation), and with personal hazards (smoking, dieting, and drinking). (p. 169) _Ch. 3, Inv. 3; Ch. 4, Inv. 2_

- Societal challenges often inspire questions for scientific research, and social priorities often influence research priorities through the availability of funding for research. (p. 169) _Ch. 3, Inv. 3_

- Technology is essential to science for such purposes as access to outer space and other remote locations, sample collection and treatment, measurement, data collection and storage, computation, and communication of information. (p. 46) _Ch. 4, Inv. 3_

- Engineers, architects, and others who engage in design and technology use scientific knowledge to solve practical problems. But they usually have to take human values

and limitations into account as well. (p. 46) _Ch. 1; Ch. 3, Inv. 2 and 3; Ch. 4, Inv. 2 and 3_

- Technology cannot always provide successful solutions for problems or fulfill every human need. (p. 55) Ch. 3, Inv. 3; Ch. 4, Inv. 3

- The interior of the earth is hot. Heat flow and movement of material within the earth cause earthquakes and volcanic eruptions and create mountains and ocean basins. Gas and dust from large volcanoes can change the atmosphere. (p. 73) _Entire Unit_

- Some changes in the earth's surface are abrupt (such as earthquakes and volcanic eruptions) while other changes happen very slowly (such as the uplift and wearing down

of mountains). The earth's surface is shaped in part by the motion of water and wind over very long times, which act to level mountain ranges. (p. 73) _Entire Unit_

- Heat can be transferred through materials by the collisions of atoms or across space by radiation. If the material is fluid, currents will be set up in it that aid the transfer of heat. (p. 85) Ch. 2, Inv. 1

- Vibrations in material set up wavelike disturbances that spread away from the source. Sound and earthquake waves are examples. These and other waves move at different speeds in different materials. (p. 90) _Ch. 3, Inv. 2 and 3_

Curriculum
INTEGRATION

Science as a discipline does not exist in isolation. An integrated approach to the teaching of science will help students understand how science connects to other school subjects as well as to technology, to diverse cultures, and to literature. The location in the unit of activities that connect to other disciplines is indicated in the chart.

THE SCIENCES

- Life Science, page B11
- Life Science, page B26
- Physical Science, page B28
- Physical Science, page B38
- Physical Science, page B64
- Physical Science, page B77
- Life Science, page B90

LITERATURE

- Sci–Fi, page B39
- Using Maps, page B40
- Volcano Story, page B105
- Science in Literature features, pages B30, B46, B66, B91

MATH

- Moving Plates, page B19
- Spreading Rate, page B30
- Faults, page B65
- Calculating, page B76
- Measuring Lava, page B89
- Rifting Rates, page B108

LANGUAGE ARTS

- Reporting News, page B57
- Mount Pinatubo, page B96
- Legends, page B102
- Robot, page B107

CONNECTING SCIENCE TO

CULTURAL CONNECTIONS

- Hot Spots, page B31
- Legends, page B48
- Visiting Nepal, page B49
- Researching, page B59
- Ancient Ideas, page B87
- Making Casts, page B92
- A Valley Visit, page B109

SOCIAL STUDIES

- Theories, page B8
- Making Maps, page B10
- Using Maps, page B14
- The Red Sea, page B20
- Find Mountains, page B45
- Making Posters, page B58
- Coordinates, page B86
- Philippines, page B97
- Yellowstone, page B103

TECHNOLOGY & SOCIETY

- Using Lasers, page B13
- Sound Off, page B27
- Space Probes, page B46
- Wave Diagrams, page B66
- Tsunamis, page B78
- Engineering, page B79
- Disasters, page B98
- Monitoring, page B104
- Robot Fair, page B106

THE ARTS

- Map Making, page B9
- Making Models, page B12
- Making Models, page B29
- Designing, page B74
- Volcano Types, page B88

Plate Tectonics

by Thomas A. Davies

Dr. Thomas Davies is presently a senior research scientist at the University of Texas Institute for Geophysics. He has previously held positions at Scripps Institution of Oceanography in La Jolla, California, and at Middlebury College in Vermont.

THE SHAPES OF THE CONTINENTS

The theory of plate tectonics is a major unifying concept that helps explain a wide range of phenomena we observe on Earth's surface, including the shape of the continents, the formation of mountain ranges, the occurrence of earthquakes, and the distribution of volcanoes. According to this theory, Earth's crust and upper mantle are made up of approximately seven large and several smaller tectonic plates, which are continually moving over Earth's surface. Convection currents of hot, molten rock in the upper parts of the Earth's mantle cause the tectonic plates to move. The movement is slow, by human standards. The fastest plates shift only a few centimeters per year. But over millions of years, this motion has caused the continents to travel across the globe, arranging and rearranging themselves in different configurations.

More than 200 million years ago, today's continents were all fused together in a continuous landmass, or supercontinent, called Pangaea. Over the next 20 million years, Pangaea began to break up into a few very large landmasses. The larger of these landmasses continued to fragment. Sixty-five million years ago, these landmasses split into the continents that are similar to today's continents. The shapes of the continents show that they could once have fit together like the pieces of a jigsaw puzzle.

Even now, the continents continue their movement. Major mountain systems form where tectonic plates collide. For instance, the Appalachians, in the eastern United States, mark where part of the old Eurasian Plate crashed into the North American Plate.

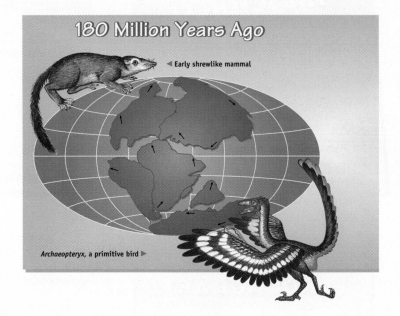

180 Million Years Ago
◄ Early shrewlike mammal
Archaeopteryx, a primitive bird ▶

ACTION AT THE BOUNDARIES

Usually when two plates collide, the heavier plate is forced under the lighter plate; the heavier plate dives deep into Earth's mantle, in a process called subduction. The subducted plate melts in the hot mantle, causing part of Earth's crust to be destroyed. Volcanoes may rise up through cracks in the overriding plate. This is one reason why volcanoes are often present along the boundaries of two colliding plates.

Subduction is a process that causes crust to be destroyed. However, another process occurring at plate boundaries causes new crust to be produced. Long, narrow chains of high underwater mountains occur where two plates are moving apart. As the plates move, hot magma from the mantle wells up into the crack. This material forms an underwater mountain chain—Earth's newest crust.

Give each student three colors of home-made or purchased modeling clay. Have students flatten the clay into layers about 1/4-inch thick and stack them, then cut the stack in half. They can use these models of Earth's plates to experiment with applying forces: pushing two plates together, sliding two plates past each other, and so on. To model a dome mountain, have students hold a stack of clay layers and gently push up from underneath with a blunt object, then cut the model through the center to see how the layers are folded.

Kathleen Swingle
Columbia, Maryland

Use a paper towel to represent the Pacific Plate and move it across the point of a pencil, held upright, to simulate the upwelling of magma producing the Hawaiian Island volcanoes. Punch the pencil through the paper towel as the paper towel is pulled on a diagonal across the pencil point. As the towel moves, representing the Pacific Plate's

movement toward the northwest, successively more holes are created. These holes represent volcanic islands, with the youngest at the southeast.

Jeanne Bishop
Westlake, Ohio

If you have your students collecting rock samples, such as volcanic rock, labeling the samples is important. Otherwise, when you're trying to describe the rocks to students, you may rely too heavily on color to distinguish them. I dab a small bit of correction fluid on the samples and put numbers on them with a thin-line permanent marker. The numbers stay there and don't interfere with observation.

Sr. Sharon Kassing
St. Louis, Missouri

Skills for LIFELONG LEARNING

Experiences provided by *Silver Burdett Ginn Science DiscoveryWorks* are aimed at developing a wide range of science processes and skills. These tools provide a basis for a lifetime of participation in society as a whole. As described in *Science for All Americans* by F. James Rutherford and Andrew Ahlgren (Oxford University Press, 1990), the skills developed through scientific inquiry foster reasoning abilities that relate directly to a person's outlook on knowledge and learning and ways of thinking and acting.

Process Skills provide a framework in which ideas can be conceptualized, tested, and evaluated. The processes listed here are developed through a wide range of hands-on experiences.

Process Skills

Activities	Page	Observing	Classifying	Measuring/ Using Numbers	Communicating	Inferring	Predicting	Collecting, Recording, and Interpreting Data	Identifying and Controlling Variables	Defining Operationally	Making Hypotheses	Experimenting	Making and Using Models
The Great Puzzle	B6	•			•								•
The Earth-Always Rockin' and Rollin'	B16	•			•	•	•						•
Volcanoes and Earth's Plates	B18	•			•			•				•	
Sea-Floor Spreading	B22	•										•	•
Building a Model of the Ocean Floor	B23												•
Mapping the Ocean Floor	B24			•	•	•		•		•			•
The Conveyor	B36	•					•	•				•	•
Colliding Continents	B42	•					•	•				•	•
A Big Fender Bender	B44	•						•				•	•
A Model of Sliding Plates	B54	•				•	•	•					•
Shake It!	B62	•				•	•				•		•
Shake It Harder!	B68	•		•			•	•	•	•			•
Locating Earthquakes	B70			•		•		•					
Be An Architect	B72	•			•		•		•			•	•
Worldwide Eruptions	B84		•		•			•			•		
Volcanoes You Can Eat!	B94	•				•							•
How Hawaii Formed	B100			•		•		•					

Critical Thinking Skills are embedded in the questioning strategies throughout the program. The chart below summarizes the processes assessed in the Think It/Write It sections that end each investigation.

Critical Thinking Skills

Process	Description	B15	B21	B32	B41	B50	B61	B67	B80	B93	B99	B110
Analyzing	Studying something to identify constituent elements or relationships among elements	•	•			•	•			•	•	
Synthesizing	Using deductive reasoning to pull together key elements		•	•	•	•	•	•	•			•
Evaluating	Reviewing and responding critically to materials, procedures, or ideas and judging them by purposes, standards, or other criteria							•	•	•		
Applying	Using ideas, processes, or skills in new situations	•	•									•
Generating Ideas	Expressing thoughts that reveal originality, specula-tion, imagination, a personal perspective, flexibility in thinking, invention, or creativity				•				•			
Expressing Ideas	Presenting ideas clearly and in logical order, while using language that is appropriate for the audience and occasion				•	•		•	•			
Solving Problems	Using critical thinking processes to find solutions to a problem	•			•						•	•

Through the development and reinforcement of science process skills and critical thinking skills, the following **Scientific Reasoning Skills** are developed. This symbol ⬢ identifies questions within the teaching material that highlight Scientific Reasoning Skills.

Scientific Reasoning Skills

Reasoning Skill	Description
Longing to Know and Understand	The desire to probe, find information, and seek explanations
Questioning of Scientific Assumptions	The tendency to hold open for further verification of presented assumptions, encounters, and ideas
Search for Data and Its Meaning	The propensity to collect information and to analyze it in context
Demand for Verification	The inclination to repeat and replicate findings and studies
Respect for Logic	The inclination to move from assumptions to testing and data collection to conclusions
Consideration of Premises	The tendency to put into context the reason for a particular point of view
Consideration of Consequences	The tendency to put into perspective the results of a particular point of view
Respect for Historical Contributions	The inclination to understand and learn from the contributions of earlier ideas, studies, events, and so on

Ongoing Assessment

Daily observations and a variety of ongoing assessment activities can provide comprehensive appraisal of student growth. *Silver Burdett Ginn Science DiscoveryWorks* provides several methods to help you monitor student growth.

Performance Assessment

Observation checklists provide concrete descriptions of student behaviors. Performance assessments allow students to demonstrate their ability to use the tools of science and science processes in hands-on activities, at the end of each investigation and chapter, and in a culminating unit performance task.

Portfolio Assessment

Portfolios of student work can be used to holistically assess student understanding and progress. The *Assessment Guide* provides support materials for developing portfolios and in using them to evaluate growth in science.

Written Reviews and Tests

Think It/Write It sections at the end of each investigation foster critical thinking and provide a snapshot of student understanding. Written tests provide additional tools for assessing how well students understand, integrate, and apply key concepts. Opportunities for periodic review are included in Analyze and Conclude at the end of each activity, in Reflect and Evaluate at the end of each chapter, and in Chapter Tests and Unit Tests in the *Assessment Guide.*

Unit Performance Assessment

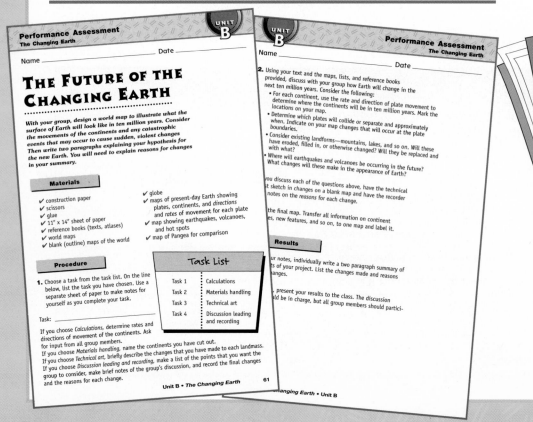

PORTFOLIO ASSESSMENT

Choose among the following products students can put in their Portfolios.

- data from activities
- data from Video, Videodisc, or CD-ROM projects
- data from outside research
- integrated curriculum projects
- projects from Investigate Further activities
- results from Think It-Write It activities

Ongoing Assessment Opportunities

	Performance	Portfolio	Written Reviews and Tests
Chapter 1			B33, AG 45–46
Investigation 1	TG B15		B15, AG 42
Investigation 2	TG B21		B21, AG 43
Investigation 3	TG B32		B32, AG 44
Chapter 2			B51, AG 49–50
Investigation 1	TG B41		B41, AG 47
Investigation 2		TG B50	B50, AG 48
Chapter 3			B81, AG 54–55
Investigation 1		TG B61	B61, AG 51
Investigation 2	TG B67		B67, AG 52
Investigation 3		TG B80	B80, AG 53
Chapter 4			B111, AG 59–60
Investigation 1	TG B93		B93, AG 56
Investigation 2		TG B99	B99, AG 57
Investigation 3	TG B110		B110, AG 58
Unit Close	AG 61–62		AG 65–68

Key: TG = Teacher Guide   AG = Assessment Guide   All other pages are from the Student Edition.

Unit Tests

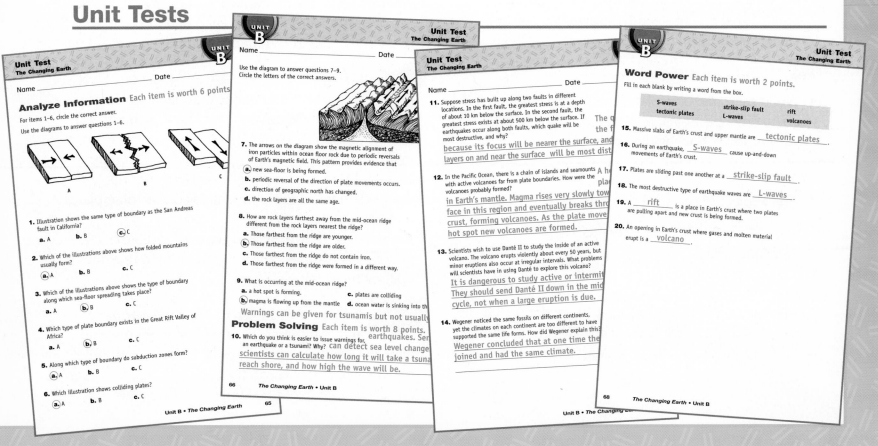

UNIT PROJECT

Earthquake and Volcano Safety Guide

Students create an earthquake and volcano safety guide to help people prepare for and survive these events.

Getting Ready

Group Size
4 to 6 students

Have each group research and brainstorm different ways people can prepare for an earthquake or a volcanic eruption and how to survive these geologic upheavals once they occur.

Materials

For Research

- Magazines, newspaper articles, books on earthquakes and volcanoes

- Pamphlets, such as government publications, on how people can protect themselves in case of earthquakes and volcanic activity

For Models and Presentations

- World map, tectonic-plates map, art paper, markers, paints, pushpins, scissors, glue, hole punch, yarn or other bookbinding materials

Other Materials

- Unit Project Masters B1–B4, TRB pp. 71–74.

- *Science Notebook* pp. 54, 72, 87, 106

- Transparencies 7, 8

Plan Ahead

Gather materials. You may also want students to begin their research on tectonic-plate activity around the world a few weeks before beginning this project.

Building the Project
Through Project Links

Chapter 1, p. B17 Students create a tectonic-plates map showing their own town and collect data from articles about earthquakes and volcanic activity around the world. Students can mark a world map with map pins to show where tectonic-plate activity is taking place. Then they can make predictions about where earthquakes might be likely to occur and where they might be less likely to occur. Students may use *Science Notebook* p. 54 to record their predictions.

Assessing Student Progress: Determine whether each group member participates in preparation of the tectonic-plates map and in placing map pins on the classroom map.

Chapter 2, p. B43 Students collect data about mountains that have grown after recent geologic upheavals. Then have students use the world map to identify the location of these growing mountains. Students can discuss and identify observed patterns, especially patterns that relate to the placement of these mountains on tectonic plates and near faults.

Assessing Student Progress: Evaluate each group's cooperative effort in researching recently uplifted mountains.

Chapter 3, p. B63 Students trace and compute how far the tsunami traveled after the Alaskan earthquake in 1964. Using the world map, students can then trace North American coastlines that might be exposed to tsunamis.

Assessing Student Progress: Evaluate whether or not each group's map represents areas likely to experience tsunamis.

Project Link **Chapter 4, p. B95** Students locate and mark the Ring of Fire on the world map and identify those islands created by volcanic activity. Then students can draw a picture of their own island paradise and describe where they think it will emerge. Students may use *Science Notebook* p. 106 to do their drawings and record their predictions.

Assessing Student Progress: Evaluate the accuracy of the placement of each island.

Wrapping Up the Project

Students should prepare a guide that gives people information on protecting themselves against earthquakes or volcanoes. Have students include maps, tables, and other visual tools to help them communicate their ideas clearly. Before students begin their guides, give them an opportunity to brainstorm on the kinds of information they want to include, such as public warnings, safety rules, improving building codes, or better prediction techniques. Use Unit Project Scoring Rubric Master B4 (TRB p. 74) to evaluate students' projects.

OTHER PROJECTS TO DO

- **Explore Use of Seismographs.** Find out how scientists use seismographs to detect earthquakes. Make a diagram to show a seismograph. Label the diagram with captions describing how the seismograph works. Make suggestions on how to improve the design of the seismograph.

- **Investigate Predicting Earthquakes.** Find out if there is any truth to predicting earthquakes based on animal behavior. Collect data on predicting earthquakes. Look for any information reporting changes in animals' behaviors prior to earthquakes. Use library resources to help you learn more about earthquake predictions.

PEOPLE TO CONTACT

In Person

- Contact a geoscientist to describe to the class the equipment used to conduct geological surveys.

By Mail

- **American Geological Institute,** 4220 King Street, Alexandria, VA 22302-1507

- **Geological Society of America,** P.O. Box 9140, 3300 Penrose Place, Boulder, CO, DC 80301

By Computer

- Connect to the *SilverShare Bulletin Board* to exchange data and the results of your investigations with other *Silver Burdett Ginn Science DiscoveryWorks* users. Watch for our Internet address, coming soon!

PLACES TO VISIT

- **Science museums** often have displays explaining how earthquakes and other large disturbances occur.

- **Parks** are a source of information on geological changes that have occurred.

- **Petroleum or natural gas industries that employ geologists** are sources of information on the local geology.

The Changing Earth

Overview The CD-ROM activities in this unit enable students to explore Earth's changing surface. Through animation, video, and Data Packs, students gather information on plate tectonics, earthquakes, and volcanoes. They use this knowledge to predict where future earthquakes and volcanoes may develop. This CD-ROM unit consists of five parts: a unit opening and four investigations.

Using the CD-ROM

Unit Opening On the Edge *(Beginning the Unit)*

On a world map, students click on information about plate boundaries by type of movement and predict where violent earthquakes might occur. They then view animation that illustrates the breakup of the supercontinent Pangea and the resulting continents' movement over time to their present positions.

Investigation 1 Map It! *(Enhances or replaces Chapter 1, Inv. 2)*

What is the relationship of tectonic plates to earthquakes and volcanoes?

In Map It! students describe how earthquakes and volcanoes are related to tectonic plates. Using the Earthquakes and Volcanoes Data Pack, they view tectonic plates on a world map, then place earthquakes and volcanoes in appropriate places along the plates. After analyzing the locations of earthquakes and volcanoes relative to the tectonic plates, students predict where these events may occur in the future.

Investigation 2 On the Move *(Enhances or replaces Chapter 2, Inv. 2)*

How were mountains formed?

In On the Move, students observe various types of plate movement that result in mountain building. They click on areas of a world map showing the tectonic plates to see the type of movement and the resulting mountain formation. They use the Mountains Data Pack to identify various mountain ranges around the world and discover how they were formed.

Investigation 3 Feel the Quake! *(Enhances or replaces Chapter 3, Inv. 3)*

How is the epicenter of an earthquake determined?

A video introduces students to a seismologist who shows them how the epicenter of an earthquake is located. Then students use wave information from three cities to determine the epicenter of an earthquake. They try the same activity with a different earthquake and three other cities. In the Earthquake Data Pack, students find information on several actual earthquakes, then use the Writer to describe the similarities and differences they discover.

Investigation 4 Thar She Blows *(Enhances or replaces Chapter 4, Inv. 1)*

How is a volcano formed?

Students watch a video in which a volcanologist describes how a volcano forms. Students then gather information on different types of volcanoes by clicking on colored dots on a world map to identify the locations of volcanoes. Using various Volcano Super-Packs, students create a Spreadsheet and a bar graph to compare different types of volcanoes.

CD-ROM Interactive

The CD-ROM includes Data Packs and Tools that can be used to enhance The Changing Earth.

Using the Data Packs

The Data Packs listed below can be accessed for information that relates to this unit.

Dinosaurs	**Oceans and Seas**
Earthquakes	**Rivers**
Minerals	**Rocks**
Mountain Ranges	**Volcanoes**

Geologic Time: Eras; Periods; Epochs

Using the Tools

On-screen tools can help students report results of activities, produce reports, or organize data.

Spreadsheet   Students can use this tool to chart data collected on worldwide volcanic eruptions and the data on volcanic islands in Chapter 4 activities.

Painter   Students can use this tool to reproduce their earthquake pattern, draw their sea floor spreading model, and reproduce their ocean floor map in Chapter 1.

Calculator   Students can use this tool to compare distances between volcanic islands in Chapter 4.

OTHER TECHNOLOGY RESOURCES

Science DiscoveryWorks
Videodisc Problem

Island Factory   Students investigate sea-floor spreading, plate tectonics, and hot spots to determine which of the Hawaiian Islands is the youngest. Use with Chapter 4.

Video

Discovering the Changing Surface of Our Earth   Students explore geologic phenomena such as faulting, folding, earthquakes, volcanoes, erosion, and glaciers. Use with Chapter 3 or 4. (Knowledge Unlimited Video 1–800–356–2303)

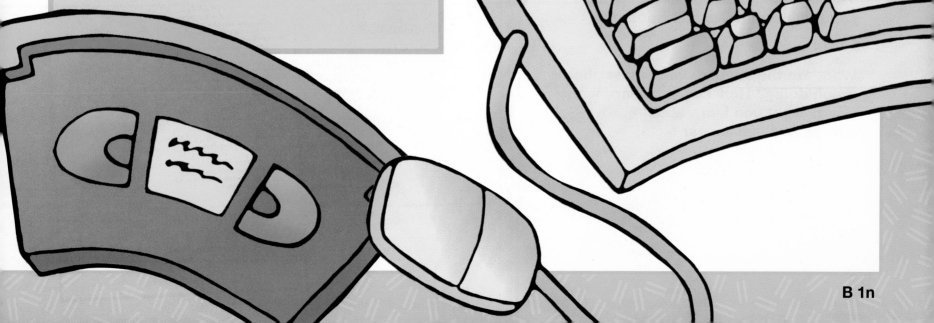

UNIT B

The Changing Earth

GET READY TO INVESTIGATE!

Overview

In this unit, students will be examining ways in which Earth changes over time. They will learn how volcanoes, earthquakes, and mountains are related to the theory of plate tectonics. Students will also learn why tectonic plates move and what happens as a result of this movement.

Warming Up

As students look at pages B2–B3, stimulate discussion with these questions:

- **What do you see in the photograph in the first column? How might a volcano erupting in one part of the world affect other places on Earth?**

- **What are the students in the photograph in the second column doing? How can measuring and locating earthquakes help in making new discoveries?**

- Point out the book cover to students. Invite them to read the summaries. The book pictured is in the Trade Book Library. **What do you think fumaroles and hot springs are?**

- **What are the students in the last photograph doing? How can you share with others what you learn about earthquakes and volcanoes?**

 Have students use *Science Notebook* p. 45.

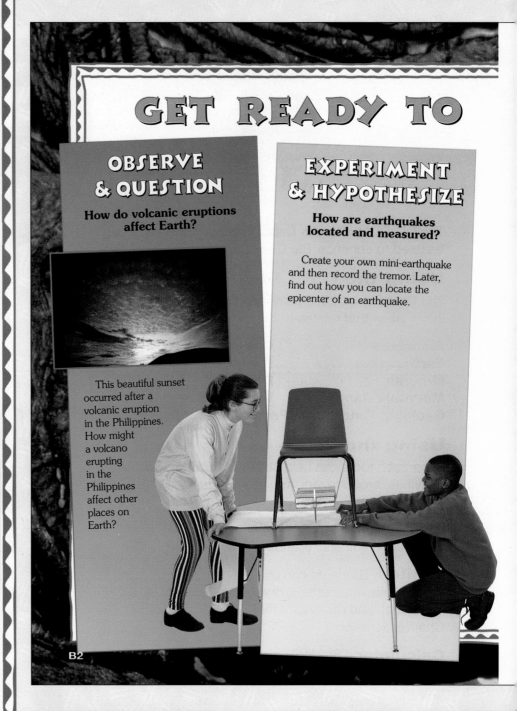

GET READY TO

OBSERVE & QUESTION

How do volcanic eruptions affect Earth?

This beautiful sunset occurred after a volcanic eruption in the Philippines. How might a volcano erupting in the Philippines affect other places on Earth?

EXPERIMENT & HYPOTHESIZE

How are earthquakes located and measured?

Create your own mini-earthquake and then record the tremor. Later, find out how you can locate the epicenter of an earthquake.

B2

Home-School Connection

The Opening Letter at the beginning of the unit introduces family members to the topic of plate tectonics. Distribute the Opening Letter (TRB p. 6) at the beginning of the unit.

Opening Letter

Dear Family,

Earth may seem "solid as a rock," but it's always changing. Our science class will be exploring some of these changes in a unit on The Changing Earth. We'll be studying the tectonic plates—thick slabs of rock—that make up Earth's crust and upper mantle. We'll learn how they move and how their movement causes changes to Earth's surface.

You can help your student keep track of some of Earth's changes by looking and listening for news stories about earthquakes and volcanoes. Share with your student any experiences or knowledge you or a friend or relative may have had with these events.

For this unit, we'll also be using the materials listed below. Can you donate any of these items? If so, we need to receive them by _____.

- shoeboxes with lids
- stirrers
- plastic straws
- oven mitts
- food coloring
- cellulose sponges
- coarse sandpaper
- shelf paper
- tracing paper

Do you or other family members have a special interest in or experience with earth science or seismology? Could you help with activities? If so, please fill out the form below and have your student return it to class.

Thank you for your help!

Opening Letter
The Changing Earth

Your name _____ Student's name _____

Home phone _____ Work phone _____

INVESTIGATE!

RESEARCH & ANALYZE

As you investigate, find out more from these books.

- **Volcanoes and Earthquakes** by Basil Booth (Silver Burdett Press, 1991). Besides learning all about volcanoes and earthquakes, you'll find out what fumaroles and hot springs are!

- **Earthquake at Dawn** by Kristiana Gregory (Harcourt Brace, 1992). Daisy Valentine watches in horror as San Francisco is rocked by an earthquake in 1906.

- **Surtsey: The Newest Place on Earth** by Kathryn Lasky (Hyperion Books for Children, 1992). The wonderful photographs in Lasky's book take you on an adventurer's tour of a newly formed island.

WORK TOGETHER & SHARE IDEAS

Is an earthquake likely to occur where you live?

Working together, you'll have a chance to apply what you've learned. With your class you'll explore the geologic events of your state and town. You'll find out whether you're likely to experience an earthquake or a volcanic eruption. Finally, you'll find out how to prepare for these events.

B3

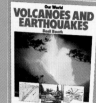

Additional Student Resources

How the Earth Works by John Farndon (Reader's Digest Association, 1992). A reference book that combines clear graphics with related hands-on activities. **(Text Correlation: Chapters 1-4)**

Volcanoes and Earthquakes by Mary Elting with Rachel Folsom and Robert Moll; illustrated by Courtney (Simon & Schuster Books for Young Readers, 1990). The true stories of famous eruptions, including Paricutín, Heimaey, Mt. Pelee, Mount St. Helens, Krakatoa, and Mount Vesuvius. **(Text Correlation: Chapter 3)**

Volcano: The Eruption and Healing of Mount St. Helens by Patricia Lauber (Aladdin Books, 1993). A photographic essay describing the eruption, devastation, and recolonization of living things on Mount St. Helens.

(Text Correlation: Chapter 4)

BOOKS AND ARTICLES FOR TEACHERS

Craters, Caverns, and Canyons: Delving Beneath the Earth's Surface by Jon Erickson (Facts on File, 1993). This fascinating book discusses meteorite impacts, caves and caverns, earthquakes, and volcanic rifts, among other topics. Good for additional information for the classroom.

"Dante's Inferno" by Judith Anne Gunther (*Popular Science,* Vol. 245, No.5, November 1994, p. 66). Dante II is a semiautonomous machine—a robot—used to collect images and samples of hostile environments. Built as part of a $1.7 million NASA-funded project, Dante II collected data on an active volcanic crater in the southern flank of Mt. Spurr in Alaska.

The Encyclopedia of Earthquakes and Volcanoes by David Ritchie (Facts on File, 1994). An A-to-Z listing of major earthquakes and volcanoes. Includes black-and-white photographs.

How the Earth Works by John Farndon (Reader's Digest Association, 1992). Guide to Earth science secrets through experiments and hands-on projects. Separate chapters on rocks and soil and the changing face of the land.

Janice VanCleave's Earthquakes: Mind-Boggling Experiments You Can Turn Into Science Fair Projects by Janice VanCleave (Wiley, 1993). A collection of experiments and projects that encourage students to explore various aspects of earthquakes. Good for classroom demonstrations.

Plate Tectonics: Unraveling the Mysteries of the Earth by Jon Erickson (Facts on File, 1992). Photographs and sketches illustrate information on plate tectonics. Includes how the plates have shifted over time and the effects of their shifting.

CHAPTER 1 · CRACKED CRUST

Subconcepts	Activities	Materials
Investigation 1 Do Continents Really Drift About?		

Evidence supports the theory that all the continents were once one large land-mass, which gradually separated into several continents.
 	
Suggested Pacing: 2–3 class periods
Standards
  pp. 160, 161
Benchmarks
  pp. 46, 73
	The Great Puzzle, p. B6
	Science Processes: observe, infer, make and use models
		scissors, Activity Support Master B1 (TRB p. 42), sheet of paper, glue, map of the world, *Science Notebook* p. 49

Investigation 2 What Do the Locations of Volcanoes and Earthquakes Tell Us?		

Earth's crust and upper mantle are composed of plates that fit together like the pieces of a broken eggshell; strong earthquakes and volcanoes occur at the edges of these plates.
 	
Suggested Pacing: 2–3 class periods
Standards
  pp. 159, 160
Benchmarks
  pp. 46, 73
	The Earth—Always Rockin' and Rollin'!, p. B16
	Science Processes: observe; communicate; infer; predict; collect, record, and interpret data; make and use models
	
	Volcanoes and Earth's Plates, p. B18
	Science Processes: observe; communicate; collect, record, and interpret data; make hypotheses
		Activity Support Master B2 (TRB p. 43), tracing paper*, *Science Notebook* pp. 52–53
		
		Activity Support Master B3 (TRB p. 44), Activity Support Master B2 (TRB p. 43), *Science Notebook* p. 55

Investigation 3 What Does the Sea Floor Tell Us About Plate Tectonics?		

The sea floor spreads away from cracks or rifts in the crust and magma rises to form new crust; sea-floor spreading is evidence for the theory of plate tectonics.
 	
Suggested Pacing: 3–4 class periods
Standards
  pp. 159, 160
Benchmarks
  pp. 46, 73
	Sea-Floor Spreading, p. B22
	Science Processes: observe, make hypotheses, make and use models
	
	Building a Model of the Ocean Floor, p. B23
	Science Processes: make and use models
	
	Mapping the Ocean Floor, p. B24
	Science Processes: measure/use numbers; communicate; infer; collect, record, and interpret data; define operationally; make and use models
		sheet of paper with 3 slits, each 10 cm long; 2 strips of notebook paper, each 9.5 x 27 cm long; metric ruler*; scissors; pencil; *Science Notebook* p. 57
		
		modeling clay*, shoebox with lid*, metric ruler*, Activity Support Master B4 (TRB p. 45), pencil, tape, *Science Notebook* p. 58
		
		coffee stirrer*, fine-tip marker*, plastic straws*, scissors, shoebox model of ocean floor, metric ruler*, plastic tape, *Science Notebook* p. 60

Overview

In this chapter students examine the theory of continental drift, the theory of plate tectonics, the world-wide pattern of earthquakes and volcanoes, and the nature of sea-floor spreading.

Chapter Concept

The position of Earth's continents has changed as the continents have ridden upon moving tectonic plates; earthquakes, volcanoes, and the formation of new crust are most common at the edges of these plates.

Advance Preparation	Curriculum Connection	Assessment
The Great Puzzle None	Social Studies TG pp. B8, B10, B14 The Arts TG p. B9, B12 Integrating the Sciences TG p. B11 Science, Technology & Society TG p. B13	**Chapter 1 Baseline Assessment:** *Science Notebook* pp. 45–46 **Investigation 1 Baseline Assessment:** TG p. B6 **Investigation 1 Review:** AG p. 42 **Think It/Write It,** p. B15; *Science Notebook* p. 51 **Following Up on Baseline Assessment:** TG p. B15 **Performance:** TG p. B15
The Earth—Always Rockin' and Rollin'! None **Volcanoes and Earth's Plates** None	Math TG p. B19 Social Studies TG p. B20	**Investigation 2 Baseline Assessment:** TG p. B16 **Investigation 1 Review:** AG p. 43 **Think It/Write It,** p. B21; *Science Notebook* p. 56 **Following Up on Baseline Assessment:** TG p. B21 **Portfolio:** TG p. B21
Sea-Floor Spreading Prepare papers with 3 slits, each 10 cm long. **Building a Model of the Ocean Floor** Collect enough shoeboxes for each group. **Mapping the Ocean Floor** None	Integrating the Sciences TG pp. B26, B28 Science, Technology & Society TG p. 27 Cultural Connection TG p. B31 The Arts TG p. B29 Math TG p. B30	**Investigation 3 Baseline Assessment:** TG p. B22 **Investigation 3 Review:** AG p. 44 **Think It/Write It,** p. B32; *Science Notebook* p. 62 **Following Up on Baseline Assessment:** TG p. B32 **Portfolio:** TG p. B32 **Chapter 1 Summative Assessment** Reflect and Evaluate, p. B33 Chapter 1 Review/Test: AG pp. 45–46 *Science Notebook* pp. 63–64

TG= Teaching Guide   TRB= Teacher Resource Book   AG= Assessment Guide   *Materials in the Deluxe Equipment Kit

Chapter Overview

Chapter Concept The position of Earth's continents has changed as the continents have ridden upon moving tectonic plates; earthquakes, volcanoes, and the formation of new crust are most common at the edges of these plates.

Theme: Models
The location of the continents has changed over time because of the slow movement of tectonic plates. Models can show how these changes occurred.

Common Misconceptions
Students probably do not think that Earth's continents move. This chapter examines evidence that explains why continents move as a result of the movement of large slabs of rock, called tectonic plates.

Options for
Setting the Stage

Warm-Up Activity
 Cut a piece of construction paper into five or six jigsaw puzzle pieces. Place the scrambled pieces on an overhead projector. Ask what clues can be used to piece the puzzle together.

 Use *Science Notebook* p.45.

Discussion Starter:
Mapping the Ocean Floor

Use the photo and text to start a discussion of how the ocean floor can be mapped.

- **How can ship navigators detect when they are passing over a mountain or a deep trench?** Sonar can be used to measure distances to the ocean floor.

- **Career:** *Geological Oceanographer*
Explain to students that geological oceanographers study the topography and structure of the ocean floor. They observe and map the ocean basins and study rock, coral reefs, and ocean sediment. Geological oceanographers need college courses in geology, biology, physics, and chemistry. Many of them hold doctoral degrees.

CHAPTER 1

CRACKED CRUST

Beneath the oceans are the highest mountains and the deepest trenches on Earth. Here molten rock erupts along underwater mountain ranges. The eruptions are part of the constant change taking place on the ocean floor.

Mapping the Ocean Floor

Few will ever see firsthand the impressive mountains and valleys below the surface of the oceans. The best view has been through sonar maps produced by ocean-floor surveys done from ships.

Now scientists in California and New York have used satellite information to produce an improved map of the ocean floor. Radar equipment on the satellite measured the distance from the satellite to Earth's surface, providing a map of the surface of the oceans. But how does this help map the ocean floor?

Because of gravity, ocean water piles up around underwater mountain ranges. Less water is found over the deep trenches. This means that the surface of the ocean has hills and valleys that imitate the contours of the ocean floor. So a map of the *surface* of the ocean provides a picture of its *floor* at the same time. Why is it important to have an accurate map of the ocean floor?

B4

Home-School Connection

The Explore at Home activity "A Puzzling Matter" encourages students to compare Earth's continents to the pieces of a puzzle. To further reinforce students' understanding of Pangaea, distribute the activity (TRB p. 7) when students have completed the chapter. Discuss the fit of the coastlines of Africa and South America.

Explore at Home

Name _____ Date _____

A PUZZLING MATTER

We have been studying how Earth changes and have learning that all of Earth's continents were once join By comparing Earth's continents to the pieces of a puzzle, we can reenact how scientists pieced togethe the idea of continental drift.

Materials
✔ paper
✔ crayons or marker
✔ scissors

Procedure
Using separate sheets of paper, you and a family member should each draw a picture that fills the page. The subject of the pictures can be anything you wish. Without letting each other see the finished drawings, cut each drawing into about 20 puzzle

pieces. Exchange your puzzles and see if you can put them back together again.

Results
Discuss what clues each of you used to reassemble the puzzles. Were you guided by the colors and patterns on each piece? Did you use the shapes of the pieces themselves? Did you try to visualize the complete picture? Talk about how your experience of putting the puzzle together was like the experience of scientists piecing together the theory of continental drift.

Coming Up

**DO CONTINENTS
REALLY DRIFT
ABOUT?**
.... B6

**WHAT DO THE
LOCATIONS OF
VOLCANOES AND
EARTHQUAKES
TELL US?**
.... B16

**WHAT DOES THE
SEA FLOOR TELL
US ABOUT PLATE
TECTONICS?**
.... B22

◀ Improved maps show that the sea
floor has features as varied as those
on land.

B5

Technology Alert

CD-ROM

Map It! Enhances or replaces Investigation 2

The activities in **Map It!** are designed to help students interpret data and hypothesize about the relationship between the location of volcanoes, earthquakes, and tectonic plates. Students become geologist-detectives and first view plate boundaries on a world map. They move earthquake and volcano symbols to appropriate locations on or near plate boundaries on the map, using the Earthquakes Data Pack and Volcanoes Data Pack for additional information. They hypothesize about a connection between earthquakes and volcanoes and plate boundaries. In the Writer, they predict where earthquakes and volcanoes might occur in the future.

Chapter Road Map

Do Continents Really Drift About?

Activities
* The Great Puzzle

Resources
Alfred Wegener and the Drifting Continents
* Evidence for Continental Drift
* Continents on the Move

What Do the Locations of Volcanoes and Earthquakes Tell Us?

Activities
* Earth—Always Rockin' and Rollin'!
Volcanoes and Earth's Plates

Resources
* The Cracked Crust: Tectonic Plates

What Does the Sea Floor Tell Us About Plate Tectonics?

Activities
* Sea-Floor Spreading
Building a Model of the Ocean Floor
Mapping the Ocean Floor

Resources
Sonar: Mapping the Sea Floor
* Magnetism Tells a Story
Heating Up Iceland

*Pressed for Time?

As you work through the upcoming investigations, focus on the activities and resources identified by the clock.

 Look for this symbol in front of questions that help develop Scientific Reasoning Skills.

DO CONTINENTS REALLY DRIFT ABOUT?

Planner

Subconcept Evidence supports the theory that all the continents were once one large landmass, which gradually separated into several continents.

Objectives

- **Make a model** showing all the continents joined and **infer** whether the fit seems reasonable.
- **Investigate** the development of the theory of continental drift and **evaluate** supporting evidence.

Pacing 2–3 class periods

Science Terms Pangaea, theory of continental drift

Activate Prior Knowledge

Baseline Assessment Ask: **If you try to glue the pieces of a broken plate back together, how can you tell which pieces fit together? How could you tell if Earth's continents once fit together?** Record responses for use in Following Up.

Activity The Great Puzzle

Preview *Students use models of the continents and should find that they can be joined to form a single landmass.*

1. Get Ready

Time about 30 minutes

Grouping groups of 4–6

Collaborative Strategy After each student completes a map of Pangaea, small groups then can compare maps.

Materials Hints Use Activity Support Master B1 (TRB, p. 42).

Safety Review safety precautions with students. Caution students to take care when using the scissors.

DO CONTINENTS REALLY DRIFT ABOUT?

About 80 years ago, Alfred Wegener suggested that at one time all the continents were joined together in one large landmass known as Pangaea. Further, he suggested that the continents split apart and drifted to their current locations. Other scientists laughed at him. Could he have been right?

Activity
The Great Puzzle

MATERIALS
- scissors
- outline map of the continents
- sheet of paper
- glue
- map of the world
- *Science Notebook*

Take a look at a map of the world. You may notice that the continents fit together like the pieces of a jigsaw puzzle. Can you reconstruct the "supercontinent" of Pangaea from today's continents?

Procedure

1. Using scissors, cut out each of the continents from the outline map. Cut along the dark outlines.

2. Arrange the continents on a sheet of paper so that they all fit together, forming one supercontinent.

3. After you have obtained your best fit, make a map by gluing the pieces onto the sheet of paper in the pattern that you obtained. Keep your map in your *Science Notebook*.

4. Use a map of the world to find the name of each continent on your map. Label the continents.

Step 1

B6

Responding to Individual Needs

Students Acquiring English Have students label each continent with its name in English and in their native language. Then help them pronounce the continents' names in both languages.

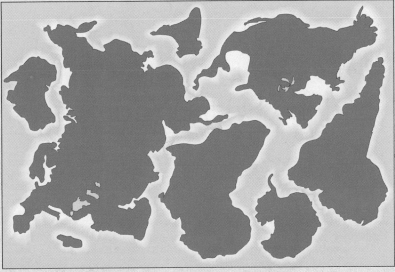

▲ Outline map of the continents

Analyze and Conclude

1. How well did the continents fit together to make a single supercontinent?

2. Compare the map that you made with one showing the present locations of the continents. What can you infer about Earth's continents if both maps are accurate?

3. In your reconstruction, what continents border on the continent of North America?

4. What evidence, besides the shapes of the continents, might scientists look for to confirm the idea that continents were once joined in a supercontinent?

INVESTIGATE FURTHER!

RESEARCH

Look in a world atlas, such as *Goode's World Atlas*, to find a map that shows Earth's landforms. Use this information to explain why Wegener thought Earth's landmasses were once joined as a supercontinent.

B7

2. Guide the Procedure

• You may wish to reproduce the outline maps on heavy paper for a firmer base. Small scissors should be used for cutting the detailed coastlines of the continents.

• Expect differences among students' maps. Even experts don't agree on exactly how all the continents should be joined.

 Have students answer questions on *Science Notebook* p. 49.

 You may wish to have students use the CD Rom Painter to display their maps.

3. Assess Performance

Process Skills Checklist

• Did students' **models** of Pangaea display how the continents once fit together to form one large land-mass?

• Did students **infer** that the present-day continents must have moved from their previous positions?

Analyze and Conclude

1. In most cases, the continents fit together reasonably well.

2. If both maps are accurate, then the continents must have moved over time.

3. Answers may vary, but probably Europe and Africa border on North America.

4. Scientists might look for similarities in landforms and in fossil plant and animal life across continental borders.

Investigate Further

Research

The mountain chain that includes the Appalachians runs through the United States and off the coast of Newfoundland. Mountains of similar structure and age are found in Greenland and Scandinavia. Similar landforms can also be matched when South America and Africa are joined. Remind students to record their information in their *Science Notebooks* on p. 50.

Alfred Wegener and the Drifting Continents

Preview *Students focus on the development of Wegener's theory of continental drift. They will find out how Wegener came to propose the idea of Pangaea and the evidence he cited to support the theory of continental drift. Students will discover that it often takes many years for a new idea to become accepted by other scientists.*

1. Get Ready

Science Terms Pangaea

Background

• After Wegener proposed his theory of continental drift, he was met with extraordinary hostility from geologists wherever he went. The notion that Earth's continents were not fixed in one place was considered bizarre and ludicrous, because it contradicted every theory of geology held in the early 1900s. At the time, most scientists believed that Earth was cooling and contracting. They did believe that the continents had once been joined by land bridges, but that the land bridges had collapsed and sunk under the oceans as the planet shrank.

Discussion Starter

• **In The Great Puzzle, which two continents seemed to best fit together?** South America and Africa

• **Why might people not have believed that the continents had drifted apart?** Students might respond that something as large and massive as a continent could not have moved.

Alfred Wegener and the Drifting Continents

The year was 1911. Nabisco introduced its cream-filled chocolate cookie called Oreo. Marie Curie won a Nobel Prize for her isolation of pure radium. The National Urban League was founded.

That same year, Alfred Wegener read a scientific paper that changed his life. The paper presented evidence that millions of years ago a land bridge may have connected South America with Africa. To Wegener the evidence suggested that the two continents were at one time a continuous landmass. Further, he thought that *all* of Earth's continents might once have been joined. But he dropped the idea when he couldn't explain how such vast landmasses had moved.

In 1912, Wegener gave a scientific talk about his ideas on moving continents. He suggested that the landmasses were once joined and had since drifted apart. Nearly all who attended the talk, as well as others in the scientific community, thought Wegener's idea was ridiculous. Wegener still held on to his hypothesis.

In 1915 he published a book explaining how Earth's continents and oceans might have formed and changed over time. His evidence came from many fields of science. Wegener noted that the continental shelves fit together like the pieces of a puzzle. A continental shelf is an underwater part of a continent that extends under shallow water from the edge of the land down to a steeper slope. He noted that the fossil remains of certain species of plants and animals were found on widely separated continents. The plants and animals that left these fossils could not have crossed the oceans.

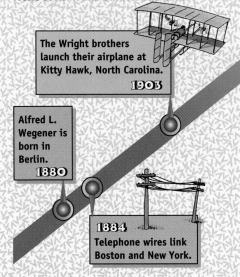

The Wright brothers launch their airplane at Kitty Hawk, North Carolina. **1903**

Alfred L. Wegener is born in Berlin. **1880**

1884 **Telephone wires link Boston and New York.**

B8

Integrating the Curriculum

Science & Social Studies

THEORIES

What to Do When the first reliable world maps were made in the 17th century, several scientists noted the remarkable fit between the west coast of Africa and the east coast of South America. The suggestion was made that the two continents had once been joined but had broken apart and moved. Ask students to find out about the theory proposed by geologist Edward Suess in 1885.

What's the Result? What did Edward Suess propose in his theory? How was Wegener's theory similar to Suess's? According to Suess, Earth's crust shrank as the planet cooled. Great slabs of crust collapsed into the mantle, creating ocean basins. Both scientists believed in the idea of an ancient supercontinent.

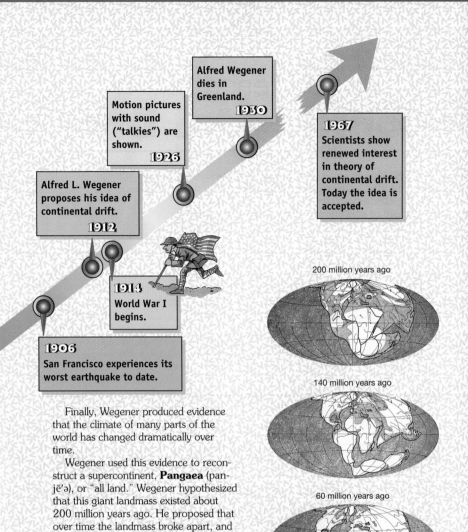

Alfred Wegener
dies in
Greenland.
1930

Motion pictures
with sound
("talkies") are
shown.
1926

1967
Scientists show
renewed interest
in theory of
continental drift.
Today the idea is
accepted.

Alfred L. Wegener
proposes his idea of
continental drift.
1912

1914
World War I
begins.

1906
San Francisco experiences its
worst earthquake to date.

Finally, Wegener produced evidence that the climate of many parts of the world has changed dramatically over time.

Wegener used this evidence to reconstruct a supercontinent, **Pangaea** (pan-jē′ə), or "all land." Wegener hypothesized that this giant landmass existed about 200 million years ago. He proposed that over time the landmass broke apart, and he concluded that continents are still moving. Wegener's hypothesis on the movement of continents is called continental drift. Despite all the evidence cited, it wasn't until the 1960s that scientists took Wegener's hypothesis seriously. ■

200 million years ago

140 million years ago

60 million years ago

▲ Wegener's maps of drifting continents

B9

Science & the Arts

MAP-MAKING

What to Do Students might enjoy using drawing paper and markers to draw a map of an imaginary planet with three or four continents that could have once been joined. Have them draw in mountain ranges and fossil locations.
What's the Result? Suggest that pairs of students exchange maps, then try to reconstruct one large landmass formed by the continents.

2. Guide the Discussion

Choose from the following strategies to facilitate discussion.

Connecting to the Activities

• *The Great Puzzle, p. B6*
Think back to *The Great Puzzle*. What was probably the first bit of evidence that led some people to believe that the continents were once connected? The similarities between the coastlines of South America and Africa

Making Inferences

Do you think the continents were drifting before Pangaea broke apart? Why do you think so? Answers will vary, but students who answer "yes" will probably infer that if the continents have been moving for the past 200 million years, they were probably moving before that as well.

Responding to Individual Needs

Kinesthetic Activity To reinforce the idea of an ancient supercontinent, use oversized outlines of the continents mounted on heavy cardboard or plastic foam and cut out so that students can feel how the continental coastlines might fit together.

Thinking About the Data

• **Besides their shapes, what other evidence suggests that Africa and South America were once joined?** The discovery of fossil remains of similar plants and animals and identical patterns among rock layers found in Brazil and South Africa.

Making Inferences

• **Why didn't scientists immediately accept Wegener's theory of continental drift?** His theory didn't have an explanation as to how or why the continents moved.

3. Assess Understanding

Students can work in groups of three or four. Have them draw small maps showing the positions of the continents at 200 million, 140 million, and 60 million years ago and place them on a timeline of the last 200 million years.

Evidence for Continental Drift

Preview *Students focus on the evidence that Wegener found and used to support his theory of continental drift.*

1. Get Ready

Background

- The theory of continental drift can explain many fossil distributions. Alfred S. Romer, an authority on Permian amphibians and reptiles, has noted a great similarity between animal fossils found in Texas and those found in the Czech Republic. He has stated that the similarity is so great that if a person familiar with a Texas fossil collection were presented with a specimen from the Czech fossil collection, he or she would not realize that it was not part of the Texas collection. Although Texas and the Czech Republic were not connected, the continents of North America and Europe once were, and the animal ranges extended into both places.

Discussion Starter

- **Why was it difficult at first for people to believe Wegener's theory that the continents had drifted?** The process has been so slow that it isn't noticeable, even over many generations. Also, Wegener couldn't explain how or why the continents moved.

- **What kinds of evidence would you have looked for to support your theory if you were Wegener?** Encourage speculation from the students at this point. They might mention looking at fossil evidence or similar landforms.

Evidence for Continental Drift

Alfred Wegener was a meteorologist—a scientist who studies weather. But he was interested in many fields of science. His **theory of continental drift**, which stated that the continents were once one landmass that had broken apart and moved to their present positions, was supported by many lines of evidence.

One piece of evidence was the puzzle-like fit of continental shelves. Recall how you fitted the continents together on page B6. Wegener found that when he joined the continental shelves of Africa and South America, the fit was nearly perfect. Many of the rocks that made up mountains in Argentina were identical to those found in South Africa. It seemed unlikely to Wegener that these identical layers of rocks were formed in such widely separated places at the same time.

By the time Wegener had published the third edition of his book, he had found other similarities among certain rocks. He had discovered that diamond-rich rocks in South Africa were very similar to diamond-rich rocks in Brazil. Many of the coal beds in North America, Britain, and Belgium were deposited in the same geological period. And a thick red sandstone layer crossed continental boundaries from North America to Greenland, Britain, and Norway. Look at the map shown below. What pieces of evidence can you name that support the theory of continental drift?

The fit of the continental shelves is evidence that South America and Africa were once joined. ▶

AFRICA

SOUTH AMERICA

■ Areas of overlap
■ Continental shelf
□ Similar geologic formations

B10

Integrating the Curriculum

Science & Social Studies

MAKING MAPS **What to Do** Have students trace a world map onto paper. They can use a symbol to mark places where fossils of *Glossopteris* have been found. They can also use symbols to mark places where similar natural resources occur. Have students include a map key.
What's the Result? **Where has *Glossopteris* been found?** South America, Australia, India, and Africa **Where are similar resources found?** Answers should reflect information from the maps in an atlas.
Multi-Age Classroom Small groups could discuss what resources to put on the map and the symbols to use. Tasks could be assigned on the basis of students' capabilities and interest level.

Wegener also noted that certain fossils were preserved in rocks of the same age on different continents. He argued that the remains of these once-living organisms were so similar that they must have been left by the same kinds of organisms. One of these creatures was a small reptile called *Mesosaurus*, which lived its life in fresh water. Other fossils found in rocks that were very far apart were those of *Glossopteris*. Remains of this plant had been discovered in South America, Australia, India, and Africa. How, Wegener asked, could this plant have survived the different climates of these four landmasses?

Because of his training as a meteorologist, much of Wegener's evidence included information about climate. You probably already know that Earth can be divided into three major climate zones. The tropics are located near the equator and extend to about $23\frac{1}{2}°$ north and south of the equator. The temperate zones lie between the tropics and the polar zones. The polar climatic zones extend from about $66\frac{1}{2}°$ north and south to the poles.

Wegener noted that fossils of beech, maple, oak, poplar, ash, chestnut, and elm trees had been found on a small island named Spitsbergen, near the North

◀ **A variety of *Glossopteris*, a plant with fossil remains found in widely separated continents.**

Pole. These trees generally grow only in temperate areas. Today, however, the island is covered for much of the year with snow and ice because it has a very cold climate—a polar climate.

Coal forms in swampy marshes that receive a lot of rain each year. Today coal beds are forming in areas near the equator and in some temperate regions. Wegener proposed that coal beds in the eastern United States, Europe, and Siberia formed when the continents were joined and were located closer to the equator.

Wegener used all of these different lines of evidence to reconstruct the supercontinent Pangaea. He hypothesized that this single landmass existed about 200 million years ago. Over time, he proposed, the landmass broke apart and the continents drifted to their present positions on Earth's surface. ■

Another variety of *Glossopteris* ▼

◀ ***Mesosaurus*. Fossil remains of this reptile were found on widely separated continents.**

B11

Investigate Further

Integrating the Sciences

LIFE SCIENCE

What to Do Australia has remained isolated since its rift from Antarctica during the breakup of Pangaea. Ask students to find out how continental drift might have influenced the animal populations of Australia.

What's the Result? **What unusual kinds of animals evolved on this continent?** Answers should include marsupials, such as kangaroos and wombats. **Why were they able to survive?** They had no competition from placental mammals that evolved on other continents.

Multi-Age Classroom Students with research skills could locate sources, while others with artistic skills could prepare the collage.

2. Guide the Discussion

Choose from the following strategies to facilitate discussion.

Connecting to the Activities

• *The Great Puzzle, p. B6*

Think back to *The Great Puzzle*. On which two continents might you start looking for similar fossils or landforms? Why? South America and Africa might be a good place to start looking because they seem to fit together so well.

Responding to Individual Needs

Visual/Spatial Activity On the chalkboard, make diagrams of two columns of rocks. Using colored chalk to represent different types of rock layers, make both columns identical in the bottom five layers. Then make them different in the top three layers. Label one column *Africa* and the other *South America*. Ask: **Why do you think the bottom rock layers are the same, but the top layers are different?** Students should infer that the bottom layers formed when the two continents were joined, and the upper layers formed after the continents had separated.

Thinking About the Data

• **List all of Wegener's evidence for continental drift.** The puzzlelike fit of the continental shelves, similarities among certain rocks on different continents, identical plant and animal fossils on different continents, and fossils of temperate plants in polar climates.

Responding to Individual Needs

Gifted and Talented Activity Ask students to speculate on possible ways that similar plants and animals might have moved from one continent to another if the continents were never connected. Have them present their ideas to the class.

3. Assess Understanding

Students can work in groups of three or four and use index cards to make a simple "Go Fish" type card game using various lines of evidence that supports continental drift. Players take turns asking for certain cards and must "drift" if the requested card is not held by any of the players.

Continents on the Move

Preview *Students focus on a visual essay showing the positions of the continents and the predominant plants and animals living during different time intervals, from about 180 million years ago to the present. By examining arrows on a series of world maps, students can see how the large landmasses split apart and gradually moved over millions of years, demonstrating continental drift.*

1. Get Ready

Background

• Before the formation of Pangaea, Earth's landmasses had probably joined and separated several times. Evidence from fossils and landforms indicates that between 500 and 225 million years ago, continents from an earlier supercontinent began to collect to form Pangaea. The first collision is thought to have occurred between North America and Europe. That collision resulted in the formation of the northern Appalachian Mountains. During the period between 250 and 300 million years ago, Africa and North America collided, causing the formation of the southern Appalachian Mountains.

Discussion Starter

Do you think the continents are still moving today? Why or why not? Students might reason that if the continents were moving in the past, they are probably still moving today.

Continents on the Move

Wegener's hypothesis stated that Pangaea began to break apart about 180 million years ago. These smaller pieces of land drifted to their present position as Earth's continents. Although Wegener's idea was at first criticized, today it is accepted by scientists.

The maps on the next four pages show how landmasses—later Earth's continents—moved over time. Arrows on the continents show the direction in which they moved. Compare the location of the continents millions of years ago with their present location. ■

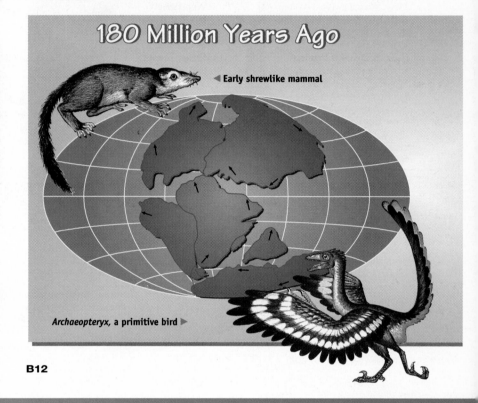

180 Million Years Ago

◄ **Early shrewlike mammal**

Archaeopteryx, a primitive bird ▶

B12

Integrating the Curriculum

Science & the Arts

MAKING MODELS

What to Do Students can make flip books from a series of ten index cards to show the drifting of South America and Africa. On the first card, the continents should be joined together. On successive cards, they should be slightly apart. On the tenth card, the continents should be located where they are today. Students can use the maps on pp. B12–B15 to help them position the two continents.

What's the Result? After the cards are stapled along on one edge, have students flip the cards to show two continents drifting apart.

Multi-Age Classroom Have older students draw the maps and collaborate with younger students to correctly sequence the cards.

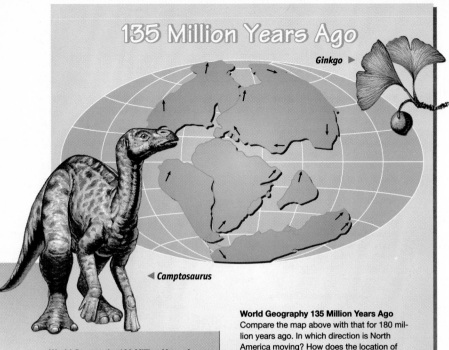

135 Million Years Ago

Ginkgo

◀ *Camptosaurus*

World Geography 180 Million Years Ago
About 180 million years ago, North America, Europe, and much of Asia began to split from South America and Africa. India separated from the landmass around the South Pole and started moving northward. Australia and Antarctica drifted to the south and west. The Atlantic and Indian Oceans began to form.

Life About 180 Million Years Ago
Green algae, corals, and sponges lived in the warm waters that covered much of Earth. Ammonites, which looked like giant snails, also inhabited Earth's oceans. Many amphibians, including ancestors of modern frogs, roamed the land. The first dinosaurs appeared on Earth. Somewhat later, *Archaeopteryx*, a birdlike animal, also lived on Earth. Conifers were the dominant plants.

World Geography 135 Million Years Ago
Compare the map above with that for 180 million years ago. In which direction is North America moving? How does the location of India compare with that on the map for 180 million years ago? In which direction is Australia moving? What has happened to South America and Africa?

Life About 135 Million Years Ago
Sea urchins, sand dollars, and green algae populated the seas. Dinosaurs such as *Camptosaurus*, *Stegosaurus*, *Allosaurus*, and *Apatosaurus* roamed the land. Birds soared through the sky. Conifers, ferns, and ginkgoes made up the plant life on the planet.

B13

Investigate Further

 ## Science, Technology & Society

USING LASERS **What to Do** Have students find out about global positioning systems (GPS), in which a laser beam is sent from a ground-based station to a satellite. The beam is reflected back to the station. By measuring the time required for the laser beam to make the trip, a person can compute the distance between the satellite and the ground station. The distance between any two Earth stations can also be calculated. Thus, if there is a change in distance between any two ground stations due to plate movement, it can be detected and measured.
What's the Result? **How might the information gathered from GPS be helpful to scientists?** Scientists can plot the distance and the rate at which continents are moving away from each other.

2. Guide the Discussion
Choose from the following strategies to facilitate discussion.

Responding to Individual Needs
Visual/Spatial Activity Place a covered transparent container of water on an overhead projector. Float several pieces of plastic foam in the water. Gently stir the water a little. Ask students to observe the movement of the pieces and compare them with Earth's drifting continents.

Connecting to the Activities
- ***The Great Puzzle, p. B6***
If you started with the continents in their present-day positions, in what directions would you move South America and Africa to form part of Pangaea? South America would move east and Africa would move westward.

Have students research climate and representative organisms on Earth during the times shown on the maps on pp. B12–B14 using the Geologic Time Data Pack on the CD-ROM.

Making Comparisons
Look at the four maps. What do they show? The movement of the continents over a period of 180 million years
- **How do the positions of Africa and South America change from one map to the next?** In each successive map, the two continents move farther and farther away from each other.
- **In what direction did each continent move from Pangaea to its position today?** North America and South America moved west, Africa moved northeast, Antarctica moved south, Australia moved south and west and then northeast, Europe and Asia moved northeast, and India moved north.

Making Inferences

■ **If the continents are still moving today, where might they be in another 50 million years?** Responses should indicate further movement in basically the same directions.

■ **If the continents continue to move in the same directions, which continents might be the next to collide?** Perhaps Australia and Asia or North America and Asia (near Alaska)

Making Comparisons

• **What kinds of plants and animals lived on Earth 180 million years ago?** Green algae, coral, sponges, and ammonoids lived in the oceans. Amphibians and reptiles lived on the land. Conifers were the main land plants.

• **What new kinds of living things lived on Earth 135 million years ago?** Sea urchins, sand dollars, dinosaurs, birds, ginkgoes, and ferns

• **What were the most numerous land animals 65 million years ago?** Insects

Drawing Conclusions

• **How did plant life on land evolve between 180 million and 65 million years ago?** The main land plants 180 million years ago were conifers, but by 65 million years ago, the main land plants were flowering plants.

3. Assess Understanding

Students can work in groups of three or four. Invite each group to draw a map that shows the probable positions of the continents 50 million years in the future.

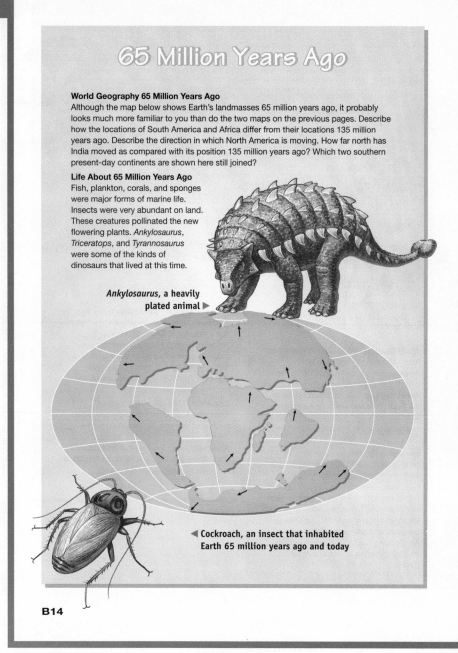

65 Million Years Ago

World Geography 65 Million Years Ago
Although the map below shows Earth's landmasses 65 million years ago, it probably looks much more familiar to you than do the two maps on the previous pages. Describe how the locations of South America and Africa differ from their locations 135 million years ago. Describe the direction in which North America is moving. How far north has India moved as compared with its position 135 million years ago? Which two southern present-day continents are shown here still joined?

Life About 65 Million Years Ago
Fish, plankton, corals, and sponges were major forms of marine life. Insects were very abundant on land. These creatures pollinated the new flowering plants. *Ankylosaurus*, *Triceratops*, and *Tyrannosaurus* were some of the kinds of dinosaurs that lived at this time.

Ankylosaurus, a heavily plated animal ▶

◀ Cockroach, an insect that inhabited Earth 65 million years ago and today

B14

Integrating the Curriculum

Science & Social Studies

USING MAPS **What to Do** Evidence of glaciation 300 million years ago is found in South America, southern Africa, India, Australia, and Antarctica. Have students locate these areas on the world map, then shade them on an outline of a world map.

What's the Result? **What does this evidence indicate about the positions of these continents 300 million years ago?** Parts of these continents were much closer to the South Pole and possibly were once joined.

Multi-Age Classroom Students could work in groups and discuss the best way to position the continents to form a single landmass.

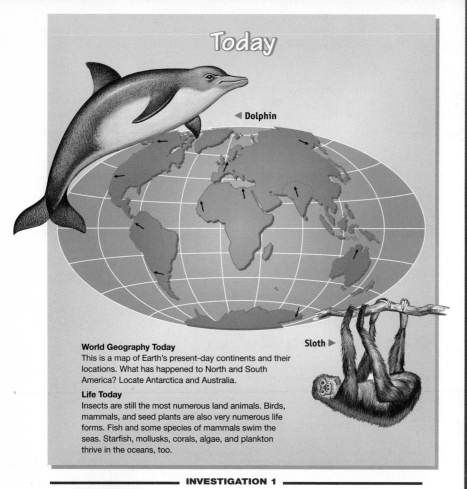

Today

◀ Dolphin

World Geography Today
This is a map of Earth's present-day continents and their locations. What has happened to North and South America? Locate Antarctica and Australia.

Life Today
Insects are still the most numerous land animals. Birds, mammals, and seed plants are also very numerous life forms. Fish and some species of mammals swim the seas. Starfish, mollusks, corals, algae, and plankton thrive in the oceans, too.

Sloth ▶

INVESTIGATION 1

1. Evidence of glaciers has been found in many parts of southern Africa! What does this information tell you about the possible location of this continent at some time in the past?

2. Describe the kinds of evidence that Alfred Wegener and other scientists have used to show that the continents move over time.

B15

Assessment

Performance
Presentation 🔲 On index cards, write statements that could and could not be used to support continental drift. Divide the class into groups of 3 or 4 and let each group pick a card from the pile. Give each group a few minutes to discuss whether the evidence would or would not support Wegener's hypothesis. Have a member from each group present the consensus.

Investigation Review
Do Continents Really Drift About?

CHAPTER 1

Name _____ Date _____

1. Underline the correct answer within the parentheses.

a. Alfred Wegener's hypothesis of (continental drift, plate tectonics) stated that all of the continents had once been joined together as a single supercontinent, which he called (Pangaea, Spitzbergen).

b. According to Wegener's hypothesis, the supercontinent began to split apart about (200, 20) million years ago. Today, the continents (have stopped moving, continue to move).

2. Match each conclusion with evidence appropriate for that conclusion. Use all the evidence.

Conclusions

I. Africa and South America were once connected.

II. North America and Europe were once connected and, together with much of Asia, were closer to the equator.

III. India, Australia, Africa, and South America were once connected.

Evidence

a. Beds of red sandstone of the same age are found on these continents.

b. The fossil *Glossopteris* is found in rocks of the same age on these continents.

c. The continental shelf outlines match almost perfectly.

d. Coal beds on these continents were formed during the same geological period.

e. Similar rock layers and diamond-rich rocks are found on these continents.

Process Skills
Making and Using a Model

How did your map in "The Great Puzzle" support Wegener's hypothesis that a single supercontinent had once existed? Write your answer on a separate sheet of paper.   The map is a model that
reveals a reasonably good fit among the borders of the continents—indirect evidence that a supercontinent existed.

Close
the Investigation

THINK IT WRITE IT

Critical Thinking Skills
Analyzing, Applying, Solving Problems
1. Since glaciers only form in very cold climates, southern Africa must have been located near the South Pole at some time in the past.

2. Evidence supporting continental drift includes matching coastlines of Africa and South America, fossils of the same organisms on different continents, similarities among rocks and mountain ranges on different continents, and evidence of glaciers in areas presently having warm climates.

Challenge
Have groups of students make cardboard cutouts of the continents. Then have them glue small magnets to the undersides of the cutouts. Next have them place the cutouts on a large metal cookie sheet and move the pieces to their positions at 180 million years ago (mya), 135 mya, and 65 mya.

Following Up

Baseline Assessment Return to the broken plate analogy. Have students explain how edges, patterns, and perhaps color could be used as a guide to glue the pieces back together. Make sure they understand that fossil evidence, rock structures, continental outlines, and climate indicators were used to piece together the supercontinent Pangaea.

Reteaching Discuss the investigation subconcept with students. Together, create a word web of supporting evidence surrounding the central idea of continental drift.

📖 Use *Science Notebook* p. 51.

◀ **Investigation Review**
Use Investigation Review p. 42 in the *Assessment Guide*.

WHAT DO THE LOCATIONS OF VOLCANOES AND EARTHQUAKES TELL US?

Planner

Subconcept Earth's crust and upper mantle are composed of plates that fit together like the pieces of a broken eggshell; strong earthquakes and volcanoes occur at the edges of these plates.

Objectives

- **Use** maps of the locations of earthquakes and volcanoes to **infer** the existence of tectonic plates.
- **Explain** the relationship between the location of volcanoes, earthquakes, and Earth's plates.

Pacing 2–3 class periods

Science Terms theory of plate tectonics, plates, tectonic plates, crust, mantle, plate boundaries

Activate Prior Knowledge

Baseline Assessment Ask: **Where and why do earthquakes and volcanoes occur?** Save responses for Following Up.

Activity The Earth— Always Rockin' and Rollin'!

Preview *Students focus on earthquakes and should find they are most common in certain places, such as around the Pacific rim and along mid-ocean ridges.*

1. Get Ready

Time about 30 minutes

Grouping groups of 4–6

Collaborative Strategy Suggest that group members come to a consensus before marking the pattern on their tracing paper.

WHAT DO THE LOCATIONS OF VOLCANOES AND EARTHQUAKES TELL US?

Earthquakes and volcanoes make our world a bit shaky! Think of all the stories you have heard about earthquakes and volcanic eruptions. Can the locations of these events give us clues about continental drift?

Activity

MATERIALS
- earthquake map of Earth
- tracing paper
- *Science Notebook*

Earth—Always Rockin' and Rollin'!

Did you ever wonder why earthquakes occur where they do? See if you can find any pattern in the locations of earthquakes.

How is Earth like a cracked eggshell? ▼

Procedure

1. Study the earthquake map. Every dot on the map represents a place where a strong earthquake has occurred. Look for a pattern that the dots form. Describe this pattern in your *Science Notebook*. Discuss your observations with your team members.

2. On tracing paper, use your pencil to trace and then darken the pattern formed by the earthquake dots. Work with your team members to decide how to draw the pattern.

3. Think about the way a cracked eggshell looks. Earth's **crust**, which is its outermost, solid layer, is a lot like a cracked eggshell, broken up into large pieces. Look again at the pattern of the earthquake dots. How is the pattern of the dots like the cracks of an eggshell? Record your answer.

B16

Responding to Individual Needs

Students Acquiring English Students can label the names of continents and/or countries on the earthquake map in their native languages and can pronounce these names for other students. Group members can help students acquiring English to pronounce the names in English.

▲ Earthquakes around the world

Analyze and Conclude

1. Earth's crust is broken into large pieces called **tectonic plates**. Use your tracing and the map to locate some of these tectonic plates.

2. Earthquakes occur mostly along cracks in Earth's crust. Predict some locations where earthquakes are likely to occur. Record your predictions.

UNIT PROJECT LINK

Create a tectonic-plates map that shows your town. Also, show the tectonic plate(s) surrounding the plate that includes your town. How close is your town to the edge of a tectonic plate? Place a map pin where your town is located. Predict how likely your town is to have an earthquake.

As you go through this unit, collect data from news articles about earthquakes and volcanic activity around the world. Place map pins on a classroom map showing where this activity is taking place. Look for relationships between earthquakes, volcanoes, and tectonic plates.

B17

Investigate Further

Unit Project Link

Unless your town is in the western U.S., Alaska, or Hawaii, you are not near any major plate boundaries. These particular areas are more likely to experience earthquakes than other parts of the U.S. Note that in addition to newspaper articles, a good source for data on recent earthquakes and volcanic eruptions is *Earth* magazine, which gives a summary of all tectonic activity for a period of several months.

Encourage students to record their data on earthquakes and volcanic activity in their *Science Notebooks* on p. 54. Then use Unit Project Master B1 (TRB p. 71) to help them develop a tectonic-plates map that shows their town.

Materials Hints Use Activity Support Master B2 (TRB, p. 43). Have students staple or tape the tracing paper to the earthquake map.

2. Guide the Procedure

• For best results, have students use colored pencils to mark the earthquake locations. Remind them to save their maps for the next activity.

• Expect some differences in students' maps. The pattern is not so obvious around the Antarctic Plate.

 Have students record their data and answer questions on *Science Notebook* pp. 52–53.

 Have students research earthquakes using the Earthquake Data Pack on the CD-ROM.

 To display worldwide earthquake patterns to the entire class, you may wish to use **Transparency 7,** "Earthquakes Around the World."

3. Assess Performance

Process Skills Checklist

• Were students able to **identify** a pattern in the earthquake locations? Did they correctly **infer** that this pattern indicates the boundaries of Earth's tectonic plates?

• Did students' maps accurately **model** some of Earth's plate boundaries?

Analyze and Conclude

1. Plate boundaries outline both oceanic plates and plates that carry continents. Students may cite the Pacific Ocean, North America, South America, Africa, the Indian Ocean (including Australia), and the Eurasian landmasses as plates.

2. Predictions may vary, but will probably include the western United States and other areas around the Pacific rim. Predictions should be based on the locations of plate boundaries.

Activity — Volcanoes and Earth's Plates

Preview
Students should recognize a pattern in the locations of volcanoes that corresponds well with the pattern of earthquake activity, reinforcing the idea that Earth's crust is broken into pieces.

1. Get Ready

Time about 30 minutes

Grouping groups of 4–6

Collaborative Strategy Suggest that group members reach agreement on their hypothesis.

Materials Hints Use Activity Support Masters B2 and B3 (TRB, pp. 43 and 44). Have students save their volcano maps for later use.

2. Guide the Procedure

- Allow groups adequate time to study both maps and to discuss their observations.
- Students may notice that volcanoes occur in some areas that are not plate boundaries.

 Have students record their data and answer questions on *Science Notebook* p. 55.

 You may wish to have students use the CD-ROM Spreadsheet to organize and display their data.

 To display patterns of volcanic activity, you may wish to use **Transparency 8,** "Volcanic Activity Around the World."

 Have students research volcanoes using the Volcanoes Data Pack on the CD-ROM.

3. Assess Performance

Process Skills Checklist
- How well did students **interpret data** to recognize the patterns formed by earthquakes and volcanoes?
- Were students able to **make a hypothesis** that explains the link between tectonic plates, earthquakes, and volcanoes?

Analyze and Conclude
1. Around the edges of the Pacific Ocean, the northern edge of the Mediterranean Sea, and in eastern Africa
2. Volcanoes and earthquakes are associated with the edges of Earth's tectonic plates.

Activity
Volcanoes and Earth's Plates

Earthquakes occur at the edges of huge slabs of crust and upper mantle called tectonic plates. *Are volcanoes and earthquakes found in the same places?*

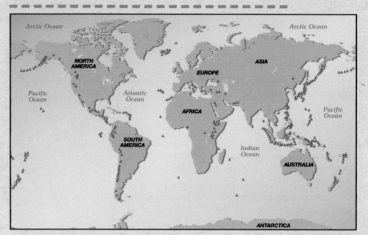

▲ Volcanic activity around the world

Procedure

Study the map of Earth's volcanoes and compare it with your map of Earth's earthquakes. In your *Science Notebook*, list the places where volcanoes occur.

Form a hypothesis about the locations of volcanoes, earthquakes, and the edges of Earth's tectonic plates. Record your hypothesis. Discuss your observations with your group.

Analyze and Conclude

1. Using the maps on B17 and B18, describe where both earthquakes and volcanoes occur.

2. How do the locations of earthquakes and volcanoes help identify Earth's tectonic plates?

B18

Responding to Individual Needs

Logical/Mathematical Activity Have students make a list of 25 major cities around the world, using a world political map as their resource. Then have them rate the probability of the occurrence of earthquakes and volcanic eruptions in these cities. Have them use the following scale: 1–Very likely; 0.5–Somewhat likely; 0–Unlikely.

The Cracked Crust:
Tectonic Plates

Floating Plates

Sometimes you'll hear the expression "It's as solid as a rock." This expression means that whatever is referred to is solid, permanent, and dependable. We may like to think that rock is solid and permanent, but even large slabs of rock move. Actually, nothing on the surface of Earth is permanent and unmoving. Even the continent of North America is moving. The movement is very slow, but it is movement, just the same. The slow movement of North America and the continents can be explained by the theory of plate tectonics.

In the late 1960s, scientists expanded Alfred Wegener's idea of drifting continents and proposed the **theory of plate tectonics**. The word *tectonics* refers to the forces causing the movement of Earth's rock formations and plates.

The theory of plate tectonics states that Earth's crust and upper mantle are broken into enormous slabs called **plates**, also called **tectonic plates**. (The **crust** is Earth's outermost, solid layer. The **mantle** is the layer of Earth between the crust and the core.) The continents are like enormous ships attached to these floating plates. Scientists believe that currents, or slow plastic movements in the mantle, cause the plates to move across Earth's surface. The currents are caused by differences in temperature in Earth's interior regions.

This theory is one of the most important theories about Earth's geologic history. It has guided scientists in the way they think Earth might have looked millions of years ago. Plate tectonics has helped them reconstruct the ways the continents might have moved over millions of years.

A wedge showing Earth's layers (*left*); a section of the crust and upper mantle (*right*)

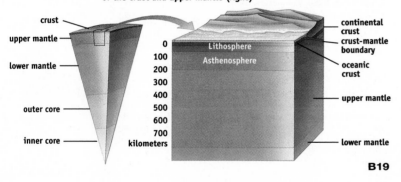

crust
upper mantle
lower mantle
outer core
inner core

0
100
200
300
400
500
600
700
kilometers

Lithosphere
Asthenosphere

continental crust
crust-mantle boundary
oceanic crust
upper mantle
lower mantle

B19

Integrating the Curriculum

Science & Math

MOVING PLATES

What to Do A plate carrying a continent is about 50 km thick. Earth's radius is about 6,400 km. How thick is a tectonic plate compared to Earth's radius?

What's the Result? What is the ratio of the thickness of a continental plate to Earth's radius? The answer is 50/6,400 or 0.008 to 1, or about 1/125.

The Cracked Crust: Tectonic Plates

Preview *Students focus on the locations and names of Earth's tectonic plates and the relative direction of movement of the plates.*

1. Get Ready

Science Terms theory of plate tectonics, plates, tectonic plates, mantle, plate boundaries

Background

- Information about plate tectonics is still developing. In 1968, Jason Morgan, an American earth scientist, had identified eight major tectonic plates. But by the mid-1980s, geologists recognized as many as sixteen plates. In the 1970s, a new technique called *seismic reflection profiling* revealed that the continental crust was much more complicated that anyone had imagined. Data from this technique indicated that plate sutures extend deep into the upper mantle.

Discussion Starter

Show students a hard-boiled egg. Allow a volunteer to gently tap the egg on the table to produce cracks in the shell. Ask: **Is this an accurate model of Earth's plates?** Most students will probably say yes. Have a volunteer carefully remove a piece or two of the shell including the membrane. Conclude that the shell represents Earth's crust and the membrane the upper mantle. Now, peel and cut the egg in half. Ask volunteers to make analogies between the egg and Earth's interior. (The egg white is the mantle; the yolk represents the core.)

2. Guide the Discussion

Choose from the following strategies to facilitate discussion.

Connecting to the Activities

- *Earth—Always Rockin' and Rollin'!, p. B16 and Volcanoes and Earth's Plates, p. B18*
  How do your earthquake and volcano maps from the activities compare to this map? Most volcanoes and earthquakes are located near the plate boundaries shown on this map.

 To show the relationship between earthquakes, volcanoes, and tectonic plates, you may wish to use **Transparency 7,** "Earthquakes Around the World;" **Transparency 8,** "Volcanic Activity Around the World;" and **Transparency 9,** "Tectonic Plates."

Thinking About the Data

- **On which plates are the following countries located: United States, France, Australia, Japan, Brazil?** North American, Eurasian, Australian, Eurasian, South American

- **Do tectonic plates carry only continents? Explain.** No, most contain both continents and ocean floor (as well as the ocean water above the ocean floor).

Responding to Individual Needs

Students Acquiring English Help students pronounce the names of the plates in English.

Making Comparisons

- **Which plates are moving toward one another?** Answers might include the Eurasian and Pacific Plates or the South American and Nazca Plates.

- **Which plates are moving away from one another?** Answers might include the South American and African Plates, the Pacific and Nazca Plates, the Australian and Antarctic Plates, or the North American and Eurasian Plates.

3. Assess Understanding

Challenge students to draw a new map of where the continents might be in 50 million years and then compare these maps with the ones they drew in the resource *Continents on the Move.*

EARTH'S TECTONIC PLATES There are seven major plates and several minor ones. Many of the plates are named after the major landmasses that are parts of the plates. The plates act like rafts that carry Earth's crust and upper mantle around on a layer of semisolid material. Study the map shown to the right. You will see that most of the United States is located on the North American Plate. In what direction is this plate moving? In what direction is the Pacific Plate moving?

Makeup of the Plates

What do the tectonic plates consist of? Each plate is formed of a thin layer of crust, which overlies a region called the upper mantle. In a plate that carries a continent, the crust can be 40 to 48 km (25 to 30 mi) thick. In a plate that is under an ocean, the crust can be only 5 to 8 km (3 to 5 mi) thick. The drawing at the bottom of this page shows the makeup of a tectonic plate.

Interacting Plates

Plates can interact in three ways: (1) They can come together, (2) they can move apart, and (3) they can slide past one another. Places where plates interact are called **plate boundaries.** As you probably know by now, earthquakes and volcanoes occur along plate boundaries. In Chapter 2 you will find out much more about what happens along these boundaries. ■

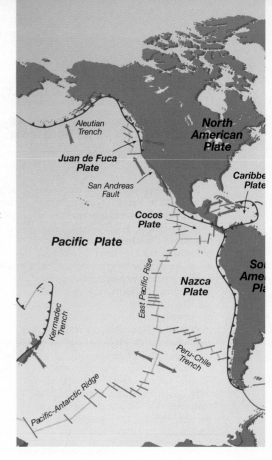

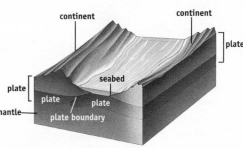

Tectonic plates can carry a continent, an ocean, or both a continent and an ocean. ▶

Integrating the Curriculum

Science & Social Studies

THE RED SEA **What to Do** Have students locate the Red Sea on a world map. Inform them that the plates on either side of the sea are moving away from each other. Challenge them to use the theory of plate tectonics to predict how the size of the sea will change in the future.

What's the Result? **How might this narrow sea change?** As the plates move farther and farther apart, the size of the sea will continue to increase, gradually forming a large ocean.

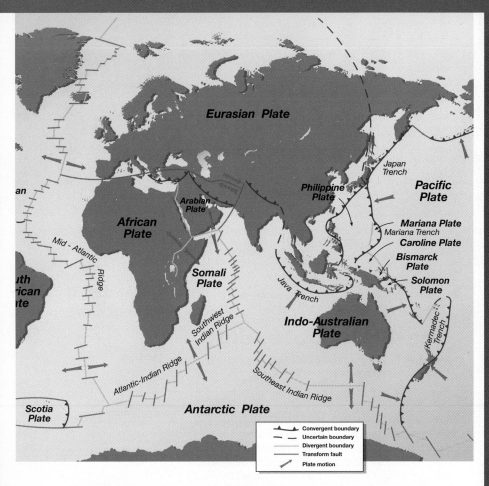

Eurasian Plate

Japan Trench

Philippine Plate

Pacific Plate

Arabian Plate

African Plate

Mariana Plate
Mariana Trench

Caroline Plate

Mid - Atlantic Ridge

Somali Plate

Bismarck Plate

Solomon Plate

Java Trench

Southwest Indian Ridge

Indo-Australian Plate

Kermadec Trench

Atlantic-Indian Ridge

Southeast Indian Ridge

Scotia Plate

Antarctic Plate

Convergent boundary
Uncertain boundary
Divergent boundary
Transform fault
Plate motion

INVESTIGATION 2

1. Predict what might happen in 10 million years to Los Angeles (on the Pacific Plate) and San Francisco (on the North American Plate) if the two plates carrying these cities continue to move in the direction in which they are now moving.

2. What is the connection between earthquakes, volcanoes, and tectonic plates? Give evidence to support your answer.

B21

Assessment

Performance

Modeling Have students use felt cutouts of Earth's plates and a globe to model the movement of tectonic plates.

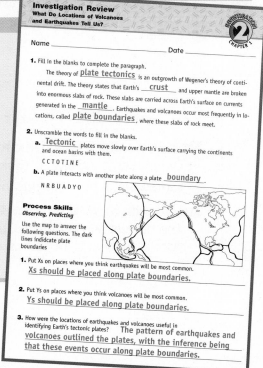

Investigation Review
What Do Locations of Volcanoes and Earthquakes Tell Us?

Name _____ Date _____

1. Fill in the blanks to complete the paragraph.
The theory of <u>plate tectonics</u> is an outgrowth of Wegener's theory of continental drift. The theory states that Earth's <u>crust</u> and upper mantle are broken into enormous slabs of rock. These slabs are carried across Earth's surface on currents generated in the <u>mantle</u>. Earthquakes and volcanoes occur most frequently in locations, called <u>plate boundaries</u>, where these slabs of rock meet.

2. Unscramble the words to fill in the blanks.
a. <u>Tectonic</u> plates move slowly over Earth's surface carrying the continents and ocean basins with them.
C C T O T I N E

b. A plate interacts with another plate along a plate <u>boundary</u>.
N R B U A D Y O

Process Skills
Observing, Predicting
Use the map to answer the following questions. The dark lines indidcate plate boundaries

1. Put Xs on places where you think earthquakes will be most common.
<u>Xs should be placed along plate boundaries.</u>

2. Put Ys on places where you think volcanoes will be most common.
<u>Ys should be placed along plate boundaries.</u>

3. How were the locations of earthquakes and volcanoes useful in identifying Earth's tectonic plates? <u>The pattern of earthquakes and volcanoes outlined the plates, with the inference being that these events occur along plate boundaries.</u>

Close
the Investigation

INVESTIGATION 2

Critical Thinking Skills
Analyzing, Synthesizing, Applying

1. Los Angeles and San Francisco are moving toward one another. In another 10 million years, Los Angeles will be just southwest of San Francisco.

2. Earthquakes and volcanoes are both common along the edges of tectonic plates. Most of the earthquakes occur along plate boundaries, but some occur in other places. Most of the volcanoes are also located along plate boundaries, but some are located within tectonic plates.

Challenge Based on the information provided in this investigation, have students hypothesize *how* earthquakes occur and *why* volcanoes erupt. Have them save their hypotheses to refer to in Chapters 2 and 3.

Following Up

Baseline Assessment Return to the class list of responses about where earthquakes and volcanoes occur and their relationship. Ask students if they would like to modify or add to any responses, and if so, how.

Reteaching As students add map pins for volcanoes and earthquakes to the world map for the Unit Project, have them compare the locations to those of the plate boundaries shown on the map on pp. B20–21.

Use *Science Notebook* p. 56.

◀ **Investigation Review**
Use Investigation Review p. 43 in the *Assessment Guide*.

WHAT DOES THE SEA FLOOR TELL US ABOUT PLATE TECTONICS?

Planner

Subconcept The sea floor spreads away from cracks or rifts in the crust, and magma rises to form new crust; sea-floor spreading is evidence for the theory of plate tectonics.

Objectives

• **Model** the processes of sea-floor spreading and mapping the ocean floor

• **Explain** how magnetic records in rocks support the theory of plate tectonics.

Pacing 3–4 class periods

Science Terms mid-ocean ridge, sea-floor spreading, magnetic field, magnetic reversal

Activate Prior Knowledge

Baseline Assessment Ask: **What happened to the Atlantic Ocean as South America and Africa moved apart?** Record responses for Following Up.

INVESTIGATION ③

WHAT DOES THE SEA FLOOR TELL US ABOUT PLATE TECTONICS?

How do scientists know what the sea floor looks like? Is there evidence for plate tectonics hidden beneath the waters? Find out in this investigation.

Activity

Sea-Floor Spreading

New rock is being added to the sea floor all the time. Model this process in this activity.

Procedure

Prepare a sheet of white paper as shown in the top drawing. Draw mountains. The middle slit represents a very long crack in the ocean floor, called a **mid-ocean ridge**.

Pull strips of notebook paper up through the middle slit and down through the side slits, as shown. These strips represent magma that is flowing up through the ocean ridge and then hardening. The strips are a model of the way the ocean floor spreads. This process is often called **sea-floor spreading**.

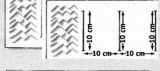
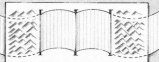

Analyze and Conclude

Consider that the magma coming up through the ridge is hardening into rock. What can you **infer** about the age of the rock along each side of the ridge? **Record** your ideas in your *Science Notebook*. Where do you think the oldest rock on the sea floor is?

B22

Activity Sea-Floor Spreading

Preview *Students make a model of the sea floor to show how the sea floor expands.*

Advance Preparation *See p. B4b.*

1. Get Ready

Time about 20 minutes

Grouping groups of 4–6

 Collaborative Strategy Students can share the tasks of drawing the mountains and manipulating the model.

2. Guide the Procedure

• Have students color the exposed parts of both strips the same color. Then have them pull them out about 6 cm more and color the newly exposed parts of both strips another color.

Have students answer questions on *Science Notebook* p. 57.

You may wish to have students use the CD-ROM Painter to create a diagram of their observations.

3. Assess Performance

Process Skills Checklist

• Did students accurately **make** the **model**?

• Did students **observe** how new sea floor forms?

Analyze and Conclude

The newest sea floor is closest to the ridge; the oldest sea floor is farthest from the ridge.

Activity

Building a Model of the Ocean Floor

The sea floor is much like the dry land. Tall mountains and deep valleys exist there. You can build your own model of these structures.

MATERIALS
- modeling clay
- shoebox with lid
- metric ruler
- grid
- pencil
- tape
- *Science Notebook*

Procedure

1. Place modeling clay along the bottom of a shoebox until the clay is about 2.5 cm (1 in.) deep in all places.

2. Add enough clay to mold an underwater valley, mountain, and an uneven surface.

3. Tape the grid to the lid of the shoebox.

4. Use your pencil to punch holes in the grid and lid wherever there are small circles on the grid. Put the lid on the shoebox.

Analyze and Conclude

1. Which ocean floor features does your model illustrate? Record your answer in your *Science Notebook*.

2. How could someone determine the shape of the "ocean floor" without looking inside the shoebox?

INVESTIGATE FURTHER!

RESEARCH

Find out the height and extent of underwater mountains. Where are the highest underwater mountains? Are these mountains related in any way to Earth's plates?

Steps 2 and 4

B23

Investigate Further

Research

Some of the highest underwater mountains along the mid-Atlantic Ridge (a divergent plate boundary) form the islands of Iceland and the Azores. One of the highest underwater mountains, Mauna Loa, is a volcano on the island of Hawaii. Measured from its base on the Pacific Ocean floor to its summit, which is above water, Mauna Loa is 9,170 m high. Students will find out that the Hawaiian volcanoes formed as a tectonic plate moved over a hot spot in Earth's mantle. Students should record the information in their *Science Notebooks* on p. 59.

Activity — Building a Model of the Ocean Floor

Preview *Students model the topography of the ocean floor.*

Advance Preparation *See p. B4b.*

1. Get Ready

Time about 40 minutes

Grouping groups of 4–6

Collaborative Strategy Group members should discuss and come to a consensus on where to locate the valley and mountain in their model.

Materials Hints Use Activity Support Master B4 (TRB, p. 45), which will give you the grid to be taped to the shoebox lid. You might want to line the shoebox with plastic wrap so the clay won't stick to the box.

Safety Review safety precautions with students. Have them use caution when punching holes in the grid.

2. Guide the Procedure

- Don't allow different groups to compare their models at this time. Remind students to save their models for the next activity.

- Have students answer questions on *Science Notebook* p. 58.

- You may wish to have students use the CD-ROM Spreadsheet to organize and display their data.

3. Assess Performance

Process Skills Checklist

- Did students' **models** of the ocean floor contain the required features?

- Were students able to **use models** to propose a method for determining the shape of the ocean floor?

Analyze and Conclude

1. The model illustrates an underwater mountain and valley.

2. Answers will vary, but students should be able to infer that a probe, marked in linear units, could be inserted into each hole. The measurements could be recorded and graphed to produce a profile of the clay's surface.

Activity Mapping the Ocean Floor

Preview *Students map a model of the ocean floor.*

1. Get Ready

Time about 40 minutes

Grouping groups of 4–6

Multi-Age Strategy Have group members check one another's measurements to be sure they agree. If there are discrepancies, they should recheck their measurements and come to a consensus on each value.

Safety Review safety precautions with students. Remind them to take care when using the scissors to avoid cutting themselves.

2. Guide the Procedure

- Have groups exchange models made in the previous activity so that each group has an "unknown" model to work with.

- Caution students to gently push the stirrer into the grid holes until they feel the resistance of the clay surface. If they push too forcefully, they will embed the stirrer into the clay and get inaccurate measurements.

- Results will vary, depending on the model used, but all models will contain trenches and ridges. The cut straws taped to, and hanging from, the shoebox lid, should provide a reverse image of the clay "ocean floor."

 Have students record their data and answer questions on *Science Notebook* p. 60.

 You may wish to have students use the CD-ROM Spreadsheet and CD-ROM Grapher to organize and display their data.

Activity
Mapping the Ocean Floor

The water is too deep to swim through, and there's no light. So how do scientists figure out the shape of the ocean floor? Use the ocean floor structures that you built in the last activity to model one way scientists do it!

MATERIALS

- coffee stirrer
- fine-tip marker
- plastic straws
- scissors
- shoebox model of ocean floor, including grid taped to shoebox lid
- metric ruler
- *Science Notebook*

Procedure

1. Cut a coffee stirrer so that it is the same length as the height of the shoebox. Beginning at one end of the stirrer, mark each centimeter along its length.

2. The stirrer is a model for a sound beam from a ship's sonar system. After a ship's sonar transmits a "ping," it "hears" (receives and records) an echo from the ocean bottom a short time later. The length of time needed for the echo to return to the ship is related to the depth of the ocean at that point. Each hole in the grid on top of the shoebox represents the location on the surface of the ocean from which a ship's sonar has sent out a sound beam or "ping."

3. Locate hole *A1* on the grid taped to the shoebox lid. Place your stirrer into this hole, inserting the 1-cm end first. In your *Science Notebook*, set up a chart for recording the depth to the surface of the clay below each hole. **Record** the depth for the hole at *A1*. **Measure** and **record** the depth to the surface of the clay under each hole on the grid.

4. Cut a piece of straw to match the depth that you measured under each point on the grid. For example, if you measured a depth of 4 cm, cut a straw piece that is 4 cm long.

Hole	Depth (cm)
A1	
A2	
A3	
A4	

Hole	Depth (cm)
B1	
B2	
B3	
B4	

Hole	Depth (cm)
C1	
C2	
C3	
C4	

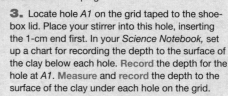

B24

👤 Responding to Individual Needs

Kinesthetic Activity Encourage students to place one palm against the clay model and the other against the surface of the straws to compare how closely the two models match.

5. Now stick a piece of straw in the hole to match the depth you measured under that hole. For example, if you measured 4 cm at *A1*, stick a 4-cm straw into hole *A1*. Next, *push the piece of straw through the shoebox lid* so that the straw hangs down below the lid. Tape the top end of the straw in place so that it is even with the shoebox lid. Insert a length of straw in each hole on the grid until every hole has a straw hanging from it. These straws represent sonar beams that are sent down to the ocean bottom. What do you think the lid represents?

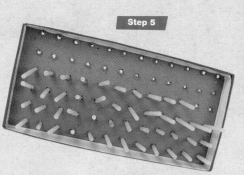

Step 5

Analyze and Conclude

1. Remove the lid, cut away one side of the shoebox, and replace the lid. Look at all the straws. How well does the pattern of the straws match the highs and lows of your ocean floor?

2. Would your straw model be more accurate if you had taken more depth readings? Why?

INVESTIGATE FURTHER!

RESEARCH

Find out where the deepest ocean trench is located and how deep that trench is. How did oceanographers determine the depth of that trench?

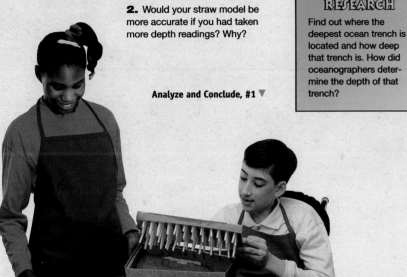

Analyze and Conclude, #1 ▼

B25

---

3. Assess Performance

Process Skills Checklist

- Did students accurately **measure** the distance from the grid to the clay at different points?

- Did students create three-dimensional straw **models** that correctly matched the topography of the shoebox model they used?

Analyze and Conclude

1. If students made accurate measurements, their straw models should closely mirror the topography of the clay model. In other words, the pattern of the straws should be the *reverse* of the highs and lows of the clay surface.

2. Yes, some features that were missed because they are between depth readings would be included.

Investigate Further

Research

The deepest spot on Earth is in the Mariana Trench, in the western Pacific Ocean near the island of Guam. It is 36,198 ft (11,033 m) deep. Oceanographers determined the depth of the trench by using sonar and by exploring the trench with a bathyscaphe. You might wish to have students compare this depth with the highest point above Earth's surface—Mt. Everest 29,0025t (8,708 m), which is a peak in the Himalaya mountain range in central Asia.

 Have students research Mt. Everest and the Himalayas using the Mountain Ranges Data Pack on the CD-ROM.

Sonar: Mapping the Sea Floor

Preview *Students focus on how a profile of the ocean bottom can be determined by using sonar.*

1. Get Ready

Background

- Although echo-sounding methods are still widely used, particularly for reconnaissance surveys, over the past few years several new tools for mapping the sea floor have become available. These include SeaBeam and SeaMark, which extend the echo-sounding principle to allow scientists to construct highly detailed maps and images of areas of the sea floor. These methods employ satellites that aid in the gathering of data to produce global sea-floor maps, which would have taken years of echo-sounding from surface ships to produce.

Discussion Starter

- **If you were on a boat in a small lake, what are some ways that you could determine the depth of the lake in different spots?** Students might suggest lowering the anchor overboard until it reaches the bottom, marking the waterline on the rope, then pulling it back up and measuring the rope. Accept all suggestions that students are able to justify with logical reasons.

Sonar:
Mapping the Sea Floor

 Did you try the activity on pages B24 and B25? If you did, then you built a model of sonar—a method for finding the shape and depth of the ocean floor. *Sonar* stands for *sound navigation and ranging.*

British naval scientists first developed sonar in 1921. During World War II (1939–1945), sonar was used to detect enemy submarines. Scientists realized that sound could be used to measure the distance from a ship on the surface of the water to the bottom of the ocean. A sonar device sends out a sound and then listens for an echo to return. By using sonar, scientists can measure the time between sending out a sound and receiving the echo of that sound. Then, by knowing this time and the speed at which sound travels through sea water,

they can compute the depth of the ocean at that point. In the activity "Mapping the Ocean Floor," the straws you pushed through each hole in the grid represented a sound impulse that might have been sent out by a ship carrying a sonar device.

As a ship with sonar moves along the surface of the ocean, it sends out frequent sound impulses. The sound impulses travel down through the sea water, strike the ocean floor, and then send back an echo. Each echo arrives at a receiver

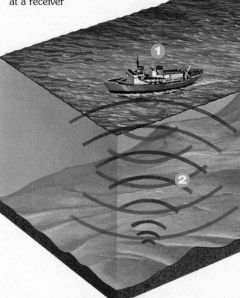

1 Ship sending out signals from sonar device

2 Sound sent out by sonar device and returning echo

3 Sea floor

How sonar is used to map the sea floor ▶

B26

Investigate Further

Integrating the Sciences

LIFE SCIENCE **What to Do** Have students find out that some bats navigate using a natural sonar system called echolocation. Students could make posters to illustrate how these animals use sonar.

What's the Result? How do bats use echolocation? Bats navigate and locate food with echoes. These echoes result from a series of short, high-frequency sounds generated by the bat. The sounds are reflected from and analyzed by the animals for purposes of orientation, obstacle avoidance, food procurement, and social interaction.

Multi-Age Classroom Set up a learning station on the topic of echolocation. Provide resource materials at different levels of difficulty.

back at the ship and is recorded on a recording chart. The sonar device records the length of time required for the echo to return from the ocean floor. It then computes the depth of the ocean floor at that point. Finally, the depth is registered on a scale.

If the total time for a sound to travel from the ship to the ocean floor and back is 6.60 s, and sound travels through sea water at 1,530 m/s, the sound has traveled a total of 10,098 m. The distance from the ship to the ocean floor is half the total, or 5,049 m. By assembling all the measurements taken as the ship moves through the water, scientists can produce a map of a section of the

ocean floor. The more readings they take, the more accurate their map will be. Sonar has allowed scientists to discover many new features of the ocean floor. For example, they have found some places that are over 10,600 m (6.3 mi) deep. That's over 10 km! They also have found undersea mountains higher than Mount Everest, which is 8,848 m (29,028 ft) high!

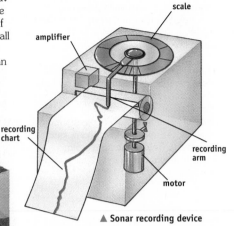
▲ Sonar recording device

Probing the Land with Sonar
Sonar can also be used on land. Sound pulses can be sent through the ground, and the returning echoes can be used to identify different layers of soil and rock as well as to locate deposits of natural gas and oil. ■

B27

Science, Technology & Society

SOUND OFF **What to Do** During the early years of sea exploration, there was no accurate way to determine what the ocean floor looked like. Explorers tried to find out using a method called sounding. Invite interested students to research this method and plan a demonstration for the class of how it was done.

What's the Result? **How was sounding done? What were its problems?** Sounding was done by lowering ropes with weights attached to them. When the weights touched bottom, the length of wet rope showed the depth of the water. It was inaccurate in deep water because currents moved the rope so it did not go straight down. Thus, the length of the wet rope was greater than the actual depth. Each sounding took many hours to do.

2. Guide the Discussion

Choose from the following strategies to facilitate discussion.

Connecting to the Activities

• **Mapping the Ocean Floor, p. B24**
In the activity, what did you use to represent a ship's echo sounder? The stirrer represented the echo sounder.

Making Comparisons

• **What does an echo sounder do and how is it used? Compare it to what you used in Mapping the Ocean Floor.** An echo sounder sends out sound waves and measures the time it takes to return. The stirrer was also used to gather data to map a model of the ocean floor.

Thinking Critically

A fishing boat might use sonar to locate schools of fish. How might this practice be helpful? How might it be harmful? Using sonar increases the amount of fish caught, but increasing the catch could lead to endangerment or extinction of species of fish.

Responding to Individual Needs

Kinesthetic Activity Have pairs of students use yo-yos to model sonar. As the toy is released from the hand and returns, have students call out the phrases "Signal sent," "Echo returns," and "Wave hits bottom," at the appropriate times.

3. Assess Understanding

Students can work in groups of three or four. Sound waves travel at 1,530 m/s in ocean water. Give students the following readings from a ship's echo sounder as it travels across a section of ocean. Have students assume that the ship takes a reading every kilometer. Ask each group to make a graph that will show the depth of the ocean. Time (in seconds) for echoes to return: 1.0, 2.0, 3.0, 6.0, 3.0, 3.0, 2.0, 0.5, 3.0, 0.5, 2.0, 2.0, 1.0, 1.0. After the groups have made the graph, have them label the features the profile shows.

Magnetism Tells a Story

Preview *Students focus on how magnetic records in rocks provide evidence for the process of sea-floor spreading.*

1. Get Ready

Science Terms
magnetic field, magnetic reversal, magnetometer, sea floor spreading

Background

- Earth is like a giant bar magnet, with magnetic north and south poles. The magnetic poles are in slightly different locations than the geographic north and south poles. As molten rock rises up from mid-ocean ridges and solidifies, magnetic material in the rock lines up with the Earth's magnetic field. Scientists have found that the location of the magnetic north and south poles reverses approximately every half-million years. Bands of ocean crust record each of the magnetic pole reversals.

Discussion Starter

- **What do you know about magnets?** Responses might include that they pick up or attract certain metal objects and that each has a north and a south pole.

Responding to Individual Needs

Kinesthetic Activity Allow students to experiment with magnets of various sizes. Have students classify the magnets as either "strong" or "weak" by feeling the relative attraction between each magnet and a single paper clip. Students can quantify these observations by seeing how many paper clips (attached magnetically end to end) each magnet can hold.

Magnetism Tells a Story

You have probably used magnets many times. Perhaps you used one to pick up a string of paper clips or to hold notes on the refrigerator door. How is Earth like a magnet?

A magnet is an object that attracts certain metals, including iron, steel, and nickel. A magnet has two ends, or poles. When hung from a string, the pole that turns toward north is called the *north pole* of the magnet. The pole that points south is the *south pole* of the magnet. A **magnetic field** is the area around a magnet where the effects of magnetism are felt.

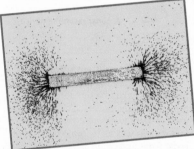

▲ Iron filings show the magnetic field around a magnet.

Earth is like a giant magnet, and it has two magnetic poles. These poles are inclined, or tilted, about 11° from the

geographic poles. The magnetic field around Earth is thought to be due to movements within Earth's fluid outer core, which is composed mainly of iron and nickel. For reasons unknown, Earth's

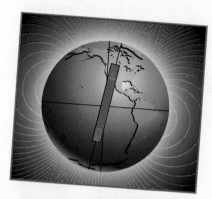

▲ The earth is like a giant magnet surrounded by a magnetic field.

magnetic field reverses, or flips, from time to time. Such a change in the magnetic field is called a **magnetic reversal**.

At present, the magnetic field is said to be normal. This means that the north-seeking needle of a compass will point toward Earth's north magnetic pole. What do you think will happen when the field is reversed?

You probably know that some of Earth's rocks contain iron. When these

Investigate Further

Integrating the Sciences

PHYSICAL SCIENCE

What to Do Allow students to simulate magnetic reversal by having them stroke an iron nail against one end of a strong magnet about twenty times, always stroking in the same direction. Have them determine which end of the nail is attracted to the north pole of the magnet. Then have them stroke the iron nail toward the opposite end of the magnet about twenty times, always stroking in the same direction. Ask them to test the nail after ten strokes and after twenty strokes. **What's the Result? What happened to the nail when you stroked it in the opposite direction?** The nail became demagnetized at first, but then became magnetized with opposite poles.

rocks formed from magma, the particles in the iron lined up with the magnetic field of the time, much as a compass needle lines up with Earth's magnetic field. Scientists can use this lining up of iron particles to find the direction of Earth's magnetic field at the time the rock formed.

Scientists use a device called a magnetometer (mag nə tăm'ət ər) to detect magnetic fields. This device can show how particles of iron line up within rock. Magnetometers have been used by oceanographers to study the magnetic fields of rock on the ocean floor. What the scientists found surprised them!

When the scientists studied the sea floor at mid-ocean ridges and on either side of the ridges, they found a magnetic pattern. There were long stretches of rock in which iron particles were lined up in one direction. Then there were other stretches of rock, parallel to the first, in which the iron particles lined up in the reverse direction. This pattern of reversals continued from the mid-ocean ridge outward, away from the ridge. A further

finding was that the pattern on one side of the ridge was exactly the same as the pattern on the other side of the ridge.

The drawing below helps explain the magnetic patterns on the ocean floor. At the center of the drawing is a mid-ocean ridge. Magma flows up from below the ridge and then hardens into rock on the sea floor. Only when iron-containing rock is fluid can the iron particles line up in a magnetic field. Once the rock hardens, the iron does not change its direction. The arrows show the magnetic directions of the iron in the rock at the mid-ocean ridge and on either side of the ridge. Note the repeating pattern.

Scientists have found that rocks closer to mid-ocean ridges are younger than rocks farther from the ridge. The magnetic patterns in the sea-floor rocks and the different ages of the rocks led scientists to a startling conclusion. New sea floor is continually being formed along underwater mountain chains, or mid-ocean ridges! As two plates separate along a ridge, magma fills the separation. As it is carried away from the ridge due

Sea-floor spreading. Magma bubbles up and flows out along the ridge. When it hardens, it forms rock. On either side of a mid-ocean ridge are layers of magnetized rock. Each arrow represents a magnetic reversal. ▼

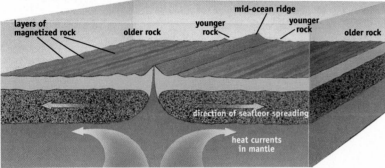

layers of magnetized rock   older rock   younger rock   mid-ocean ridge   younger rock   older rock

direction of seafloor spreading

heat currents in mantle

B29

Integrating the Curriculum

Science & the Arts

What to Do Have pairs of students use two different colors of modeling clay to make a model illustrating magnetic reversal patterns on either side of a mid-ocean ridge. Suggest that they place sheets of waxed paper between the different colors of clay.
What's the Result? **What do the different-colored bands in the model represent?** Each color change represents a magnetic reversal. **Why are the color bands the same on both sides of the mid-ocean ridge?** The molten magma comes out of the rift and flows in both directions as rifting occurs. The patterns are symmetrical with respect to the ridge.

2. Guide the Discussion

Choose from the following strategies to facilitate discussion.

Making Inferences

What do you think will happen when Earth's magnetic field reverses? Magnetic compasses will reverse the direction they now point.

Connecting to the Activities

• *Sea-Floor Spreading, p. B22*
Think back to the activity *Sea-Floor Spreading*. Where is new ocean floor being formed? Along the mid-ocean ridges **How does magnetism help prove that new sea floor is being formed?** Magnetic particles in the rock line up with Earth's magnetic field at the time the rock forms. As rifting takes place, records of Earth's magnetic orientation become "frozen" in the rocks.

To point out the direction of sea-floor spreading and the magnetic reversal pattern on either side of the mid-ocean ridge, you may wish to use **Transparency 10,** "Sea-Floor Spreading." To add the illusion of motion, use **Transparency 1,** "Moiré Overlay," with **Transparency 10**.

Thinking About the Data

- **On the map that shows rates of sea-floor spreading along the Mid-Atlantic Ridge, where is the fastest spreading occurring?** Southwest of the southern tip of Africa **Where is the slowest spreading?** Southeast of Iceland

3. Assess Understanding

 Students can work in groups of three or four. Have each group imagine that they have recently discovered the magnetic bands in the rocks of the sea floor. They are going to present their findings to a group of earth scientists at a convention. Their presentations should include a description of the magnetic bands, an explanation of how the magnetic bands were formed, and why this discovery is significant.

SCIENCE IN LITERATURE

Volcanoes and Earthquakes*
by Basil Booth

The map on pp. 14–15 shows the San Andreas fault. It is harder to predict an earthquake in Los Angeles than in San Francisco because L.A. is *not* directly on the fault; San Francisco lies *directly* on the fault.

*Available in the Trade Book Library.

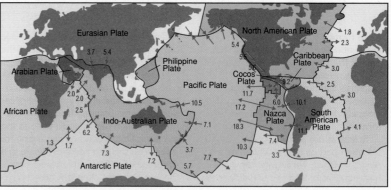

▲ Map showing rates at which plates separate and move together. The rates are in centimeters per year.

to convection currents in the mantle, the magma cools. As it cools, the iron in the magma lines up with Earth's magnetic field. This process by which new ocean floor is continually being added is called **sea-floor spreading**. Recall that you constructed a model of sea-floor spread-ing on page B22. Sea-floor spreading is strong evidence for the theory of plate tectonics.

Look at the map above that shows rates of sea-floor spreading along the Mid-Atlantic Ridge. Where is spreading the fastest? Where is it the slowest? ■

SCIENCE IN LITERATURE

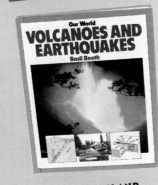

VOLCANOES AND EARTHQUAKES
by Basil Booth
Silver Burdett Press, 1991

B30

What are some famous earthquakes? How is one volcanic eruption different from another? What makes a geyser, such as Old Faithful in Yellowstone Park, erupt like clock-work about every 65 minutes? You can look up the answers to these questions and more in *Volcanoes and Earthquakes* by Basil Booth.

The edges of tectonic plates can get pretty complicated. Find the San Andreas Fault on the big map on pages 14–15 of *Volcanoes and Earthquakes*. It looks like a straight line. Now look at the close-up map of the San Andreas Fault system. What might make it harder for scientists to predict the next earthquake in Los Angeles than it is to predict one in San Francisco?

Integrating the Curriculum

Science & Math

SPREADING RATE

What to Do Students could use the rates given on the map to calculate an average rate of spreading along the Mid-Atlantic Ridge. To determine the average, they must add all the values and divide by the number of values. Remind them to include units in their answers.

What's the Result? What is the average rate of sea-floor spreading along the Mid-Atlantic Ridge? 4.1 cm/yr + 3.0 cm/yr + 2.5 cm/yr + 3.0 cm/yr + 2.3 cm/yr +1.8 cm/yr = 16.7 cm/yr; 16.7 cm/yr ÷ 6 = ~2.8 cm/yr

Have students use the CD-ROM Calculator.

Heating Up Iceland

In Iceland, some families don't need ovens to bake their bread; they simply place the dough inside a hole in the ground. Do they have underground ovens? Yes, but these ovens are created by natural processes taking place inside Earth. Below ground, but still close to the surface, there are very hot rocks. These rocks are heated by magma that bubbles up from deep inside Earth. Icelanders use these heated rocks to bake things in their underground ovens.

Helpful Shifting Plates

Movement of Earth's plates can cause trouble. Earthquakes and volcanic eruptions often occur along the edges of moving plates. But there are regions where plate movement can be helpful. In Iceland, for example, moving plates produce underground ovens that use an inexpensive kind of energy—geothermal energy.

Why It Is Hot

Iceland lies on the Mid-Atlantic Ridge, a chain of mountains running through the middle of the Atlantic Ocean. This small country is also located on the edge of two plates—the North American Plate and the Eurasian Plate. As these two plates move away from each other, hot

◄ **A geothermal plant in Iceland**

A geyser formed by the heating of water within Earth ▼

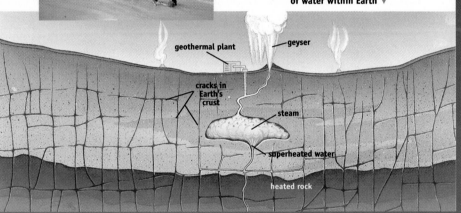

geothermal plant — geyser

cracks in Earth's crust

steam

superheated water

heated rock

Investigate Further

Cultural Connection

HOT SPOTS

What to Do Islands located along plate boundaries include New Zealand, Japan, the Azores, and the Philippines. All these islands use geothermal energy to a certain extent, but only in New Zealand is underground steam an important source of power. Near Wairakei on North Island, engineers have drilled many deep holes to release geothermal steam that is used to generate electricity. Have volunteers locate the above-mentioned islands on a world map.
What's the Result? Which of the islands is also located on the Mid-Atlantic Ridge? The Azores How do the locations of the other islands differ from that of Iceland? The other islands are located near deep ocean trenches.

Heating Up Iceland

Preview *Students find out how Iceland is affected by being on the Mid-Atlantic Ridge.*

1. Get Ready

Background

• Iceland lies just south of the Arctic Circle in the North Atlantic Ocean. It is sometimes called the *land of fire and ice* because large glaciers lie next to steaming hot springs, geysers, and volcanoes. A rift in the Mid-Atlantic Ridge runs through Iceland, causing the island to have more hot springs and sulfur springs than any other country. Some of the hot springs are geysers, which spray streams of hot water into the air. The word *geyser* comes from the name of Iceland's most famous hot spring, *Geysir*, which spouts hot water 59 m (195 ft) into the air.

Discussion Starter

• Ask: **What do you think causes hot springs and geysers?** Students may speculate that the water from hot springs and geysers is heated by very hot rocks below Earth's surface.

2. Guide the Discussion

Use the following strategy to facilitate discussion.

Connecting to the Activities

• *Sea-Floor Spreading, p. B22*

Explain that when rocks in Iceland were dated, scientists found that rocks at the middle of the island were the youngest. The rocks got progressively older toward the outer edges of the island. Ask: **Think back to Sea-Floor Spreading. How do the ages of rocks on Iceland support sea-floor spreading?** The island formed due to rifting.

3. Assess Understanding

Students can work in pairs to create a poster illustrating ways that geothermal energy is used by people.

Close the Investigation

 Critical Thinking Skills
THINK IT WRITE IT

Synthesizing, Generating Ideas, Expressing Ideas, Solving Problems

1. Descriptions will vary, but they should indicate an understanding of the processes involved in sea-floor spreading.

2. Features along the mid-ocean ridge include mountains, volcanoes, and rifts. These features form when molten magma from within Earth breaks through the crust that makes up the sea floor.

Challenge Ask students to find out how the research of the Mid-Atlantic Ridge by the submersible *Alvin* contributed to knowledge of plate tectonics.

Following Up

Baseline Assessment Return to the responses to questions about how the Atlantic Ocean has changed. Ask students if they would like to change any of their responses and, if so, how.

Reteaching Place two desks side by side about 1 meter (3 ft) apart. Explain that the desks represent the mid-ocean ridge and the space between them represents the rift zone. Select four pairs of students. Have the first pair walk side by side between the desks and take one step away from each other in front of the desks. Have the second pair of students do the same thing, noting that the first pair of students will have to move outward from the rift to make room for them. Repeat the process with the third and fourth pairs of students. Ask: **Which students walked between the desks first? Which students are farthest away from the opening between the desks? How does this simulate sea-floor spreading?** The oldest rocks are farthest from the mid-ocean ridge.

 Use *Science Notebook* p. 62.

Investigation Review ▶
Use Investigation Review p. 44 in the *Assessment Guide*.

magma rises up from inside Earth, heating the underground rock. The heated rock in turn heats any nearby ground water, changing it to steam. Some of this steam spurts out of the ground in the form of huge geysers.

Energy From Earth

Icelanders use this heated underground water as geothermal ("hot earth") energy. This energy, which comes from heat produced inside Earth, is used by the Icelanders to heat their homes, businesses, swimming pools, and greenhouses. The steam produced by the heated water runs generators that produce electrical energy.

Value of Geothermal Energy

Compared to other forms of energy, geothermal energy has many advantages, as you can see in the table below. Which form of energy is used where you live?

Geothermal energy is used now in several parts of the world besides Iceland—such as in Italy, Japan, Australia, New Zealand, Russia, and the United States. Some of the same processes that can lead to a volcanic eruption can also be turned to useful purposes. The use of geothermal energy in Iceland shows that processes inside Earth can provide people with the heat and electricity they need every day. ■

Comparison of Forms of Energy

Energy	Advantages	Disadvantages
Fossil fuels	no toxic waste	nonrenewable, polluting
Geothermal	less polluting than fossil fuels or nuclear energy	produces sulfur, boron, and ammonia wastes
Hydroelectric	cheap form of energy; renewable, nonpolluting	dams cause flooding of valuable land
Nuclear	cheap, renewable, powerful	toxic waste; risk of radiation leaks
Solar	renewable, nonpolluting	expensive development and maintenance

— **INVESTIGATION 3** —

1. You are planning a TV program about the mysteries at the bottom of the sea. How would you explain sea-floor spreading to your viewers?

2. Describe some of the most important features you might find along a mid-ocean ridge. Explain how these features are formed.

B32

Assessment

Investigation Review
What Does the Sea Floor Tell Us About Plate Tectonics?

CHAPTER 1

Name _____ Date _____

1. Use these terms to complete the paragraph below.

| sea-floor spreading | mid-ocean ridges | magma | rock |

Along deep cracks in the ocean floor, hot ___magma___ continually flows and hardens to form new ___rock___. These cracks where new ocean floor is being formed are known as ___mid-ocean ridges___. This constant activity, resulting in expansion of the ocean floor, is called ___sea-floor spreading___.

2. Fill in the blanks to complete the paragraph.

Movements in Earth's outer core, which contains iron and nickel, generate Earth's ___magnetic field___. Evidence of magnetic reversals found in rocks on the ocean floor led to the idea that new ocean floor is constantly being formed, in a process called ___sea-floor spreading___. This process provided direct evidence for the theory of ___plate tectonics___.

Process Skills
Making and Using Models

Why does an oceanographer's map of the ocean floor get more accurate as more sonar readings are taken? How does the model you made help you to understand this? The ocean floor varies with depth and breadth—it has ridges, mountains, and valleys. The more sonar readings that are taken, the more detailed the map will be. As more straws were added to the shoe box model, the topography of the clay surface became more obvious.

Performance

Demonstration Have each student design and make a "flip book" that demonstrates sea-floor spreading. Books can be included in students' portfolios.

REFLECT & EVALUATE

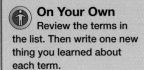
WORD POWER

crust   Pangaea
mantle   plates
magnetic field
magnetic reversal
mid-ocean ridge
plate boundaries
sea-floor spreading
tectonic plates
theory of continental drift
theory of plate tectonics

On Your Own
Review the terms in the list. Then write one new thing you learned about each term.

With a Partner
Use the terms in the list to make a word-search puzzle. See if your partner can find the hidden terms and tell you what each one means.

BUILD YOUR PORTFOLIO

Write a story that tells what you would see if you were the pilot of a research submarine that dived around a mid-ocean ridge.

Analyze Information

The maps on pages B17 and B18 show the location of earthquakes and volcanoes. Why are there so many earthquakes and volcanoes located around the shores of the Pacific Ocean? _____

Assess Performance

The two strips of paper in the model on page B22 represent the spreading sea floor. Make a similar model and use it to show how magnetic reversals occur on each side of a mid-ocean ridge. Write an explanation of how your model shows what happens at mid-ocean ridges. _____

Problem Solving

1. Oceanographers have found a large mountain range that runs down the middle of the South Atlantic Ocean between Africa and South America. Careful measurements show that South America is moving away from Africa at about 3 to 5 cm each year. How would you explain this?

2. Explain how the same kinds of rock could be found in Norway, Scotland, and parts of eastern Canada and the eastern United States.

3. Dinosaur skeletons have been found in Antarctica, but they could not have lived in such a cold climate. How could they possibly be there?

B33

REFLECT & EVALUATE

Word Power

 On Your Own Students' sentences should reflect some new information related to each term.

 With a Partner Remind students to check the terms in their puzzles for correct spelling.

Analyze Information

The boundaries of several tectonic plates occur along the Pacific rim and earthquakes and volcanoes often occur at plate boundaries.

Assess Performance

Students' models should show a pattern similar to that shown in the model on p. B 29. Evaluation could be based on how well students model and describe magnetic reversals at mid-ocean ridges.

Problem Solving

1. The movement of the continents can be explained by sea-floor spreading. South America and Africa are part of separate plates—the South American Plate and the African Plate, which are separating from each other.

2. At one time, all the continents were joined in one large landmass but later split apart and drifted to their current locations. Such rocks probably formed at the same time and were separated by continental drift.

3. The presence of dinosaur skeletons can be explained by the theory of continental drift.

 Use *Science Notebook* pp. 63–64.

BUILD YOUR PORTFOLIO

Students' stories should reflect understanding of the characteristics of the sea floor and mid-ocean ridges. Students might enjoy illustrating their stories.

Chapter Test   pp. 45–46 in the Assessment Guide

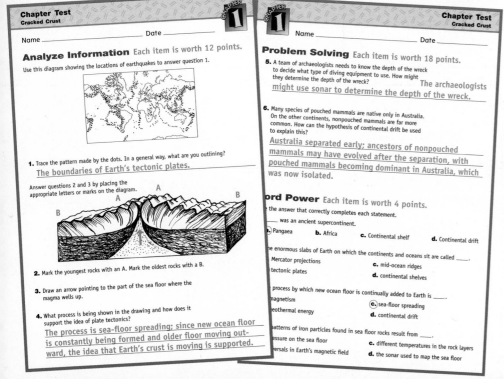

Chapter Test
Cracked Crust

Name _____ Date _____

Analyze Information Each item is worth 12 points.

Use this diagram showing the locations of earthquakes to answer question 1.

1. Trace the pattern made by the dots. In a general way, what are you outlining?
The boundaries of Earth's tectonic plates.

Answer questions 2 and 3 by placing the appropriate letters or marks on the diagram.

2. Mark the youngest rocks with an A. Mark the oldest rocks with a B.

3. Draw an arrow pointing to the part of the sea floor where the magma wells up.

4. What process is being shown in the drawing and how does it support the idea of plate tectonics?
The process is sea-floor spreading; since new ocean floor is constantly being formed and older floor moving outward, the idea that Earth's crust is moving is supported.

Chapter Test
Cracked Crust

Name _____ Date _____

Problem Solving Each item is worth 18 points.

5. A team of archaeologists needs to know the depth of the wreck to decide what type of diving equipment to use. How might they determine the depth of the wreck? The archaeologists might use sonar to determine the depth of the wreck.

6. Many species of pouched mammals are native only in Australia. On the other continents, nonpouched mammals are far more common. How can the hypothesis of continental drift be used to explain this?
Australia separated early; ancestors of nonpouched mammals may have evolved after the separation, with pouched mammals becoming dominant in Australia, which was now isolated.

Word Power Each item is worth 4 points.
the answer that correctly completes each statement.
_____ was an ancient supercontinent.
a. Pangaea   b. Africa   c. Continental shelf   d. Continental drift

he enormous slabs of Earth on which the continents and oceans sit are called _____.
Mercator projections   c. mid-ocean ridges
tectonic plates   d. continental shelves

process by which new ocean floor is continually added to Earth is _____.
magnetism   c. sea-floor spreading
eothermal energy   d. continental drift

patterns of iron particles found in sea floor rocks result from _____.
essure on the sea floor   c. different temperatures in the rock layers
eversals in Earth's magnetic field   d. the sonar used to map the sea floor

Subconcepts	Activities	Materials
Investigation 1 Why Do Tectonic Plates Move?		

The theory of plate tectonics proposes that the tectonic plates are moved by convection currents in Earth's mantle.
 	
Suggested Pacing: 2–3 class periods
Standards
  pp. 159, 160
Benchmarks
  pp. 73, 85
	The Conveyor, p. B36
	Science Processes: observe; predict; collect, record, and interpret data; make hypotheses; make and use models
		aquarium*, cold water, milk carton (0.24 L), 2 lengths of string (60 cm)*, duct tape*, measuring cup*, hot water, food coloring*, scissors, metric ruler*, paper towels, *Science Notebook* p. 67

Investigation 2 How Does the Motion of Tectonic Plates Build Mountains?		

Folded mountains form when plates carrying continents collide, thrusting up the crust; the interaction of plates can also result in the formation of volcanoes and other types of mountains.
 	
Suggested Pacing: 2–3 class periods
Standards
  p. 160
Benchmarks
  p. 73
	Colliding Continents, p. B42
	Science Processes: observe; predict; collect, record, and interpret data; define operationally; make and use models
	
	A Big Fender Bender, p. B44
	Science Processes: observe; predict; make hypotheses; make and use models
		sheet of cardboard*, Activity Support Master B5 (TRB p. 46), Activity Support Master B6 (TRB p. 47), *Science Notebook* pp. 70–71
		
		2 cellulose sponges*, water, *Science Notebook* pp. 73–74

Overview

In this chapter students investigate how mountains form, including how the movement of tectonic plates is related to mountain-building.

Chapter Concept

The theory of plate tectonics states that the flow of molten rock in the mantle moves tectonic plates; the movements of tectonic plates can cause mountains to form.

Advance Preparation	Curriculum Connection	Assessment
The Conveyor Collect enough milk cartons for each group	Integrating the Sciences TG p. B38 Literature TG pp. B39, B40	**Chapter 2 Baseline Assessment:** *Science Notebook* pp. 65–66 **Investigation 1 Baseline Assessment:** TG p. B36 **Investigation 1 Review:** AG p. 47 **Think It/Write It,** p. B41; *Science Notebook* p. 69 **Following Up on Baseline Assessment:** TG p. B41 **Performance:** TG p. B41
Colliding Continents None **A Big Fender Bender** None	Social Studies TG p. B45 Science, Technology & Society TG p. B46 Cultural Connection TG pp. B48, B49	**Investigation 2 Baseline Assessment:** TG p. B42 **Investigation 2 Review:** AG p. 48 **Think It/Write It,** p. B50; *Science Notebook* p. 76 **Following Up on Baseline Assessment:** TG p. B50 **Portfolio:** TG p. B50 **Chapter 2 Summative Assessment** Reflect and Evaluate, p. B51 Chapter 2 Review/Test: AG pp. 49–50 *Science Notebook* pp. 77–78

TG= Teaching Guide   TRB= Teacher Resource Book   AG= Assessment Guide   * Materials in the Deluxe Equipment Kit

Chapter Overview

Chapter Concept The theory of plate tectonics states that the flow of molten rock in the mantle moves tectonic plates; the movements of tectonic plates can cause mountains to form.

Theme: Models

Using physical models of plate movement and mountain formation, students can imagine how such processes happen in the real world.

Common Misconceptions

Students might believe all mountains are on land, but many are on the ocean floor. Some islands are mountaintops rising above the surface of the water.

Options for
Setting the Stage

Warm-Up Activity

 Give pairs of students two empty spools of thread, two pencils, a strip of paper (4" x 16") and some tape. Help them construct a conveyor belt by looping the paper around the spools. One student can hold the pencils and turn the spools while the other student places an object on the belt. Suggest that students think about how Earth's tectonic plates might be moved by a similar conveyor.

Use *Science Notebook* pp. 65–66.

Discussion Starter:
The Strangest Volcano

Use the photo and text to discuss volcanoes.

- **How can there be a volcano under a thick sheet of ice?** The volcano probably formed long before it was covered over by snow and ice, which formed the glacier.

- **Career:** *Geophysicist*
Many geophysicists concentrate their study on rocks and minerals. Geophysicists usually spend part of their time in the field observing and collecting data. Some work for large companies, searching for oil or mineral deposits. They use their knowledge of rocks to aid in the search.

TECTONIC PLATES AND MOUNTAINS

The Himalayas, the Andes, and other great mountain ranges have existed for millions of years. The largest of all mountain ranges is actually beneath an ocean. How do mountains form? Do mountains on land and beneath the ocean form in the same way?

The Strangest Volcano

The West Antarctic ice sheet stretches for hundreds of kilometers across the continent of Antarctica. This seemingly unchanging land with its 1.6-km thick (1-mi thick) ice holds a secret that reminds us of how highly active Earth is.

Donald Blankenship and Robin Bell are both geophysicists (jē ō fiz′i sists), scientists who deal with Earth's weather, wind, earthquakes, and so forth. Blankenship and Bell were flying over the West Antarctic ice sheet when they noticed a caved-in area that measured 48 m deep and 6.4 km across. What could cause such a strange hole in the thick ice?

Using radar to see through the ice, the researchers discovered a 630-m mountain—a volcano. Imagine finding a volcano under a thick sheet of ice!

B34

Home-School Connection

The Explore at Home activity "Build A Mountain!" encourages students to investigate the forces inside Earth that form mountains. Distribute the activity (TRB p. 8) when students have completed the chapter. Discuss what happens when you shake up a bottle of soda and release the cap.

Explore at Home

Name _____ Date _____

BUILD A MOUNTAIN

In our science class we have been studying how different kinds of mountains form. By building a model, we can learn more about how molten rock causes Earth's crust to bulge, forming dome mountains.

Materials

✓ dish towel
✓ round balloon
✓ plastic straw
✓ rubber band or tape
✓ paper clip

over the edge. Place a dish towel over the balloon. Blow through the straw slowly until a dome mountain forms. Fold the straw over and clamp it with a paper clip. Draw pictures of your "Earth's surface" both before and after you have made your mountain.

Procedure

Put one end of the straw into the balloon and use a rubber band to hold it securely in place. Lay the balloon and straw on a table or countertop so that the straw extends

Results

With family members, talk about how the pressure caused the dish towel to rise. Compare the result to the way pressure from magma causes Earth's crust to bulge, forming a dome mountain.

My Dome Mountain	
Before	After

Coming Up

INVESTIGATION 1

WHY DO TECTONIC PLATES MOVE? B36

INVESTIGATION 2

HOW DOES THE MOTION OF TECTONIC PLATES BUILD MOUNTAINS? B42

◄ Map showing presence of volcanic rock under the ice sheet.

Technology Alert

CD-ROM

On The Edge and **On The Move** Enhances or replaces Investigations 1 and 2

In **On The Edge** students examine how tectonic plates interact at plate boundaries. They "click" to learn about convergent, divergent, and transform-fault boundaries. When they correctly match the type of plate boundary to "hot spots" highlighted on a world map, an inset picture shows the plate movement that results. Students record their observations in a Spreadsheet.

In **On The Move** students hypothesize about the relationship between plate movement and mountain formation. They "click" to hear narration about plate movement on a tectonic world map. Using the Mountains Data Pack, students identify mountain ranges.

Chapter Road Map

INVESTIGATION 1

Why Do Tectonic Plates Move?

Activities	Resources
* The Conveyor	* Moving Plates

INVESTIGATION 2

How Does the Motion of Tectonic Plates Build Mountains?

Activities	Resources
* Colliding Plates	* Mountain-Building
A Big Fender Bender	Life at the Top

*Pressed for Time?

As you work through the upcoming investigations, focus on the activities and resources identified by the clock.

Look for this symbol in front of questions that help develop Scientific Reasoning Skills.

WHY DO TECTONIC PLATES MOVE?

Planner

Subconcept The theory of plate tectonics proposes that the tectonic plates are moved by convection currents in Earth's mantle.

Objectives

- **Predict** and **observe** how convection currents in water move and **hypothesize** how similar currents might move tectonic plates.

Pacing 2–3 class periods

Science Terms lithosphere, asthenosphere, convection, convection current, theory of plate tectonics, plate boundary, convergent boundary, divergent boundary, transform-fault boundary

Activate Prior Knowledge

Baseline Assessment Ask: **What force do you think makes Earth's tectonic plates move?** List students' responses and save them for use in Following Up at the end of the investigation.

Activity The Conveyor

Preview *Students use a model to investigate how heat energy from inside Earth moves tectonic plates.*

Advance Preparation *See p. B34b.*

1. Get Ready

Time about 30 minutes

Grouping groups of 4–6

 Collaborative Strategy Group members can jointly decide on a group hypothesis.

Materials Hints Use rinsed milk cartons from the school cafeteria.

Safety Wipe up spills promptly.

WHY DO TECTONIC PLATES MOVE?

Wegener's hypothesis on continental drift helped to explain why the continents appear to be just so many pieces of a jigsaw puzzle. However, his hypothesis didn't explain why the continents moved. What force can move such huge plates of rock?

Activity
The Conveyor

Heat is a form of energy. Energy can do work. How can heat energy from Earth's interior move tectonic plates? In this activity you'll construct a model that shows what moves tectonic plates.

MATERIALS
- aquarium
- cold water
- milk carton (0.24 L)
- 2 lengths of string (60 cm)
- duct tape
- measuring cup
- hot water
- food coloring
- scissors
- metric ruler
- paper towels
- *Science Notebook*

Procedure

1. Fill an aquarium with cold water.

2. Punch a 5-mm hole in the side of a milk carton, near the bottom. Punch another hole near the top of the carton.

3. Place a length of string over the hole near the bottom so that it extends down 2.5 cm below the hole. Cover the string and hole securely with a strip of duct tape, as shown.

4. Repeat step 3, this time covering the hole near the top of the carton.

B36 | Step 3

Responding to Individual Needs

Students Acquiring English Pair students who are working to acquire English with those who are English-proficient. Ask each pair to draw diagrams showing the movements of hot and cold water that they observed in the activity. In addition, pairs should label their diagrams and be prepared to explain them. Students may also add tectonic plates to the diagrams to show how convection currents might move them.

5. Using a measuring cup, fill the milk carton with hot water colored with food coloring. Seal the carton with duct tape.

6. Place the carton in the middle of the aquarium. Predict what will happen when the holes in the carton are opened. Record your predictions in your *Science Notebook*.

7. Have a group member hold down the milk carton while you carefully pull the strings to peel the tape off the holes. Watch what happens. Record your observations.

8. Form a hypothesis on how the movement in the aquarium is a model of the movement of material in Earth's crust and upper mantle. Discuss your hypothesis with your group.

Analyze and Conclude

1. What happened in step 7 when you removed the tape from the holes?

2. Did the hot water do what you predicted it would do? Compare your predictions with what actually happened.

3. If the hot and cold water represent the layer of Earth known as the mantle, which is just below the crust, how might the mantle move tectonic plates?

INVESTIGATE FURTHER!

EXPERIMENT

Predict what would happen if you floated a small piece of paper directly over the milk carton before you opened the holes. Then try it and compare your prediction with what actually happened.

B37

Investigate Further

Experiment

Students should find that if paper or another light, floating object is placed above the carton before opening the holes, the object will move on the convection currents horizontally toward the edge of the tank. Students can also try the experiment using two milk cartons and several pieces of paper cut to resemble adjacent plates. Students should record their observations in their *Science Notebooks* on p. 68.

---

2. Guide the Procedure

- Make certain that students use hot water and that the outsides of the milk cartons are dry before attaching the duct tape.

Have students record their answers on *Science Notebook* p. 67.

Have students use the CD-ROM Speadsheet to organize and display their data.

3. Assess Performance

Process Skills Checklist
- Were students' **predictions** reasonable and were their **observations** accurate?
- Did the students' **hypotheses** reflect their knowledge of Earth's layers and were they based on observations made during the activity?

Analyze and Conclude

1. The hot, colored water flowed out of the top hole in the carton and rose to the surface. The cold water sank to the bottom of the aquarium and flowed into the bottom hole in the carton, replacing the hot water and forcing it to rise to the surface.

2. Students' predictions may vary. They should observe that the hot water flowed out the top hole and rose to the surface.

3. Students should hypothesize that heat energy from inside Earth partially melts rock in the mantle. The melted rock rises just like the hot water in the activity. When the melted rock reaches the base of a tectonic plate, it moves horizontally, carrying the tectonic plate with it. As the melted rock cools, it sinks back into the mantle, like the cold water in the activity.

Moving Plates

Preview *Students focus on how convection currents in the asthenosphere may move tectonic plates.*

1. Get Ready

Science Terms lithosphere, asthenosphere, convection, convection current, theory of plate tectonics, plate boundary, convergent boundary, divergent boundary, transform-fault boundary

Background

- At convergent boundaries where both plates are carrying continental crust, folded mountains form as the plates collide. The continents become fused into a single continent, with a mountain range where the plates joined. For example, Europe and Asia are joined at the Ural Mountains. When the two plates carrying continental crust collided to form one plate, the Ural Mountains formed.

- Where both plates carry oceanic crust or where one plate carries continental crust and the other plate carries oceanic crust, volcanoes form as oceanic crust is carried back down into the mantle to be recycled.

Discussion Starter

What do you think is inside Earth? What makes you think so? Students might respond that there are different layers inside Earth. They may mention the mantle and the core as being composed of molten rock. Students probably have seen pictures of volcanoes erupting and pouring out molten rock from inside Earth.

Moving Plates

Recall from Chapter 1 that Earth's crust and upper mantle are broken into seven large slabs and several small ones. The slabs are called tectonic plates. These plates move over Earth's surface an average of several centimeters a year. Just what keeps these enormous slabs in motion?

Tectonic plates make up a part of Earth called the lithosphere. The word part *litho-* means "rock." You probably know that *sphere* means "ball."

The **lithosphere** (lith'ō sfir), then, is the solid, rocky layer of Earth. It is about 100 km (62 mi) thick. This part of Earth includes the crust, with the oceans and continents, and the rigid uppermost part of the mantle.

Have you ever slowly pulled on some silicon putty? What happened to the putty as the result of the force you applied? It stretched, didn't it? Suppose you gave the putty a quick, sharp tug. What would happen? The putty would snap and break. What do these two activities tell you about the putty? The putty has properties of both liquids and solids. Like a liquid, it flows when the force is applied slowly. Like a solid, putty snaps when the force is applied quickly.

(Left), Pulling slowly on silicon putty
(Right), Giving silicon putty a sharp tug

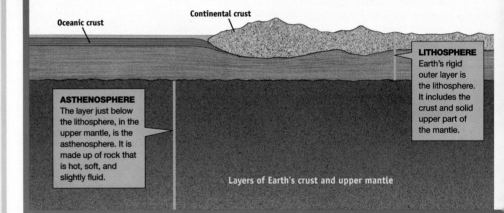

Oceanic crust   **Continental crust**

LITHOSPHERE Earth's rigid outer layer is the lithosphere. It includes the crust and solid upper part of the mantle.

ASTHENOSPHERE The layer just below the lithosphere, in the upper mantle, is the asthenosphere. It is made up of rock that is hot, soft, and slightly fluid.

Layers of Earth's crust and upper mantle

Investigate Further

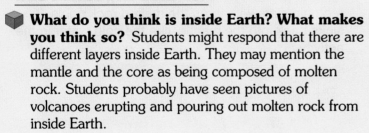

Integrating the Sciences

PHYSICAL SCIENCE

What to Do After discussing how tectonic plates move, have students explore the concept of buoyancy. Gather a pan of water, wood or foam blocks, and small weights to make models of moving tectonic plates with and without mountains. Have students place weights on some blocks and float both weighted and unweighted blocks in the pan of water.

What's the Result? Students should find that the blocks with weights float lower in the water than the blocks without weights. The blocks represent tectonic plates; the water—the asthenosphere, and the weights—mountains. Explain that the principle of buoyancy determines whether some plates float higher or lower in the asthenosphere.

The **asthenosphere** (as then'ə sfir), the layer of Earth below the lithosphere, is not rigid.

The upper part of the asthenosphere is made of rock that behaves like a plastic and is much like silicon putty when the putty is gently stretched. The rock in the lower asthenosphere is partially melted.

Convection currents in a pot of boiling pasta ▼

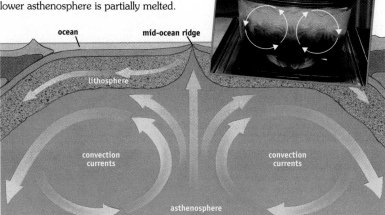

▲ Convection currents in the asthenosphere are thought to drive the movement of the tectonic plates.

Heating and Cooling Rock

Scientists think that Earth's plates move over its surface because of convection in the asthenosphere. **Convection** (kən-vek′shən) is a process by which energy is transferred by a moving fluid. Convection occurs when a fluid is placed between a hot lower surface and a cold upper surface. A **convection current** is the path along which the energy is transferred.

You are probably familiar with several kinds of convection currents. Have you ever watched rice or pasta whirl around in a pot of boiling water? Convection currents are set in motion when water or air

is heated. The heated fluid then rises because it is less dense than the surrounding fluid. In a pot of rice or pasta, when the heated water reaches the top of the pot, it cools and flows back down to begin another journey around the pot. When you did the activity on pages B36 and B37, you saw the effect of convection currents as you watched the movement of the hot and cold water in the aquarium.

Convection in the Mantle

How does convection occur in Earth's mantle? The partly melted hot rock in the asthenosphere rises because it is less

B39

Integrating the Curriculum

Science & Literature

SCI-FI

What to Do Read descriptive passages from the book *Journey to the Center of the Earth* by Jules Verne. Discuss with students whether the information in these passages about Earth's interior is accurate and whether such a journey would be possible.

What's the Result? Students should conclude that the author's descriptions of Earth's interior are inaccurate and that such a journey would be impossible because the interior of Earth is extremely hot and the rocks below the lithosphere are molten.

Multi-Age Classroom Working in groups, students can discuss ideas for their own stories about traveling to Earth's center. Some group members can be writers and others can be illustrators of their stories.

---

2. Guide the Discussion

Choose from the following strategies to facilitate discussion.

Connecting to the Activities

- **The Conveyor, p. B36**

How is the asthenosphere like the water you observed in the activity? How is it different? Like the water in the activity, the partly melted rock in the asthenosphere flows like a liquid. Also, like the water, the heated part of the asthenosphere rises, and the cooled part sinks. Unlike the water, the rock in the asthenosphere has the properties of a plastic, such as silicon putty. **Where did the heat energy come from in the activity?** The heat energy came from the hot water in the milk carton. **Where does the heat energy come from in the asthenosphere?** In the asthenosphere, the heat energy comes from within Earth.

Making Inferences

- **Why are the tectonic plates in constant motion?** Because rock in the asthenosphere is constantly being heated and cooled, creating convection currents.

Responding to Individual Needs

Visual Activity For students who have difficulty visualizing less dense rock rising to the surface, partially fill a small plastic bottle with cooking oil. Then fill a small aquarium with colored water. Holding a finger over the bottle's spout, lower the bottle on its side into the water. Remove your finger from the spout to release the oil. The less dense oil will rise to the surface of the water.

Making Comparisons

If you think of the lithospheric plates as rafts and the continents and oceans as passengers, what is the asthenosphere? The water on which the rafts are floating

Thinking About the Data

🔲 **What do you think happens when two plates collide?** Encourage speculation about surface features that might form as a result of plate collisions.

Making Comparisons

- **What do you think happens as tectonic plates move?** Students might mention that some plates move together, some move apart, and others slide past each other. Suggest that students use pieces of cardboard to simulate plate movement.

- **How are convergent and divergent boundaries similar?** Both are places where plates interact. **How are they different?** At a convergent boundary, plates are moving together. At a divergent boundary, plates are moving apart.

👤 Responding to Individual Needs

Gifted and Talented Activity Students can preview the content of Investigation 2 by researching and comparing the formation of the volcanic mountains in the Cascades with the formation of the Appalachian Mountains. Have them share their information with the class. They should find that both were formed at convergent boundaries. The Appalachian Mountains were formed when two plates collided and the rock folded. The volcanic mountains in the Cascades were formed when two plates collided, and one plate was forced under the other. Some of the plate that was pushed down melted and produced magma that rose to the surface, forming volcanic mountains.

3. Assess Understanding

👥 Working in groups of three or four, students should explore the formation and breakup of Pangaea based on their knowledge of plate boundaries. Ask each group to share their explanations with the entire class.

---

dense than the surrounding materials. It slowly makes its way toward the lithosphere. When the melted rock reaches the cooler lithosphere, the melted rock begins to cool and harden. The cooler rock then moves horizontally along the bottom of the lithosphere. When the rock reaches the edge of a plate, it sinks down under the plate into the mantle. As the rock moves down into the asthenosphere, it begins to melt, and the cycle starts again.

Moving Tectonic Plates

Today scientists generally agree that convection currents in the asthenosphere are the force that moves tectonic plates. Recall from Chapter 1 that Alfred Wegener, despite all his evidence, could not explain what caused the continents to move over Earth's surface. Thus, his idea of continental drift was a hypothesis, or a guess based on observations. In the 1960s the theory of plate tectonics was

HOW PLATES INTERACT

Places where plates interact are called **plate boundaries**. Examples of three kinds of interacting plates are shown on this page and the next.

COLLIDING PLATES Plates collide, or come together, at **convergent boundaries**. What do you think might happen when two enormous slabs of rock collide? What kinds of features do you think you'll find along convergent boundaries?

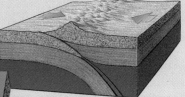

▲ Colliding plates

▲ The walls of this riverbank in Iceland are on plates that separated.

SEPARATING PLATES Plates move away from one another at **divergent boundaries**. Most divergent boundaries are found on the ocean floor. These boundaries are places where new oceanic crust forms through the process of sea-floor spreading. The photograph shows a divergent boundary.

B40

Investigate Further

📚 Using the Trade Book

USING MAPS **What You Need** *Volcanoes and Earthquakes*, by Basil Booth

What to Do Direct students to examine the text and map on pp. 16 and 17 to learn where Earth's tectonic plates are colliding, sliding, or separating. They can compare the map on pp. 16 and 17 to a physical map of the world to see what geographic features develop where plates meet.

What's the Result? 🔲 **How well does the theory of plate tectonics explain the geographic features observed?** There are geographic features along every plate boundary that can be explained by the theory of plate tectonics: colliding plates produce mountains or volcanoes; sliding plates produce fault lines; and new oceanic crust forms.

proposed. A theory carries more weight than a hypothesis because a theory is an idea that is supported by evidence. And a theory can be used to make accurate predictions about future events. The **theory of plate tectonics** states that Earth's crust and upper mantle are made up of a series of rigid or nearly rigid plates that are in motion. The map on this page shows these plates and the direction in which they move. ■

▲ This map shows the location of Earth's major tectonic plates. A full-size map is on pages B20 and B21.

SLIDING PLATES Plates move past one another at **transform-fault boundaries**. A fault is a very large crack in Earth's rocks, along which movement has taken place. The photograph shows the San Andreas Fault, found in the western United States. This fault, one of the longest and most famous in the world, is the site of many earthquakes.

▲ San Andreas Fault, California, as seen from an airplane

--- **INVESTIGATION 1** ---

1. Can convergent and divergent plate boundaries be considered opposites? Write a paragraph comparing these two kinds of plate boundaries.

2. Define the term *tectonic plate* and explain what might cause tectonic plates to move.

B41

Assessment

Performance

Interview Have pairs of students work together to present an interview on tectonic activity. One student can be the interviewer and the other a geologist who has been asked to explain tectonic activity. Students should present their interviews to the rest of the class.

Investigation Review
Why Do Tectonic Plates Move?

Name _____ Date _____

1. Match the descriptions on the left with the words on the right.

a. My upper regions are composed of partly melted rock. _____ lithosphere
b. I am the solid, rocky layer of Earth. _____ plate boundary
c. I am the region where tectonic plates interact. _____ asthenosphere

2. Use the following characteristics or descriptions associated with each type of plate interaction to complete the chart.

Convergent boundaries	Transform-fault boundaries
Sea-floor spreading occurs here	Plates come together here
Faults occur here	

Colliding Plates	Separating Plates	Sliding Plates
convergent boundaries	divergent boundaries	transform-fault boundaries
plates come together here	sea-floor spreading occurs here	faults occur here

A convection current is the flow of a fluid due to temperature
Process Skills differences in the fluid. In the model, warm
Making and Using Models water flowed across the surface and eventu-
In *The Conveyer* activity, you constructed a model to show ally sank. Convection
how tectonic plates move. How did your model demonstrate
how convection might cause tectonic plates to move? in the fluid mantle could
carry the tectonic plates as the fluid flowed.

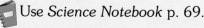

Close
the Investigation

Critical Thinking Skills
Synthesizing, Expressing Ideas

1. Paragraphs should reflect an understanding that plates are moving apart and new crust is being formed at divergent boundaries, and that plates are moving together and old crust is being destroyed at convergent boundaries.

2. A tectonic plate is a huge slab of Earth's lithosphere. Earth's crust and upper mantle are made up of a series of tectonic plates that float on the asthenosphere. Convection currents within the asthenosphere cause plates to move.

Challenge Students can work in groups of three or four to discuss the following statement: Since new crust is being formed at divergent boundaries, Earth must be getting larger. Groups should be able to explain why the statement is false.

Following Up

Baseline Assessment Return to the class list of ideas about what makes Earth's tectonic plates move. Ask students if they would like to revise any of their ideas now and, if so, how.

Reteaching Place a beaker filled with water on a ring stand. Place a lighted candle under the beaker to one side. Heat the water more on one side of the beaker than on the other. Add a spoonful of rice grains to the opposite side of the beaker. Have students observe the movement of the rice grains as convection currents are set up in the water. You might also place two small pieces of plastic foam in the center of the water's surface and have students discuss how these pieces of foam behave like tectonic plates.

Use *Science Notebook* p. 69.

◀ **Investigation Review**
Use Investigation Review p. 47 in the *Assessment Guide*.

How Does the Motion of Tectonic Plates Build Mountains?

Planner

Subconcept Folded moutains form when plates carrying continents collide, thrusting up the crust; the interaction of plates can also result in the formation of volcanoes and other types of mountains.

Objectives

- **Make a model** of colliding plates, **infer** what happens when plates collide, and **describe** how different kinds of mountains are formed.

Pacing 2–3 class periods

Science Terms folded mountain, fault-block mountain, dome mountain, volcano

Activate Prior Knowledge

Baseline Assessment Ask: **How do you think mountains form?** List students' hypotheses and save them for use in Following Up.

Activity Colliding Plates

Preview *Students make a model of what happens when two tectonic plates collide and find that, like the crust, the cardboard bends and crumples.*

1. Get Ready

Time about 20 minutes

Grouping group of 4–6

Collaborative Strategy One student can press the cardboard against the wall, while the others draw a picture showing what happens.

Materials Hints Use Activity Support Masters B5 and B6 (TRB pp. 46 and 47). For best results, use medium-weight cardboard.

How Does the Motion of Tectonic Plates Build Mountains?

The tectonic plates that make up Earth's surface are large, thick, and massive. When they move, something has to give! Find out what "gives" in Investigation 2.

Activity
Colliding Plates

MATERIALS
- sheet of cardboard
- tectonic-plates map
- Earth-features map
- *Science Notebook*

Plates are enormously big and heavy. What might happen when one plate runs into another? In this activity you'll demonstrate a simple model of colliding plates.

- -

Procedure

1. Imagine that the sheet of cardboard is a tectonic plate and that a wall is another tectonic plate. Predict what will happen when the two plates collide. Record your predictions.

2. Take the sheet of cardboard and press one edge of it firmly against a wall and push.

3. In your *Science Notebook*, record what happens to the cardboard.

4. Your map of the tectonic plates shows the edges of tectonic plates and the directions in which the plates are moving. Study your map and find one or more places where the boundary between plates is a convergent boundary.

Step 1

B42

Responding to Individual Needs

Students Acquiring English Pair students who are acquiring English with English-proficient peers. Have each pair discuss observations of colliding plates and explain their hypothesis to each other. They may also wish to compare findings from their *Science Notebooks* pp. 70–71 as a means to share information.

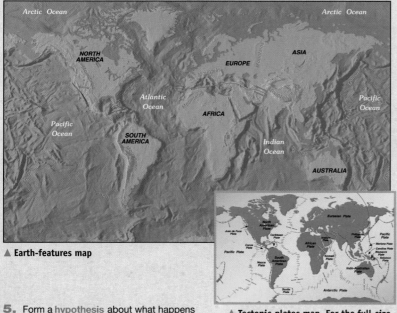

▲ Earth-features map

▲ Tectonic-plates map. For the full-size map, see pages B20 and B21.

5. Form a hypothesis about what happens when two plates meet at a convergent boundary.

Analyze and Conclude

1. What feature forms when two plates collide at a convergent boundary? Locate several such features on the Earth-features map.

2. In what parts of the world are two plates now colliding? Infer how these regions may change in the future.

UNIT PROJECT LINK

After several earthquakes shook California in the 1990s, the Sierra Nevada range became more than 0.3 m (1 ft) taller. What other mountains in the world are still growing? Use newspapers and magazines to find out about earthquakes and volcanoes that have recently lifted mountains. Find out what form of mountain building caused the uplift. Use a map to identify the location of the growing mountains.

B43

Safety Review safety precautions with students.

2. Guide the Procedure

• Make sure that all students use the same type of medium-weight, flexible cardboard.

Have students record their data and answers on *Science Notebook* pp. 70–71.

You may wish to have students use the CD-ROM Spreadsheet and Painter to organize and display their data.

3. Assess Performance

Process Skills Checklist
• Did students follow directions correctly when **making their models?**
• Did students **predict** and accurately **record observations** of what happened to the model?
• Are students' **hypotheses** based on observations and data from maps?

Analyze and Conclude
1. Mountains

2. Possible examples include the Himalayas in northern India and Nepal, and the Zagros Mountains in western Iran, where the Arabian Plate is pushing up into the Eurasian Plate. These regions may become more mountainous and experience earthquakes as plates continue to push into one another.

Investigate Further

Unit Project Link

The best location for viewing the effect of converging plates within continents is where India pushes up into the edge of the Asian Plate, resulting in the Himalaya Mountains. Other examples are the Zagros Mountains, where the Arabian Plate pushes northward, and the Alps, where the African Plate pushed into Europe. Students should record information in their *Science Notebook* on p. 72. Have students use Unit Project Master B2 (TRB p. 72) to help them visualize continental plates.

Activity A Big Fender Bender

Preview *Students construct models of moving continents and draw conclusions.*

1. Get Ready

Time about 20 minutes

Grouping groups of 4-6

Collaborative Strategy As an alternate strategy, have students work in pairs. Both members of the pair should agree on a hypothesis before testing with the model. One student should push the sponges together, while the other records observations.

Materials Hints Thin sheets of foam rubber cut into rectangular shapes can be substituted for the sponges. The foam rubber need not be moistened.

Safety Wipe up any spills promptly.

2. Guide the Procedure

- Sponges should be just moist enough to be flexible, but not sopping wet.

Have students record and graph their data and answers on *Science Notebook* p. 73.

You may wish to have students use the CD-ROM Painter to organize and display their data.

3. Assess Performance

Process Skills Checklist

- Were students' **hypotheses** reasonable?
- Were their **predictions** reasonable?
- Did students **use the model** to test their hypotheses?

Analyze and Conclude

1. One or both of the sponges buckled as they were pushed together.
2. Answers will vary but should include whether the sponges buckled.
3. Just as sponges crumple and fold upward when pushed together, so do continents. The behavior of the sponges models mountain-building.

Activity
A Big Fender Bender

Think about what happens when two cars collide. What happens to the metal? What do you think happens when two continents collide? You'll use a simple model to find out.

Procedure

1. Form a hypothesis about what you think will happen when one continent bumps into another. Discuss your hypothesis with other members of your group. Record your hypothesis in your *Science Notebook*.

2. Moisten two cellulose sponges so that they are flexible. Predict what will happen if you place the sponges end to end and push them slowly into each other.

3. Then place the sponges end to end and push them into each other. Record your observations.

Step 2

Analyze and Conclude

1. What did you observe?

2. Did the sponges do what you predicted they would do? If not, what was different?

3. Explain how the moist sponges are a model of continents colliding. How is this model related to what you did in the preceding activity?

> ### INVESTIGATE FURTHER!
> #### RESEARCH
> When North America collided with North Africa to form part of Pangaea, a large mountain range was thrust upward on the North American Plate. Find out which mountains they were and what has happened to them.

B44

Investigate Further

Research

The mountain range formed by the collision of North America and Africa is the Appalachian Range. Originally it was much higher—perhaps as high as the Himalayas—but erosion has worn it down. Students should record information they have researched in their *Science Notebooks* on p. 74.

Mountain-Building

Have you ever gone mountain climbing? A mountain is any feature that rises above the surrounding landscape. So whether you've climbed the steep slopes of the Rocky Mountains or just hiked a local hill, you've gone mountain climbing!

Mountains form as the result of four basic processes: folding, faulting, doming, and volcanic activity—so mountains can be classified as folded mountains, fault-block mountains, dome mountains, or volcanoes. Three of these kinds of mountains—folded, fault-block, and volcanic—result from plate movements.

Folded Mountains

Have you ever made a paper fan? If you have, then you've squeezed paper to make a series of pleats, or folds. If you were to look at the folded edge of the fan, you would see a series of crests, or high points, and troughs, or low points. Folded mountains form when masses of rock are squeezed from opposite sides. In the activities on pages B42 to B44, you saw that folded mountains form when two plates collide. The Appalachians, the Alps, the Urals, and the Himalayas can be classified as folded mountains. Locate these mountain ranges on a globe of Earth.

FOLDED MOUNTAINS These form when two tectonic plates collide.

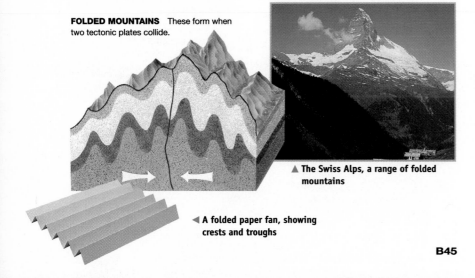

▲ The Swiss Alps, a range of folded mountains

◄ A folded paper fan, showing crests and troughs

B45

Integrating the Curriculum

Science & Social Studies

FIND MOUNTAINS **What to Do** Using a physiographic globe or wall map, ask students to locate and name mountains on each continent. Lead students to observe that mountains often occur near the coasts of continents. Discuss why this is so.

What's the Result? 📦 **How do you think the Andes Mountains formed? What makes you think so?** They formed when the Nazca and South American Plates converged and the South American Plate folded.

Multi-Age Classroom Some students could use outline maps of the world to color in mountain ranges they see on the globe or wall map. They could then label these mountain ranges.

Mountain-Building

Preview *Students focus on four mountain-building processes: folding, faulting, doming, and volcanic activity.*

1. Get Ready

Science Terms volcano

Background

- Until the Himalayas were surveyed in the early 19th century, the Andes of South America were thought to be the world's highest mountains.

- The Andes were formed by the collision of tectonic plates some 180 million years ago. They stretch 7,520 km (4,700 mi) from the Caribbean to Cape Horn. Much of the Andes Range is above 3,000 m (about 10,000 ft) and dotted with hundreds of active volcanoes. At 6,960 m (22,835 ft), Aconcagua in the Argentine Andes is the highest point in the Western Hemisphere.

Discussion Starter

- **Have you ever seen tall mountains? Where were these mountains? How do you think they formed?** Answers will vary, but encourage students to give details about the mountains they have seen. Students may respond that some mountains formed when continents collided and other mountains may have formed from volcanic activity.

2. Guide the Discussion

Choose from the following strategies to facilitate discussion.

Connecting to the Activities

- **Colliding Plates, p. B42**
  What type of mountains did you make in **Colliding Plates**? Folded mountains

Making Inferences

■ **Along what types of boundaries would you expect to find folded mountains?** Along convergent boundaries **Why?** Because where plates collide, one or both of the plates crumple and fold

■ **Along what types of boundaries would you expect to find fault-block mountains?** Along divergent boundaries and convergent boundaries

Drawing Conclusions

■ **The Himalayas continue to grow each year as the plates collide. What processes occur to prevent the Himalayas from growing indefinitely?** Erosion removes some rock each year, even as the mountain-building process continues.

Responding to Individual Needs

Kinesthetic Activity Provide papier-mâché and paint so that students can create three-dimensional mountain chains or individual mountains. Students might work in pairs and consult resource books and atlases to determine an appropriate scale for their models.

SCIENCE IN LITERATURE

Volcanoes and Earthquakes
by Basil Booth

Students should find that the Andes Mountains were formed when the Nazca and South American Plates converged. The Cascade Range formed when the Pacific Plate converged with and was subducted under the North American Plate.

Fault-block Mountains

Recall that a fault is a large crack in Earth's rocks, along which movement has taken place. Forces produced by moving plates can move rock along faults. When blocks of rock move up or down along a fault, a mountain can form.

Examples of fault-block mountains include those in the Dead Sea area, the Grand Tetons in Wyoming, and those in the Great Rift Valley of Africa. Among the mountains in the Great Rift Valley, scientists have unearthed some of the oldest known human fossils.

Dome Mountains

Have you ever heard of Pikes Peak? This granite summit in the Colorado Rockies is 4,341 m (14,110 ft) tall! It was explored in 1806 by Zebulon Pike. Although the peak was eventually named after him, Pike never even reached its summit! Pikes Peak is a dome mountain that formed millions of years ago when forces deep within Earth pushed magma toward the surface, where it cooled and hardened. Although dome mountains have an igneous core, sedimentary rocks can border such mountains. But erosion often strips away the sedimentary rocks to reveal the harder igneous core.

Other dome mountains in the United States are the Sangre de Cristo Mountains, the Bighorn Mountains, the Black Hills, and Longs Peak. Find these dome mountains on a map of the United States. Are any of them in your state or in nearby states?

SCIENCE IN LITERATURE

VOLCANOES AND EARTHQUAKES
by Basil Booth
Silver Burdett Press, 1991

Reference books are good sources when you want to find information about a specific topic.

Read pages 18–19 in *Volcanoes and Earthquakes* to find out how the Andes Mountain range of South America and the Cascade Range of North America were formed. Then try to explain to a classmate how water trapped in crustal rocks is related to mountain building. When you get to Chapters 3 and 4 in this unit, use *Volcanoes and Earthquakes* to find the answers to your own questions.

Investigate Further

STS Science, Technology & Society

SPACE PROBES **What to Do** Until the development of space probes, nothing was known about mountain-building or plate tectonics elsewhere in the solar system. Interested students could research information on what space probes have uncovered about other bodies in the solar system.

What's the Result? Encourage students to examine how information gathered by space probes helps scientists better understand the processes that occur on Earth and to share information with the class.

Multi-Age Classroom Provide resource materials at different levels of difficulty so that each student can find information at his or her own reading level.

FAULT-BLOCK MOUNTAINS These mountains form when masses of rock move up or down along a fault.

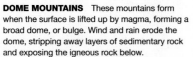

▲ Wasatch Range, Utah, fault-block mo

DOME MOUNTAINS These mountains form when the surface is lifted up by magma, forming a broad dome, or bulge. Wind and rain erode the dome, stripping away layers of sedimentary rock and exposing the igneous rock below.

▲ Pikes Peak, Colorado, a dome mountain

INVESTIGATE FURTHER!

EXPERIMENT

Use a few different colors of modeling clay to demonstrate how folded mountains form. Then use the clay and a plastic knife to show how fault-block mountains form. USE CARE IN HANDLING THE KNIFE. Make sketches of your models in your *Science Notebook*.

B47

Making Comparisons

- **How are dome mountains different from folded or fault-block mountains?** Unlike folded or fault-block mountains, dome mountains don't necessarily form on plate boundaries.

Responding to Individual Needs

Kinesthetic Activity Students could use one color of clay to form the igneous rock at the core of a dome mountain and another color of clay to form the sedimentary rock that sometimes lies over the igneous rock. Suggest that students make colored drawings of their models.

Drawing Conclusions

Dome mountains often are surrounded by gradually sloping land. Why? Sediments may erode from the top of the mountain, leaving the igneous core. The sediments may then be deposited along the sides of the mountain, creating gentle slopes.

Experiment

Students might use different colors of clay to make horizontal layers. Ask students to push on the layers from opposite ends to create folded mountains. Using plastic knives, students might cut through the horizontal layers of clay to make blocks that are then raised or lowered along a fault line to create fault-block mountains. Encourage students to make drawings of their models on *Science Notebook* p. 75.

Making Comparisons

- **How are volcanoes different from dome mountains?** Volcanoes form when hot melted rock erupts from an opening in Earth's crust. Dome mountains form from melted rock that has cooled and hardened and been pushed upward by forces deep within Earth.

 Use **Transparency 11,** "Mountain Building," here. Have students fill in the second and third columns of the chart on the transparency.

- **Look at the photos of Mount St. Helens. Compare its appearance before and after the 1980 eruption.** Before the eruption, Mount St. Helens was a conical volcano surrounded by miles of rich vegetation. After the eruption, the volcano lost much of its height, took on a more rounded appearance, and was surrounded by thick layers of ash and trees burned to charred sticks.

3. Assess Understanding

Have the students compile a list of all of the kinds of mountains discussed in this resource. Then students can use a map of the United States to locate and identify examples of each type of mountain found on their list.

Volcanoes

Have you ever opened a bottle of warm soda and had it spray all over you? The spraying of the soda is a bit like the eruption of magma when a volcano forms. **Volcanoes**, a fourth type of mountain, are common along convergent and divergent plate boundaries. They form when magma, or molten rock, erupts from an opening in Earth's surface. Sometimes the eruption is quiet; at other times it is quite forceful.

Mount St. Helens is a volcano in the Cascade Range. This mountain chain extends from northern California to British Columbia, in Canada. On May 18, 1980, Mount St. Helens blew its top and threw dust, ash, and volcanic rocks 18,000 m (59,400 ft) above the ground! As the ash rained back down to Earth, it blanketed some places with as much as 2 m (6.6 ft) of fine material. In some places the ash was so thick that it looked like midnight when it was actually noon! You will learn much more about volcanoes in Chapter 4. ■

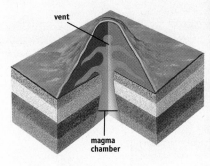

▲ A typical volcano

Mount St. Helens, Washington State. (*Top*), before the 1980 eruption; (*middle*), during the eruption; and (*bottom*), after the eruption.

B48

Investigate Further

Cultural Connection

LEGENDS

What to Do Tell students the Hawaiian legend of Pele and refer them to p. B102–B103. According to the legend, the goddess Pele went from island to island searching for a home. Finally she reached the island of Hawaii, where she used her magic spade to dig a huge fire pit within the volcano Kilauea. According to myth, the volcano has been Pele's home ever since. Encourage students to write their own legends and stories about how volcanoes or other types of mountains form. Have students read their stories to the class.

What's the Result? Ask students to point out the way in which explanations in their legends differ from the factual explanations of how different kinds of mountains form.

Life at the Top

You now know that folded mountains are formed by the interactions of tectonic plates. The Himalaya Mountains, for example, were formed millions of years ago when the plate carrying India, then a separate continent, rammed into the plate carrying Asia. This enormous collision of plates crumpled the crust and lifted up sediment from the ocean floor, forming the Himalayas. In some places the sediment was raised up thousands of meters, forming folded mountains.

People used to living at low altitudes experience problems as they move up into higher country. Climbers of very high mountains—the Himalayas, for example—can experience many difficulties. Newcomers experience problems with breathing. The lower air pressure at higher altitudes means that less oxygen is taken in with each breath. A lack of oxygen can affect vision and make walking dangerous. Heart rate quickens sharply, and the heart tries to supply more oxygen to the body. Climbers often have to stop to rest every few meters.

People in Nepal, a country in the Himalayas, have adapted to living high

The world's highest mountains, compared to the Empire State Building ▼

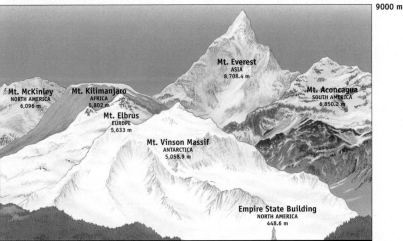

9000 m

Mt. Everest
ASIA
8,708.4 m

Mt. McKinley
NORTH AMERICA
6,096 m

Mt. Kilimanjaro
AFRICA
5,802 m

Mt. Aconcagua
SOUTH AMERICA
6,850.2 m

Mt. Elbrus
EUROPE
5,633 m

Mt. Vinson Massif
ANTARCTICA
5,058.9 m

Empire State Building
NORTH AMERICA
448.6 m

0 m

Cultural Connection

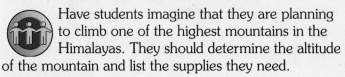

What to Do Invite small groups to find out more about the Sherpa, Bhutanese, and Tibetan people who live high in the Himalayas. Encourage them to prepare reports on lifestyles, religion, and languages, as well as a description of the climate and area where they live. Other students may be interested in learning more about high-altitude sickness. Suggest that they include illustrations such as pictures, drawings, and charts.

What's the Result? Plan a "Travel to the Himalayas" day and invite groups to present their reports as tour guides for people planning a trip to Nepal or Tibet. Encourage them to explain what people should expect to see. Those who researched high-altitude problems could advise travelers on precautions they should take.

Life at the Top

Preview *Students focus on how humans have adapted to living at high altitudes.*

1. Get Ready

Background

- La Paz, Bolivia, sits more than 3,960 m (13,000 ft) high in the Andes. Although La Paz is closer to the equator than Tahiti, fireplaces and electric heaters are often used to keep homes in La Paz warm.

- People who are not accustomed to high altitudes begin to feel the effects of lack of oxygen at about 3,000 m (10,000 ft). These effects can include headache, nausea, and shortness of breath.

Discussion Starter

Why do you think you breathe more rapidly when you run? More rapid breathing supplies the extra oxygen the muscles need.

2. Guide the Discussion

Choose from the following strategies to facilitate discussion.

Connecting to the Activities

- *A Big Fender Bender, p. B44*
  How could you have made the mountains in your model taller? By increasing the pressure of the sponges, or colliding plates

Identifying and Solving Problems

What types of problems might a hiker have on a high mountain? Difficulty breathing, vision problems, thickening blood, accelerated heart rate

3. Assess Understanding

Have students imagine that they are planning to climb one of the highest mountains in the Himalayas. They should determine the altitude of the mountain and list the supplies they need.

Close the Investigation

Critical Thinking Skills
Synthesizing, Analyzing

1. Both folded and fault-block mountains result from movement of tectonic plates. Folded mountains form when masses of rock are squeezed from opposite sides. Fault-block mountains form when large blocks of rock move up or down along a fault.

2. When tectonic plates collide, bands of rock can be squeezed together until they crumple and fold, forming folded mountains. If plates are pushing together along a fault, one block of rock can slide up and over the other, causing fault-block mountains to form.

Challenge Suggest that students find out how miners work in Earth's highest mines, such as Chile's Aucanquilcha sulfur mine (nearly 4 mi high in the Andes). One source they might use is "The High Andes," *National Geographic*, April 1987.

Following Up

Baseline Assessment Return to the class list of hypotheses about how mountains form. Ask students if they would like to change any of their hypotheses and, if so, how.

Reteaching Help students make a chart comparing the formation of the four different types of mountains. Students might want to draw each type of mountain and include examples of each from around the world.

Use *Science Notebook* p. 76

Investigation Review ▶
Use Investigation Review p. 48 in the *Assessment Guide*.

▲ Tenzing Norgay climbed Mount Everest.

▲ Sherpa women in their mountain village

up in the mountains. Nepal is the home of the highest mountain peak in the world—Mount Everest, which towers 8,848 m (29,028 ft) above sea level.

The Sherpas, a people of Tibetan ancestry who live mainly in Nepal, are known for their ability to live and work in the high terrain of their country. How have the Sherpas adapted to their life high in the mountains?

The Sherpas' most important adaptation has to do with their blood. Because the Sherpas have lived all their lives in the mountains, their blood contains more oxygen-carrying red blood cells than that of most other people. So, with each

breath the Sherpas take, they can absorb more available oxygen and pump it throughout their bodies. The ability to move enough oxygen throughout the body prevents many problems. In fact, Tenzing Norgay, a Sherpa, was one of the first two men to climb to the top of Mount Everest!

Visitors to the high mountains adapt to the lower air pressure after several weeks. What happens? Like the bodies of the native peoples, their bodies produce more of the oxygen-carrying red blood cells. In time, newcomers to the high mountains can also pump more oxygen throughout their bodies. ■

INVESTIGATION 2

1. How are folded mountains like fault-block mountains? How are the two kinds of mountains different? Write a paragraph comparing and contrasting these kinds of mountains.

2. Describe the relationship between the collision of plates and the formation of mountains.

B50

Assessment

Investigation Review
How Does the Motion of Tectonic Plates Build Mountains?

Name _____ Date _____

1. Which types of mountains seem to be directly related to interactions of plates?
   Folded mountains, volcanoes, and, possibly, fault, block mountains.

2. Match the type of mountain to the processes involved in its formation.
   a. Forces within Earth push magma upward, where it cools and hardens under the surface. — Folded mountains
   b. Magma erupts along convergent and divergent boundaries. — Fault-block mountains
   c. Masses of rock are squeezed together as plates collide. — Volcanoes
   d. Forces cause sections of rock to move up or down along cracks in the crust. — Dome mountains

Process Skills
Predicting
Based on what happened to the two sponges in the activity, *A Big Fender Bender*, predict what would happen if two tectonic plates collided in this way. Name a geological feature that forms this way.
The two sponges represent plates that are colliding. Forces are being exerted from opposite sides of the two plates. This process forms folded mountains. Examples of geological features that formed this way are the Appalachians, Alps, Urals, and Himalayas.

Portfolio
Make a Concept Map
Encourage students to make concept maps to organize what they have learned about mountains in this investigation. Hang the maps around the classroom.

REFLECT & EVALUATE

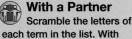

WORD POWER

asthenosphere   convection
plate boundary   volcano
dome mountain   lithosphere
convection current
convergent boundary
divergent boundary
fault-block mountain
folded mountain
theory of plate tectonics
transform-fault boundary

On Your Own
Define each term.

With a Partner
Scramble the letters of each term in the list. With terms of two or more words, keep the scrambled letters separate for each word. Exchange scrambled terms with your partner. Who can unscramble them first?

Collect photos of mountains. Classify them as folded, fault-block, dome, or volcano. Make a poster of your collection.

Analyze Information

The map below shows a convergent boundary between two tectonic plates. Describe what features you might see along this convergent boundary.

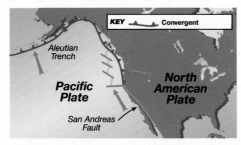

KEY — Convergent

Aleutian Trench

Pacific Plate

North American Plate

San Andreas Fault

Assess Performance

Make a double-decker peanut-butter-and-jelly sandwich. Cut it in half and use it to show how fault-block mountains are formed.

Problem Solving

1. Imagine that you are in a special kind of submarine that has entered Earth's upper mantle. The submarine is riding along in the convection currents. Describe your journey.

2. You skid on a small rug into a wall. How is what happens to the rug like tectonic plates building mountains?

3. The San Andreas Fault in California is a transform-fault boundary between the North American Plate and the Pacific Plate. Describe and model how the plates are moving along this boundary.

B51

REFLECT & EVALUATE

Word Power

On Your Own
Students should use the Glossary to check their definitions.

With a Partner
Remind students to check that the unscrambled terms are spelled correctly.

Analyze Information

Students should mention that folded mountain ranges and possibly volcanoes would be found.

Assess Performance

Students' cut sandwiches should resemble the drawing on p. B47. The layers of bread, peanut butter, and jelly in one half of the sandwich should be raised and tilted at an angle with respect to the other half.

Problem Solving

1. The submarine would move with the current in the liquid rock until it reaches the cooler lithosphere. The liquid rock would begin to cool. The submarine and the rock would move horizontally along the bottom of the lithosphere, but when the rock reached the edge of a plate, it and submarine would be dragged into molten mantle. The submarine would stay in the mantle until the rock changed into a hot liquid and began to rise.

2. The rug wrinkles and forms "hills" and "valleys."

3. The Pacific Plate is moving north with respect to the North American Plate along the San Andreas Fault.

Use *Science Notebook* pp. 77–78.

PORTFOLIO

Students' posters should include examples of folded, fault-block, dome, and volcanic mountains.

Chapter Test   pp. 49–50 in the Assessment Guide

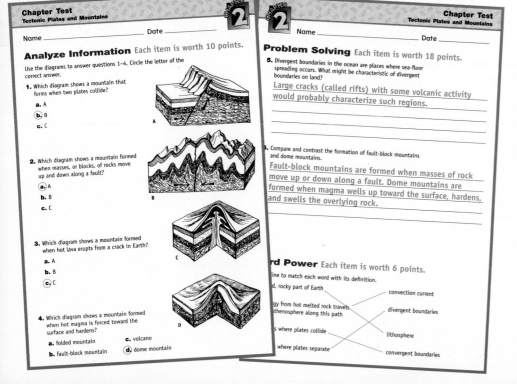

Chapter Test
Tectonic Plates and Mountains

Name _____ Date _____

Analyze Information Each item is worth 10 points.
Use the diagrams to answer questions 1–4. Circle the letter of the correct answer.

1. Which diagram shows a mountain that forms when two plates collide?
a. A
(b.) B
c. C

A

2. Which diagram shows a mountain formed when masses, or blocks, of rocks move up and down along a fault?
(a.) A
b. B
c. C

B

3. Which diagram shows a mountain formed when hot lava erupts from a crack in Earth?
a. A
b. B
(c.) C

C

4. Which diagram shows a mountain formed when hot magma is forced toward the surface and hardens?
a. folded mountain   c. volcano
b. fault-block mountain   (d.) dome mountain

D

Problem Solving Each item is worth 18 points.
5. Divergent boundaries in the ocean are places where sea-floor spreading occurs. What might be characteristic of divergent boundaries on land?
Large cracks (called rifts) with some volcanic activity would probably characterize such regions.

6. Compare and contrast the formation of fault-block mountains and dome mountains.
Fault-block mountains are formed when masses of rock move up or down along a fault. Dome mountains are formed when magma wells up toward the surface, hardens, and swells the overlying rock.

Word Power Each item is worth 6 points.
Draw a line to match each word with its definition.

... rocky part of Earth   convection current
... gy from hot melted rock travels
... asthenosphere along this path   divergent boundaries
... where plates collide
... where plates separate   lithosphere
     convergent boundaries

CHAPTER 3

SHAKE, RATTLE, AND ROLL

Subconcepts	Activities	Materials
Investigation 1 What Causes Earthquakes and How Can They Be Compared?		

Earthquakes are sudden releases of energy stored in rocks ; most earthquakes occur near the margins of tectonic plates that are sliding past each other, colliding, or moving apart.
 	
Suggested Pacing: 3 class periods
Standards
    pp. 160, 168
Benchmarks
    p. 73
	A Model of Sliding Plates,
	p. B54
	Science Processes: observe; infer; predict; collect, record, and interpret data; make and use models
		2 blocks of wood*, coarse sandpaper*, 4 rubber bands*, Activity Support Master B5 (TRB p. 46), Activity Support Master B6 (TRB p. 47), *Science Notebook* pp. 81–82

Investigation 2 What Happens To Earth's Crust During an Earthquake?		

Various kinds of rock movements along the faults result in earthquakes; earthquakes produce three kinds of energy waves, each resulting in a characteristic ground motion.
 	
Suggested Pacing: 2–3 class periods
Standards
    pp. 160, 168
Benchmarks
    pp. 73, 76, 90
	Shake It!, p. B62
	Science Processes: observe, infer, predict, experiment, make and use models
		small block of wood*, 2 clear plastic bowls*, sand*, water, measuring cup*, gelatin*, *Science Notebook* pp. 85–86

Investigation 3 How Are Earthquakes Located and Measured?		

Earthquakes can be located and measured using seismographs; information about earthquakes is used to help design earthquake-resistant structures and to warn of tsunamis.
 	
Suggested Pacing: 2–3 class periods
Standards
    pp. 160, 168, 169
Benchmarks
    pp. 46, 55, 73, 90
	Shake It Harder!, p. B68
	Science Processes: observe; measure/use numbers; predict; collect, record, and interpret data; identify and control variables; define operationally; make and use models
	
	Locating Earthquakes, p. B70
	Science Processes: measure/use numbers; infer; collect, record, and interpret data
	
	Be an Architect, p. B72
	Science Processes: observe, communicate, predict, identify and control variables, experiment, make and use models
		string*, chair, metric ruler*, two heavy books, masking tape, fine-point marker*, table, shelf paper (2 m long)*, *Science Notebook* p. 89
		
		metric ruler*, Activity Support Master B7 (TRB p. 48), Activity Support Master B8 (TRB p. 49), drawing compass*, *Science Notebook* pp. 91–92
		
		several small cardboard boxes, masking tape, large aluminum pan*, clay*, sand*, soil*, dowels*, timer*, *Science Notebook* pp. 93–94

Overview

In this chapter students investigate the nature of earthquakes—what they are, where they occur, how they can be located and measured, and how they are related to tectonic plates.

Chapter Concept

Earthquakes, which often occur at the margins of tectonic plates, can be described by their energy waves and can be located and measured.

Advance Preparation	Curriculum Connection	Assessment
A Model of Sliding Plates None	Science, Technology & Society TG p. B56 Language Arts TG p. B57 Social Studies TG p. B58 Cultural Connection TG p. B59	**Chapter 3 Baseline Assessment:** *Science Notebook* pp. 77–78 **Investigation 1 Baseline Assessment:** TG p. B54 **Investigation 1 Review:** AG p. 51 **Think It/Write It,** p. B61; *Science Notebook* p. 84 **Following Up on Baseline Assessment:** TG p. B61 **Performance:** TG p. B61
Shake It! In advance, prepare one bowl of gelatin for each group.	Integrating the Sciences TG p. B64 Math TG p. B65 Science, Technology & Society TG p. B66	**Investigation 2 Baseline Assessment:** TG p. B62 **Investigation 2 Review:** AG p. 52 **Think It/Write It,** p. B67; *Science Notebook* p. 88 **Following Up on Baseline Assessment:** TG p. B67 **Performance:** TG p. B67
Shake It Harder! None **Locating Earthquakes** None **Be an Architect** In advance, you may wish to open the boxes and tape them.	The Arts TG p. B74 Math TG p. B76 Integrating the Sciences TG p. B77 Science, Technology & Society TG pp. B78, B79	**Investigation 3 Baseline Assessment:** TG p. B68 **Investigation 3 Review:** AG p. 53 **Think It/Write It,** p. B80; *Science Notebook* p. 96 **Following Up on Baseline Assessment:** TG p. B80 **Portfolio:** TG p. B80 **Chapter 3 Summative Assessment** Reflect and Evaluate, p. B81 Chapter 3 Review/Test: AG pp. 54–55 *Science Notebook* pp. 97–98

TG= Teaching Guide   TRB= Teacher Resource Book   AG= Assessment Guide   *Materials in the Deluxe Equipment Kit

Introducing the Chapter

Chapter Overview

Chapter Concept Earthquakes, which often occur at the margins of tectonic plates, can be described by their energy waves and can be located and measured.

Theme: Models

Models can help students understand earthquakes and their relationship to plate tectonics.

Common Misconceptions

Students might think that earthquakes result in gaping cracks that swallow up objects on Earth's surface. This chapter will explain how plate movement causes earthquakes and affects Earth's surface.

Options for
Setting the Stage

Warm-Up Activity

Groups of students can use pencils like logs to build a hollow square or use index cards to construct a house on a table. Ask them to predict what will happen when the table shakes. Students should check their predictions by shaking the table. Does the strength of the shaking affect the structures differently? Try it and find out.

Use *Science Notebook* pp. 79–80.

Discussion Starter:
Shake, Rattle, and Roll

Use the photo and text to start a discussion.

Movement along a previously unknown fault caused the earthquake damage shown in the photograph. **What can Waverly Person and his staff learn from their monitoring of this earthquake?** Among other things, they can learn that other faults could lie close to the fault that caused this earthquake.

• **Career:** Seismologist
Explain that seismologists explore the causes and effects of earthquakes. Using a seismograph and monitors along fault lines, they study and interpret the shock waves (seismic waves) produced by earthquakes. Resulting information is used to design earthquake-resistant structures, explain Earth's structures, and help locate petroleum deposits.

SHAKE, RATTLE, AND ROLL

Many men and women in science try to solve problems that affect people's daily lives. Earthquakes have terrified people throughout history, and they continue to threaten loss of life and property today. How can science help?

Scientists on the Scene

Among the first people to investigate an earthquake are the seismologists (sīz mäl' ə jists). These scientists study how and why earthquakes happen. Waverly Person is the chief of the National Earthquake Information Service in Denver, Colorado. He and his staff monitor movements in Earth's crust, using seismographs and other technology.

Seismologists examine the strength of each earthquake, how long it lasts, and where it is located. They exchange ideas about *why* an earthquake has happened. Over the years, seismologists have developed hypotheses about where future earthquakes will happen. How might such predictions be useful?

B52

Home-School Connection

The Explore at Home activity "Earthquake Safety" encourages students to develop a home earthquake safety plan. Distribute the activity (TRB p. 9) when students have completed the chapter. Discuss what happens inside people's homes during an earthquake.

EARTHQUAKE SAFETY

In our science class, we have been learning about what causes earthquakes. We have also been studying how certain materials can help buildings withstand earthquake damage. What can you do around your home to help prepare for an earthquake emergency?

Procedure

With a family member, develop an earthquake safety plan. Where would you go in the event of an earthquake? Draw a map of your home that shows supported archways, interior walls, and even large heavy pieces of furniture, such as desks, that you could crawl under. On your map, mark potential danger areas, such as windows, heavy mirrors, book shelves, and hanging planters. Consider putting together an earthquake emergency kit, with a flashlight, portable radio, first aid kit, fire extinguisher, food, water, tools, and other necessities, such as medications. Then arrange a family earthquake drill so that each family member can practice what he or she would do during a real earthquake.

Results

Discuss ways that you could make your home safer in case of an earthquake. Do you have heavy or breakable objects stored on high shelves from which they could fall? Could you move flammable liquids, such as paint or cleaning supplies, from inside your home to a garage or shed? Why is it a good idea to clearly label water valves and gas shut-off valves?

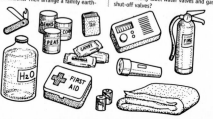

◀ Waverly Person checking a seismograph

B53

Chapter Road Map

What Causes Earthquakes, and How Can They Be Compared?

Activities	Resources
＊ A Model of Sliding Plates	Sliding Plates
	＊ Our Active Earth

What Happens to Earth's Crust During An Earthquake?

Activities	Resources
＊ Shake It!	＊ Bend Till It Breaks

How Are Earthquakes Located and Measured?

Activities	Resources
＊ Shake It Harder!	The Seismograph
Locating Earthquakes	＊ Earthquakes on the Sea Floor
Be an Architect	Designing for Survival

Technology Alert

CD-ROM

Feel The Quake Enhances or replaces Investigation 3

The activities in **Feel The Quake** help students determine how to locate earthquakes. First, students view a video that shows how seismologists use seismic data to locate the epicenter of an earthquake. Then they "become" seismologists and determine the epicenter of an earthquake on a map of the U.S. Using the Seismograph Probe, students take seismic readings and record in a Spreadsheet the delay between the P and S waves at various cities to determine the epicenter of the earthquake.

＊ Pressed for Time?

As you work through the upcoming investigations, focus on the activities and resources identified by the clock.

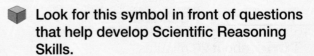 Look for this symbol in front of questions that help develop Scientific Reasoning Skills.

WHAT CAUSES EARTHQUAKES, AND HOW CAN THEY BE COMPARED?

Planner

Subconcept Earthquakes are sudden releases of energy stored in rock; most earthquakes occur near the margins of tectonic plates that are sliding past each other, colliding, or moving apart.

Objectives

• **Make** and **use a model** of how Earth's plates move past one another.

• **Investigate** what happens during an earthquake.

Pacing 3 class periods

Science Terms earthquake, fault, aftershock, Richter scale, magnitude

Activate Prior Knowledge

Baseline Assessment Ask: **What do you think happens when two huge slabs of Earth's crust suddenly slip past each other?** Record and save students' response for use in Following Up.

Activity — A Model of Sliding Plates

Preview *Students make a model of sliding plates and apply it to real tectonic plates. They should find that the blocks in their model do not move until moderate pressure is applied; then they jerk past each other.*

1. Get Ready

Time about 20 minutes

Grouping groups of 4–6

 Collaborative Strategy Students can cover the blocks of wood with sandpaper and then take turns rubbing them together.

INVESTIGATION 1 — WHAT CAUSES EARTHQUAKES AND HOW CAN THEY BE COMPARED?

Picture two railroad cars rolling by each other on side-by-side tracks. Could they get past each other if their sides were touching? Some tectonic plates are a little like these trains. This investigation is about the sudden changes that can occur when plates that touch move past one another.

Activity

A Model of Sliding Plates

MATERIALS
• 2 blocks of wood
• coarse sandpaper
• 4 rubber bands
• tectonic-plates map
• Earth-features map
• *Science Notebook*

Did you ever try to slide a heavy box over a rough sidewalk and have the box get stuck? Tectonic plates have rough surfaces, too. What happens when the plates keep pushing but the rocks don't slide?

Procedure

1. Cover two blocks of wood with coarse sandpaper. Use rubber bands, as shown, to hold the sandpaper on the blocks of wood.

2. Predict what will happen if you hold the sandpaper surfaces tightly against each other and then try to slide the blocks past each other. Record your prediction in your *Science Notebook*.

Step 1

B54

Responding to Individual Needs

Students Acquiring English Have students point out several features from the Earth-features map. Then ask them to list the kind of feature both in English and in their native language. They might include *mountain, trench,* and *ocean.*

▲ Tectonic-plates map. For a larger map, see pages B20 and B21.

3. Try sliding the blocks past each other. (Hold together the surfaces on which there are no rubber bands.) **Observe** what happens and **record** your observations.

4. Explain how this action might be like two tectonic plates passing each other.

5. Now list the places shown on your tectonic-plates map where plates are sliding past each other. For example, note that the Pacific Plate and the North American Plate are sliding past each other near the west coast of the United States.

6. Find the same places on the Earth-features map. List any features you find in those places that seem to be related to the motion of the plates.

Analyze and Conclude

1. Think about the places you identified in steps 5 and 6. Have you read or heard anything about either of these locations that might involve changes in Earth's crust? What do you conclude might happen when two tectonic plates slide past each other?

2. Did you find anything that looks like it might be caused by the sliding of two plates? If so, what did you find?

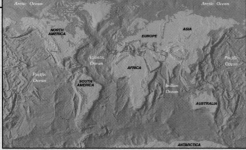

▲ Earth-features map. For a larger map, see page B43.

INVESTIGATE FURTHER!

EXPERIMENT

Find two bricks. Slide one over the other. Do they slide easily? What do you hear? What do you feel? What happens when two smooth rock surfaces slide past each other?

B55

Investigate Further

Experiment

The ease with which objects slide against each other depends on the roughness of their surfaces. Rough bricks and rocks will not slide easily. Students should recognize that they can use more than one of their senses to observe the sliding of the bricks. Encourage them to record in their *Science Notebooks* on p. 82 observations of what they see, hear, and feel. Students might record that they see the rocks move jerkily past each other, hear them grind as the surfaces catch on each other, and feel the vibrations.

Materials Hints Each piece of sandpaper should be large enough to cover a block of wood.

Safety Review safety precautions with students.

2. Guide the Procedure

• Referring to the opening paragraph at the top of p. B 54, ask: **What would happen to the railroad cars rolling past each other if the two trains happened to graze each other?** The cars would be shaken and rocked but probably would remain intact.

• Be sure students place the rubber bands so they are not on the surfaces that will be rubbed together.

Have students record their data and answer questions on *Science Notebook* pp. 81–82.

You may wish to have students use the CD-ROM Spreadsheet to organize and display their data. They can also use the Painter to make maps showing what features occur where plates slide past each other.

3. Assess Performance

Process Skills Checklist

• Did students correctly **make and use a model** of sliding plates? Did the blocks of wood move suddenly when enough pressure was applied?

• Were students' **predictions** reasonable? Were they detailed enough to be compared to students' observations?

• Were students' **observations** detailed? Were they descriptive?

• Did students **conclude** that the ground shakes or earthquakes occur when two plates suddenly slide past each other? Did students make the connection between the model and its real-life application?

Analyze and Conclude

1. Students should conclude that earthquakes can occur when two plates slide past each other.

2. The Earth-features map shows two faults—one on the west coast of the United States and the other running from the Atlantic Ocean westward to Europe. These faults might be caused by sliding plates. Students might find that abrupt changes in surface features, such as a river that suddenly changes direction or an offset line of mountains, might result from the sliding of two plates.

Sliding Plates

Preview *Students focus on the effects of the 1906 San Francisco earthquake and the movements within Earth that caused this earthquake.*

1. Get Ready

Background

- Sometimes the lessons of nature go unheeded. An earthquake that struck San Francisco in 1868 took its greatest toll on landfill--dry land that was "made" by filling in part of the bay. Landfill is made of loose materials that shift easily. It is therefore unstable in an earthquake. After the 1868 earthquake, warnings to limit construction on such reclaimed land were not heeded, and extensive landfill damage occurred again in the 1906 quake. Despite the 1906 disaster, people continued to use landfill to reclaim the shoreline. During the Loma Prieta earthquake of 1989, the unstable landfilled areas again sustained significant damage.

Responding to Individual Needs

Auditory Activity Ask volunteers to read aloud the account of the San Francisco earthquake.

Discussion Starter

- **What do you think happens when an earthquake occurs?** Encourage speculation about the movements of Earth that take place during earthquakes. Students might mention shaking of the crust, cracks in the surface, and giant sea waves.

- **What kinds of damage could these events cause?** Students might mention twisting roads or bridges, damage or destruction of buildings, fires, falling rocks and landslides on mountains, and so on.

Sliding Plates

It was a little after 5:00 A.M. on April 18, 1906. Many San Franciscans were awakened by a deep rumbling of the ground beneath them. Homes, stores, offices, hotels, churches, and bridges collapsed. Sergeant Jesse Cook, a police officer, observed, "The whole street was undulating [waving]. It was as if the waves of the ocean were coming toward me."

An editor from the *Examiner* newspaper noted that trolley tracks were twisted like wriggling snakes and that water and gas spurted high into the air.

Scientists estimate that the earthquake that struck San Francisco in 1906 would have had a reading of about 8.3 on the Richter scale. (You'll read more about the Richter scale in "Our Active Earth" on pages B58 and B59.) The earthquake

▲ City Hall after the 1906 San Francisco earthquake; a 1906 newspaper headline

Gold is discovered at Sutter's Mill.
1848

Cable cars climb the hills of San Francisco for the first time.
1873

B56

Investigate Further

STS Science, Technology & Society

ANALYZING NEWS

What to Do Explain that news of the 1906 San Francisco earthquake spread slowly. In contrast, television enabled millions of people worldwide to be eyewitnesses to the 1989 earthquake that struck San Francisco during the broadcast of the World Series baseball game. Encourage students to compare newspaper coverage of an event with television coverage of the same event.

What's the Result? How might the time frame in sending news differ between newspapers and television? Newspaper transmission of news can take one day. Once camera and transmission equipmewnt is on the scene, television news is instantaneous. **How might the quick spread of news be helpful?** Help can reach the affected area faster; updates can be reported instantly.

lasted for only a little over a minute. But its effects were enormous. About 500 people died, and nearly 250,000 were left homeless. Water mains were destroyed. Fires due to broken gas lines raged throughout the city for days. More than 28,000 buildings were destroyed by the fires.

Shortly after the quake, San Franciscans began to rebuild their destroyed city and their disrupted lives. By December 1906, many new buildings stood where others had collapsed. Within about three years, 20,000 buildings had been constructed to replace those lost to fire and to the quake itself.

Today, just as in 1906, people ask "What are earthquakes? Why do these tremors happen in some places and not in others?" An earthquake is a vibration of the Earth, caused by a sudden release of energy stored in the crust. Most earthquakes occur along tectonic plate boundaries, places on Earth where vast slabs of rock separate, collide, or slide past one another.

Faults

The 1906 earthquake occurred when blocks of rock deep within Earth's surface began to move along a crack called the San Andreas Fault. A fault is a large crack in layers of rock along which movement has occurred. The San Andreas Fault runs through much of California and separates the North American Plate from the Pacific Plate. The 1906 San Francisco earthquake wasn't the first "earth-shaking" event to occur along the San Andreas Fault and it wasn't the last. Many large earthquakes have struck that region since 1906. A major earthquake struck the San Francisco Bay area in October 1989. That quake, measuring 7.1 on the Richter scale, caused $7 billion in damage and 63 deaths. Scientists predict that a much larger earthquake—the "Big One"—is yet to come. ■

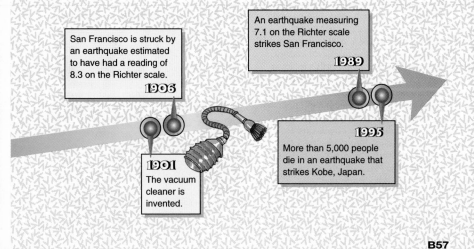

San Francisco is struck by an earthquake estimated to have had a reading of 8.3 on the Richter scale.
1906

1901
The vacuum cleaner is invented.

An earthquake measuring 7.1 on the Richter scale strikes San Francisco.
1989

1995
More than 5,000 people die in an earthquake that strikes Kobe, Japan.

B57

Integrating the Curriculum

Science & Language Arts

REPORTING NEWS **What to Do** Provide students with books or articles about the San Francisco earthquake of 1906. Student "journalists" can write articles reporting on how it was just before, during, or after the quake. Articles can be compiled to make newspapers.
What's the Result? Ask volunteers to play the role of "newsies" from the early part of the century, encouraging other classes to "read all about it."
Multi-Age Classroom Encourage students to work cooperatively in groups, assigning pairs of students to gather research, write copy, proofread, make drawings to resemble photographs, write headlines, and produce a newspaper.

2. Guide the Discussion

Choose from the following strategies to facilitate discussion.

Connecting to the Activities

- **A Model of Sliding Plates, p. B54**
  Which part of the model that you made with wooden blocks represents the San Andreas Fault? The plane along which the blocks move represents the fault. Students might describe this plane as a line, space, or crack.

Thinking About the Data

What did you find most interesting or surprising about the 1906 San Francisco earthquake? Students should refer to information in the text or information they discovered while producing their newspapers for the Science & Language Arts activity.

Thinking Critically

Why might scientists predict that a much larger earthquake is yet to come in California? Students might suggest that by looking at data on past earthquakes, scientists can see a pattern of large quakes occurring every so often. Other responses might refer to knowledge scientists gain by studying the movement of rocks along faults. Point out that the work of many scientists, both past and present, contributes to the current understanding of earthquakes.

3. Assess Understanding

Suggest that students pretend to be city council members and concerned citizens of a city that has just had an earthquake. During a council meeting, they should summarize the damage that has been done, suggest ways to deal with this damage, and make proposals for what might be done to limit such damage in the future.

Our Active Earth

Preview *Students focus on predicting earthquakes, the causes of quakes, and how scientists measure the amount of energy released in an earthquake.*

1. Get Ready

Science Terms earthquake, aftershock, Richter scale, magnitude

Background

- Thus far, seismologists have not been able to predict earthquakes consistently; however, some successful predictions have been made. The most dramatic success occurred in China during the winter of 1974–1975. Observers noticed several warning signs associated with impending quakes. Well water rose and fell. The ground tilted unusually. Animals behaved strangely: hibernating snakes left their burrows early and froze, groups of rats scurried about, and cattle refused to enter their stalls.

  The occurrence of a swarm of 500 tremors on February 4 led seismologists to issue a prediction that a major earthquake would strike within a day or two. Hundreds of thousands of people left their work and homes to wait outside in the cold. That evening, a quake with a magnitude of 7.3 leveled many buildings in the area. The prediction probably saved hundreds of thousands of lives.

Discussion Starter

- **What natural changes take place in, on, or around Earth?** Natural changes include daily weather changes; slow processes such as erosion; and catastrophic changes, such as earthquakes and volcanic eruptions. Living things also change daily and over months and years.

- **How long do you think an earthquake lasts?** Show pictures of earthquake damage. Students might think earthquakes last longer than the usual few minutes or less.

Our Active Earth

Earth is an ever-changing planet. Some changes happen in a matter of seconds or minutes. Other changes occur over months or years. Soils are eroded by water, wind, and gravity. Mountains take hundreds, thousands, or even millions of years to form and just as long to be worn away. And some changes, such as those caused by earthquakes, occur suddenly and violently.

Earthquakes

Earthquakes usually last for only a few minutes. But it takes many years to build up the energy that is released during an earthquake. As blocks of rocks move past one another along faults, friction prevents some sections of rock from slipping very much. Instead, the rocks bend and change shape, until the force becomes too great. It is only when the rocks suddenly slide past each other that an earthquake occurs.

An **earthquake** is a vibration of Earth, caused by the release of energy that has been stored in Earth's rocks as they have ground past one another over time. Most earthquakes occur in parts of the world where tectonic plates are colliding, separating, or moving horizontally past each other. California is one area where earthquakes are likely to occur. Part of southern California is on the edge of the Pacific Plate, which is moving slowly toward the northwest.

The San Andreas Fault

During the 30-million-year history of the San Andreas Fault in California, hundreds of earthquakes and many thousands of aftershocks have occurred along its length of 1,200 km (720 mi). An **aftershock** is a shock that occurs after the principal shock of an earthquake. Recall that one of these tremors nearly destroyed the city of San Francisco in 1906.

A more recent earthquake, which was centered in Loma Prieta, California, in October 1989, was felt as far away as Oregon and Nevada. This earthquake caused more than 60 deaths and registered 7.1 on the Richter scale.

Damage caused by the Loma Prieta, California, earthquake in October 1989. ▼

Integrating the Curriculum

Science & Social Studies

MAKING POSTERS

What You Need art materials, almanacs, news magazines, books on weather and natural disasters

What to Do List locations of some of the most recent earthquakes, such as Kobe, Japan in 1995; Northridge, California in 1994; northwestern Iran in 1990; Armenia in 1988; and Mexico City in 1985. Encourage students to find out more about these quakes and prepare a chart comparing them. Then have groups create posters listing what people should do to prepare for a possible quake.

What's the Result? Display posters. Invite students to organize and stage an earthquake drill in the classroom.

The Richter Scale

If you've ever listened to or read a news report about an earthquake, you've heard the term *Richter scale*. The **Richter scale**, with numbers ranging from 1 to 10, describes the magnitude, or strength, of an earthquake. The **magnitude** of an earthquake is the amount of energy released by the quake. The Richter scale is named after the American seismologist Charles Richter.

Minor earthquakes have magnitudes of 4 or less. The largest recorded earthquakes have magnitudes of about 8.5.

Each increase of 1.0 on the Richter scale represents a difference of about 30 times more energy than the previous number. For example, an earthquake measuring 5.0 on the Richter scale releases about 30 times more energy than a quake measuring 4.0. Likewise, an earthquake measuring 5.7 on the

The Pacific Plate and North American Plate border the San Andreas Fault. In which directions do the plates move? ▼

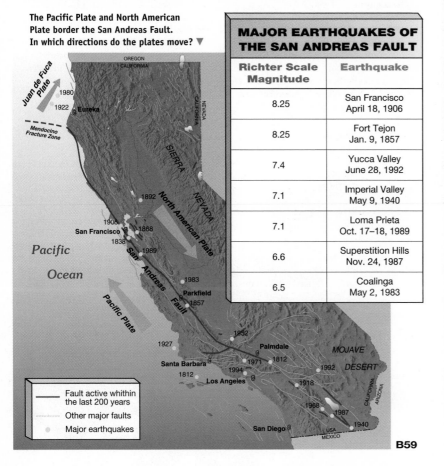

MAJOR EARTHQUAKES OF THE SAN ANDREAS FAULT	
Richter Scale Magnitude	**Earthquake**
8.25	San Francisco April 18, 1906
8.25	Fort Tejon Jan. 9, 1857
7.4	Yucca Valley June 28, 1992
7.1	Imperial Valley May 9, 1940
7.1	Loma Prieta Oct. 17–18, 1989
6.6	Superstition Hills Nov. 24, 1987
6.5	Coalinga May 2, 1983

B59

2. Guide the Discussion

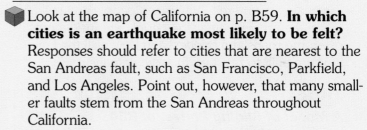

Choose from the following strategies to facilitate discussion.

Thinking About the Data

Look at the map of California on p. B59. **In which cities is an earthquake most likely to be felt?** Responses should refer to cities that are nearest to the San Andreas fault, such as San Francisco, Parkfield, and Los Angeles. Point out, however, that many smaller faults stem from the San Andreas throughout California.

You might wish to use **Transparency 7,** "Earthquakes Around the World," to reinforce where earthquakes are likely to occur.

Identifying and Solving Problems

How much more energy would be released by a quake that measures 5.5 than by a quake that measures 4.5? Thirty times

Drawing Conclusions

• **How would you respond if you experienced an earthquake that measured 3.6 on the Richter scale?** Most students would probably not be very concerned since a quake that measures 3.6 is relatively minor. However, students who have never experienced a quake would likely be nervous about any quake they could feel. A quake less than 2.0 cannot be felt—it can only be detected by instruments.

What do you think the "Big One"—the large earthquake that scientists expect in California—might measure on the Richter scale? Based on the data in the table and descriptions in the text, students should conclude that such a large quake would measure between 7.5 and 8.5.

Responding to Individual Needs

Students Acquiring English Have students write a short paragraph describing what happens when an earthquake takes place. Ask them to underline the words that describe what a person experiencing the earthquake would see or hear.

Cultural Connection

RESEARCHING

What to Do Before scientific explanations were developed, many cultures told myths and folk tales to explain frightening and dangerous events. Japanese folklore told of a giant catfish that lived under the ground and caused earthquakes by thrashing around. Suggest that students find other stories in reference books explaining the occurrence of earthquakes and then compare and contrast explanations from different cultures.

What's the Result? Lead students to understand that myths that seem odd to us today were nonetheless based on the limited information available to people at the time. Since information was so limited, myths often filled the gaps between what people knew and did not know at the time.

Making Comparisons

■ **How does the magnitude of a quake relate to the amount of damage it causes?** The magnitude generally indicates whether there will be a lot of damage or only minor damage. But exactly how much damage will occur depends on many factors: where the quake is centered; how many people and buildings are in the area; whether the people are inside, outside, or on the roads and bridges; and how well the buildings are built to resist earthquake damage.

Connecting to the Activities

• *A Model of Sliding Plates, p. B54*
As you pushed the blocks together in the activity, what information would have helped you predict when the blocks would slip past each other? The kind of sandpaper (amount of friction between the blocks), the amount of force applied to the blocks, and the angle at which that force is applied would all help you predict when the blocks would slip.

■ **How does this information apply to predicting earthquakes?** Students should recognize that such conditions as the kinds of rocks on either side of a fault and the amount of force applied to those rocks is important information to know when predicting earthquakes. Generally, the more scientists know about Earth and the forces acting on it, the better the chances of using that knowledge for the good of humanity, as in predicting earthquakes.

3. Assess Understanding

Remind students of their suggestions for what a city council should do after an earthquake.
Students can work in groups of three or four. Let the groups list their recommendations of what the city should do to prepare for an earthquake predicted for the near future. Groups can share their recommendations with the class.

Richter scale releases about 30 times less energy than an earthquake measuring 6.7 on the scale.

Now study the table and map on page B59, showing some of the earthquakes that occurred along the San Andreas Fault over the past century. Where along the San Andreas did most of the quakes occur? Where did the strongest earthquakes occur? Then look at the map below. Where is the strongest quake likely to occur in the future?

Predicting Earthquakes

Scientists know that earthquakes are more common in some parts of the world than in others. Yet the actual timing of these Earth movements is difficult to predict. Seismologists, scientists who study earthquakes, have no sure way of knowing when or where an earthquake will strike or how strong it will be. They can only give estimates of the probability that an earthquake will strike in a certain place within a certain span of years.

Once in a while, seismologists are lucky in predicting earthquakes. In 1988, seismologists of the United States Geological Survey predicted that Loma Prieta, California, was likely to have an earthquake. Loma Prieta is along the San Andreas Fault. On October 17, 1989, a severe earthquake struck Loma Prieta and nearby San Francisco and Oakland.

Seismologists have found that there are changes in Earth that come before most earthquakes. Knowing this, the seismologists closely watch instruments that measure and record these changes. Seismologists are especially careful to

A map of California showing how likely it is that the "Big One" will strike in different parts of the state ▼

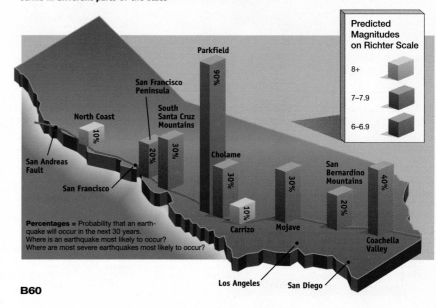

Investigate Further

Research

More than 2,200 years ago the ancient Greeks believed that animal behavior could predict earthquakes. As mentioned in the **Background** on p. B58, in 1975, Chinese scientists accurately predicted an earthquake based partly on unusual animal behavior. The prediction saved many lives. Strange animal behavior was also reported in Italy before an earthquake in May 1976. Have students research these topics and record their findings and their own thoughts in their *Science Notebooks* on p. 83.

watch the instruments in regions where earthquakes are likely to occur. For example, changes in the tilt of slabs of rock below ground can indicate that an earthquake is brewing. Studies have shown that rock formations will swell before an earthquake. Changes in Earth's magnetic and gravitational fields can mean an earthquake is soon to strike. Increases in the amount of a radioactive gas called radon from within Earth often come before an earthquake. Micro-earthquakes, or minor tremors, can also indicate that a more intense earthquake will strike an area.

Just how accurate are these warnings? Some scientists argue that watching changes in various instruments can lead to the prediction of earthquakes. Eleven days before the 1989 Loma Prieta earthquake, an instrument in the area recorded natural radio waves from Earth that were nearly 30 times stronger than usual. Just a few hours before the earthquake struck, these radio signals became so strong that they shot off the scale of the instrument.

A study by scientists at the Southern California Earthquake Center suggests that in the next 30 years there will be a severe earthquake in southern California. Exactly when and where it will strike is anyone's guess. ∎

▲ Laser beams are being used to monitor Earth's movements and to predict quakes.

INVESTIGATE FURTHER!

RESEARCH

Some people believe that animals are very sensitive to the changes that occur before events such as storms and earthquakes. Find out about this hypothesis concerning animal behavior before an earthquake as a possible warning sign for people. What do you think about this idea?

———— INVESTIGATION 1 ————

1. You are writing a news report on an earthquake that has just occurred. Tell your readers where and why the quake occurred, which plates were involved, and how severe it was.

2. Explain how the movement of tectonic plates and the occurrence of earthquakes are related.

B61

Assessment

Portfolio

Write a Story Encourage students to write a story about someone who experiences an earthquake. The story could involve friends, family, or a whole community. It should include information learned in this investigation.

Investigation Review
What Causes Earthquakes and How Can They Be Compared?

Name _____ Date _____

1. Circle the letter of the correct answer.

A. Earthquakes are common in southern California because _____.
  a. two plates are separating
  b. a continent ends
  c. very little energy is stored in Earth's crust
  d. two plates are sliding past each other

B. Which of the following leads to earthquakes along faults?
  a. constant, slow movement of the rocks
  b. magnetic reversals in the rock
  c. bending of the rocks followed by slipping
  d. seepage of magma

C. The San Francisco earthquake of 1906 measured 8.3 on the Richter scale; the 1989 quake measured 7.1. About how many times more energy was released in the 1906 quake than in the 1989 quake?
  a. 1.2 times
  b. 10 times
  c. 30 times
  d. 1000 times

2. Use the words in the box to complete the sentences.

tremors	magnitude	radon	aftershocks	magnetic

  a. Micro-earthquakes, or ___tremors___ , often occur before a major quake.
  b. The levels of the radioactive gas, ___radon___ , increase.
  c. Changes in Earth's gravitational and ___magnetic___ fields occur.
  d. Following the principle earthquake, the region may experience ___aftershocks___ .
  e. The Richter scale is used to measure the ___magnitude___ of the earthquake.

The blocks were very hard to move past each other because the sandpaper caused friction. But eventually the blocks slipped suddenly past each other. A similar situation occurs with rocks along a fault.

Process Skills
Observing, Making and Using Models
In the activity *A Model of Sliding Plates*, what happened when you tried to slide the plates over each other? Explain how this relates to the occurrence of earthquakes. Write your answer on a separate sheet of paper.

Close
the Investigation

Critical Thinking Skills
Expressing Ideas, Analyzing, Synthesizing

1. Student responses should include information on faults and plate boundaries, the Richter scale, and what damage could be expected at that level.

2. An earthquake occurs when rocks move suddenly on either side of a fault. Many earthquakes occur at plate boundaries because rocks stack and then slip as plates move past each other.

Challenge Have students find out about the Mercalli scale, which is a 12-point scale for classifying the magnitude of an earthquake. Students could illustrate the scale on poster board and explain it to the class. How does it differ from the Richter scale?

Following Up

Baseline Assessment Return to the list the class made of what they think happens when plates slide past each other. Have them delete or add to the list as necessary. Point out how the list has changed as they learned new information, just as all ideas in science change as people learn more information.

Reteaching Give groups of students two wooden blocks and clay. Students should spread the clay in a thin sheet over the blocks. Ask them to use the materials to demonstrate an earthquake at a plate boundary. Guide them as they explain how plate movement affects Earth's surface.

 Use *Science Notebook* p. 84.

◀ **Investigation Review**
Use Investigation Review p. 51 in the *Assessment Guide*.

WHAT HAPPENS TO EARTH'S CRUST DURING AN EARTHQUAKE?

Planner

Subconcept Various kinds of rock movements along faults result in earthquakes; earthquakes produce three kinds of energy waves, each resulting in a characteristic ground motion.

Objectives

- **Make** and **use a model** of how the ground vibrates during an earthquake.
- **Describe** where most earthquakes occur and how they produce ground movement.

Pacing 2–3 class periods

Science Terms focus, epicenter

Activate Prior Knowledge

Baseline Assessment Have students make a diagram of shock waves emanating from an earthquake. Save the diagrams for use in Following Up.

Activity Shake It!

Preview *Students model how earthquakes affect structures and should find that a structure shakes in a different way when the nature of the vibrations differs.*

Advance Preparation *See p. B52b*

1. Get Ready

Time about 30 minutes

Grouping groups of 4–6

Collaborative Strategy Each group member should have an opportunity to shake the model, either in sand, water and sand, or gelatin.

Safety Review safety precautions with students.

INVESTIGATION **2**

WHAT HAPPENS TO EARTH'S CRUST DURING AN EARTHQUAKE?

Have you ever pushed a desk across a floor? Sometimes the desk starts to vibrate, and you can feel the vibrations in your hands and arms. In this investigation you'll find out how this experience is similar to what happens during an earthquake.

Activity

Shake It!

In this activity you'll make a model for observing what can happen to buildings during an earthquake. In your model you'll make the vibrations.

Procedure

1. Think of a block of wood as a building and a bowl filled with sand as the surface of Earth. Stand a block of wood in a bowl full of sand.

2. Predict what will happen if you shake the bowl. Record your predictions in your *Science Notebook*.

A highway toppled during the 1995 earthquake in Kobe, Japan. ▶

B62

🧍 Responding to Individual Needs

Kinesthetic Activity After students have predicted what they think will happen when they shake their bowls, let them touch the materials in the bowls and compare and contrast the texture and thickness of the different materials used. Then give students the opportunity to change their predictions based on their observations.

3. Shake the bowl rapidly by sliding it back and forth. **Observe** what happens to the block and the surface of the sand. **Record** your observations.

4. Pour water over the sand until the water is at the same level as the sand. Again stand the wooden block on the sand. **Predict** what will happen to the block if you shake the bowl with the wet sand. Repeat the shaking, **observe** what happens, and **record** your observations.

5. Now **predict** what will happen when you set the block on the gelatin and shake the bowl. Try it; then **record** your observations.

Step 4

Analyze and Conclude

1. During the "earthquake," what happened to the dry sand? the wet sand? the gelatin? What, do you think, did the dry sand, wet sand, and the gelatin represent?

2. What happened to the "building" as it stood on the different surfaces?

3. Which model showed the most damage to the "building"? What evidence supports your conclusions?

UNIT PROJECT LINK

At 5:30 P.M. on March 27, 1964, the most powerful earthquake to hit North America struck Anchorage, Alaska. More than 130 people in Alaska and 12 people in Crescent City, California, were killed by the tsunami that followed the quake. (You'll find out about tsunamis on pages B76–77.) Use a map to trace how far the tsunami traveled. Then compute the distance that the tsunami traveled. Look at an earthquake map of the world. Outline in red those North American coastlines that might experience tsunamis.

B63

Investigate Further

Unit Project Link

The tsunami traveled about 2,880 km (1,800 mi) from Anchorage, Alaska, to Crescent City on the northern coast of California. The entire Pacific coast of North America is susceptible to experiencing tsunamis because of the number and strength of earthquakes that take place around the rim of the Pacific Ocean. Have students record their conclusions about the tsunami in their *Science Notebooks* on p. 87. Have students use Unit Project Master B2 (TRB p. 72) to help students visualize Earth's continents.

---

2. Guide the Procedure

- Tell students to shake the bowl rapidly, but to keep the movements short; about 1 cm (back and forth) works well.

- Guide students to make careful, detailed observations. For example, the observation "The block shook." would not be very helpful for this activity because it will shake during all three trials. Therefore, students' observations should be more detailed: how it shook, how long it shook, whether or not it leaned, and so on.

- In step 4, tell students to let the water soak into the sand for a few seconds, then add more water to bring the water level up to the sand.

 Have students record their data and answer questions on *Science Notebook* pp. 85–86.

 You might want students to use the CD-ROM Spreadsheet to organize and display their data.

3. Assess Performance

Process Skills Checklist

- Did students **make** and **use models** correctly by filling the bowls properly and shaking them the same way? Did students understand the need to change only one variable at a time?

- Were the **predictions** reasonable? Were they based on observations?

- Did students record their observations? Were the **observations** detailed enough to be useful?

Analyze and Conclude

1. Each of the materials—dry sand, wet sand, and gelatin—moved; gelatin moved most, followed by wet sand, followed by dry sand. These three materials represented the kind of soils on which buildings are constructed. Gelatin most closely resembles the way the ground actually behaves during an earthquake.

2. The "building" shook and moved on each surface; it sank most in dry sand, a bit less in wet sand, and even less in gelatin.

3. The "building" on gelatin shook the most and so represented the model sustaining the most damage.

Bend Till It Breaks

Preview *Students focus on the forces that push and pull at rocks, producing earthquakes and earthquake waves.*

1. Get Ready

Science Terms focus, epicenter

Background

- Although most earthquakes are associated with active plate boundaries, many faults exist far from such boundaries yet can still produce earthquakes. Of such quakes, two of the most severe occurred in 1811 and 1812 in New Madrid, Missouri. Their magnitudes have been estimated at 8.4 to 8.7 on the Richter scale. As a result of these two quakes, islands disappeared into the Mississippi River, and the course of the river itself changed. People from Canada to the Gulf of Mexico felt the ground shake. The shock waves rang church bells in Boston and swung chandeliers in Washington, D.C. The faults responsible for these quakes formed millions of years ago as a result of plate movements.

Discussion Starter

- Make a small cut in a stick. Then bend the stick slowly. Ask: **Where do you predict the stick will break? Why?** It will break where it was cut because this is its weakest point. Continue bending the stick until it snaps at that cut.

- **How is the bending and breaking of the stick similar to rocks in an earthquake?** Rocks can take only a certain amount of pressure before they break, producing an earthquake. When rocks break or move, they will do so at their weakest point, such as at a fault.

Bend
Till It Breaks

Imagine that you are holding a flexible wooden stick that is about 2 cm wide and 1 m long. You are holding one end in each hand and are gently bending the stick. If you stop bending the stick, it will return to its original shape. What will happen if you keep on bending it? Eventually it will snap!

Forces and Faults

Although Earth's rocks are hard and brittle, in some ways they can behave like the bending wooden stick. You probably know that a force is a push or a pull. If a pulling force is applied slowly to rocks, they will stretch. But like the wooden stick, the rocks will break or snap if the

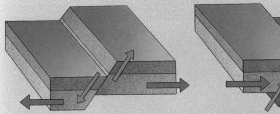

Movement Along Faults

NORMAL FAULT The rock slabs are pulling apart, and one slab has moved up, while the other has moved down along the fault.

REVERSE FAULT The rock slabs are pushing together, and one rock slab has pushed under the other along the fault.

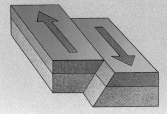

STRIKE-SLIP FAULT Slabs of rock are moving horizontally past each other along a fault. This type of fault is produced by twisting and tearing of layers of rock. The San Andreas Fault is an example of a strike-slip fault.

B64

Investigate Further

Integrating the Sciences

PHYSICAL SCIENCE

What to Do Students can experiment with friction and the amount of force needed to overcome it. Working in groups, they should first tie string around a book, then tie a rubber band to the string. Pulling slowly on a rubber band, students should observe how far the band stretches before the book moves across a variety of surfaces, such as a smooth desktop, sandpaper, and wax paper. Students should make predictions and compare their results to their predictions.
What's the Result? Have students record and display their results on a graph. ◼ **How does this experiment apply to earthquakes?** Friction causes energy to build up in rocks until a certain point is reached when the energy is released as an earthquake.

force on them is too great. A break in rocks along which the rocks have moved is called a **fault**.

What do you think would happen if rocks are squeezed together from opposite sides? If pushing forces are applied to rocks, they bend, or fold. But, just as with pulling forces, pushing forces will eventually cause rocks to break. So, pushing forces also create faults in rocks. You can see the effect of these pushing forces in the drawing of the reverse fault on page B64.

Movement Along Faults

Forces may continue to be applied to slabs of rock that contain faults. The forces, which may be either up-and-down or sideways, may continue for many

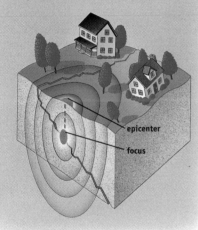

Earthquake Focus and Epicenter

Waves are sent out in all directions from the focus of the earthquake. Notice that the epicenter is the spot on the surface of Earth that lies directly above the focus. ▼

epicenter

focus

years. The three drawings on page B64 show examples of the main kinds of movement along faults. In time, the forces on the rocks become so great that the slabs overcome the friction that has held them together. Then the rock slabs move violently along the fault.

Earthquakes and Faults

Imagine that your two hands are the two rock walls on either side of a fault. Picture rubbing your hands together when they are in soapy water. Then picture rubbing them together when they are dry. Sometimes the movement of rocks along a fault is quick and smooth, like the rubbing together of soap-covered hands. But at other times, as with dry hands rubbed together, the movement can be slow and rough. As the movement causes rocks to lock and bend, energy builds up in the rocks, much as energy builds up in a flexed wooden stick. When the energy in the rocks is released, an earthquake occurs.

You know that an earthquake is a vibration of the Earth produced by the quick release of this stored energy. The point at which an earthquake begins is the **focus** of the earthquake. Most earthquakes begin below the surface. The point on Earth's surface directly above the focus is called the **epicenter** (ep′ə sen tər) of the earthquake.

Earthquakes can begin anywhere from about 5 km (about 3 mi) to 700 km (about 430 mi) below Earth's surface. Scientists have found that most earthquakes are shallow—they occur within 60 km (about 35 mi) of the surface. The most destructive earthquakes seem to be the shallow ones. The focus of the 1906 San Francisco earthquake was no deeper than about 15 km (about 9 mi).

B65

Integrating the Curriculum

Science & Math

FAULTS

What to Do To give students a better idea of the complexity of faults, have them build models of a section of Earth's crust that is heavily faulted. Provide them with wooden blocks of various sizes as building materials. The plane between each block is a fault. Challenge students to move part of their structure along a fault and see how many other faults and sections are affected.

What's the Result? How did moving one section of the structure affect the rest of it? Other sections of the structure also moved. **What did you learn about faults from this model?** Movement along one fault could affect movement along other faults.

2. Guide the Discussion

Choose from the following strategies to facilitate discussion.

Making Inferences

- **What are some things that can make movement along a fault quick and smooth or slow and rough?** The material that makes up the rock and the shape of the rock can affect the amount of friction produced as the rocks move against each other on either side of the fault.

Thinking About the Data

Besides the Pacific Ocean, where else do earthquakes happen frequently? Students should notice from the earthquakes map on p. B17 that earthquakes occur often in southern Europe and northern India. **What features exist at these places?** Mountains **What do you think is happening here?** Students might speculate that mountain building is occurring. In fact, the Himalaya Mountains, in northern India and Nepal, are continuing to build as two plates meet head-on.

You may want to use **Transparency 7,** "Earthquakes Around the World," at this point. Also have students consult a world map showing geographic features.

Responding to Individual Needs

Visual/Spatial Activity Provide clay or wooden blocks to represent slabs of rock. Using the illustrations in the text as a guide, let students demonstrate the three basic kinds of movement along faults. Students should show rock slabs being pulled apart, pushed together, and sliding horizontally past each other.

Connecting to the Activities

- ***Shake It!, p. B62***
  When you shook the bowls in the activity, you caused the model "ground" to shake. During a real earthquake, what causes things to shake? Lead students to understand that waves carrying energy disturb the surface and structures, causing both to shake.

Making Inferences

- **When an earthquake strikes, where do the earthquake waves travel?** They travel outward from the focus in all directions.

- **Why do you think there are so many earthquakes in California?** The San Andreas fault and many branch faults run along the length of California. The state is near the boundaries of two major plates.

Thinking About the Data

- **What is the risk of earthquakes in your state and neighboring states?** Students should be able to accurately analyze the earthquakes map on p. B17 to reasonably assess risk.

SCIENCE IN LITERATURE

Earthquake at Dawn,
by Kristina Gregory

Students can compare the effects of the San Francisco quake of 1906 to more recent quakes, such as those in Mexico City in 1985; in Loma Prieta, California, in 1989; or Kobe, Japan, in 1995.

3. Assess Understanding

Students can work in groups of three or four. Have each group imagine that it belongs to the news department of a television station in an earthquake-prone area. Each group should prepare a news report to help people in the area understand how forces can produce earthquakes by changing rocks and making them move. Encourage the groups to suggest illustrations for their program. Some groups might present their program to the class.

Earthquakes Around the World

When earthquake locations are plotted on a world map, patterns emerge. From the map on page B17 you can see that earthquakes occur along certain belts, or zones. Do these zones look familiar? They should! Most earthquakes occur along tectonic plate boundaries. Many occur near the edges of the Pacific Ocean.

Japan, the western United States, Chile, and parts of Central America are just a few of the areas around the edges of the Pacific Ocean that experience earthquakes.

Where do most earthquakes occur in the United States? Even without looking at a map, you probably could have guessed that most earthquakes in the United States happen in California. Now look closely at the map on page B17. Some earthquakes have occurred in the eastern part of the country—far away from the San Andreas Fault. Is your area at risk for an earthquake? Although most earthquakes occur in California, earthquakes are possible anywhere in this country. What is the risk that your state or surrounding states will experience an earthquake?

Earthquake Waves

Have you ever stood in a pool, lake, or ocean and felt water waves break against your body? Have you ever "done the wave" at a sporting event? What do all waves have in common? A wave is a

SCIENCE IN LITERATURE

EARTHQUAKE AT DAWN
by Kristiana Gregory
Harcourt Brace, 1992

It was an April morning in 1906. Aboard a boat in San Francisco harbor, 15-year-old Daisy Valentine thought the boat had struck a rock. Then there was an explosive booming sound. The city of San Francisco went dark. Someone on board screamed "Earthquake!"

Daisy Valentine, who tells the story *Earthquake at Dawn*, is a fictional character. But another character, Edith Irvine, really did take that boat ride to San Francisco. Edith, a young photographer, spent the next few days among the fires, ruins, and tragedy resulting from this famous earthquake. In *Earthquake at Dawn* you'll find Edith's photographs of the devastation and read a letter from an eyewitness.

B66

Investigate Further

STS Science, Technology & Society

WAVE DIAGRAMS **What to Do** Provide students with books on earthquakes. Encourage interested students to work in groups to find out more about earthquake waves. Does each kind of wave travel at the same speed? How is each kind of wave recorded? Do the waves look different on a seismograph? What kind of effects does each wave have on objects on the surface?

What's the Result? Suggest that students draw a diagram showing what the different waves look like on a seismograph and the kind of damage each wave causes. Let the groups share their information with the class.

rhythmic disturbance that carries energy. The energy released by an earthquake travels in all directions from the earthquake's focus. There are three kinds of earthquake waves: P waves, S waves, and L waves. The drawings below show how these waves differ. ∎

Earthquakes can severely damage property. ▶

P WAVES P waves moves out in all directions from the earthquake focus. The primary waves push and pull the rocks causing them to vibrate in the same direction in which the wave is traveling.

S WAVES S waves move out in all directions from the earthquake focus. The secondary waves cause the rocks to move at right angles to the direction in which the wave is traveling.

L WAVES When the P and S waves punch into Earth's surface, they cause the formation of L waves or surface waves. L waves move along the surface causing rocks to move up and down. These are the most destructive earthquake waves.

INVESTIGATION 2

1. Describe and make drawings of the changes taking place in Earth's crust during an earthquake. Explain the forces that caused these changes.

2. What is the connection between a fault and the production of an earthquake? Give a well-known example of such a connection.

B67

Assessment

Performance

Demonstration Ask the student to use blocks or two books to explain faults and earthquakes. Students should understand that earthquakes occur not only when a fault first develops but also as sudden movements occur along that fault.

Investigation Review
What Happens to Earth's Crust During an Earthquake?

Name _____ Date _____

1. Draw a line to match each word with its definition.

a. Focus
b. Epicenter
c. S-waves
d. L-waves
e. Normal fault
f. Reverse fault

- blocks of rock pull apart, and there is up-and-down movement along this type of fault
- surface waves that cause rock particles to move up and down and side-to-side
- where an earthquake begins, often below the surface
- waves that cause rock particles to move at right angles to the wave direction
- blocks of rock are pushed together and one rock slab moves under another along this type of fault
- point on Earth's surface directly above the earthquake's location

2. Draw the three types of faults and use arrows to show the direction of movement along each type. Include a description of what is happening along each fault.

See page B64 for drawings and descriptions.

Process Skills
Observing, Identifying Variables, Predicting

Based on the activity *Shake It!*, how might the nature of the land influence earthquake damage in a region?
Certain types of soil, and the presence of water, may vibrate and shift more easily, producing more damage.

Close
the Investigation

Critical Thinking Skills
Synthesizing, Expressing Ideas

1. Descriptions and drawings should show movement along a fault, causing an earthquake. Students should also refer to waves coming from the focus of the earthquake.

2. Sudden movement of rocks along a fault produces an earthquake. The San Andreas fault is a well-known example of a fault that has produced many earthquakes.

Challenge Have students describe and make drawings of the changes taking place in Earth's crust during an earthquake. They should explain the forces that cause these changes.

Following Up

Baseline Assessment Return to students' diagrams showing seismic waves coming from the focus of an earthquake. Ask students if they should revise their diagrams in any way. Watch for evidence that students understand that waves travel outward in all directions from the focus.

Reteaching Assist students in constructing a word web for the investigation subconcept. Build the word web against a background diagram of earthquake waves radiating from a focus.

 Use *Science Notebook* p. 88.

◀ **Investigation Review**
Use Investigation Review p. 52 in the *Assessment Guide.*

HOW ARE EARTHQUAKES LOCATED AND MEASURED?

Planner

Subconcept Earthquakes can be located and measured with seismographs; information about earthquakes is used to help design earthquake-resistant structures and to warn of tsunamis.

Objectives

- **Make** and **use a model** of a seismograph.
- **Investigate** how earthquakes are located.
- **Make and test a hypothesis** about what makes a building earthquake-proof.

Pacing 4–5 class periods

Science Terms seismograph, tsunami

Activate Prior Knowledge

Baseline Assessment Let students draw pictures of how a building might withstand an earthquake. Save drawings for Following Up.

Activity Shake It Harder!

Preview *Students make a model of a seismograph and should find that the model measures the vibrations that occur when an object is shaken.*

1. Get Ready

Time about 45 minutes

Grouping groups of 4–6

Multi-Age Strategy All group members should help build the model. Some parts of the model's construction will require finer motor skills than other parts. Group members should agree on which parts each will help build.

HOW ARE EARTHQUAKES LOCATED AND MEASURED?

The newscaster read, "The earthquake last night in Prince William Sound, Alaska, measured 8.4 on the Richter scale. It was a BIG one!" What tools and methods do scientists use to measure how strong an earthquake is or where it began?

Activity

Shake It Harder!

The energy of an earthquake is measured with a device called a seismograph. In this activity you'll build a working model of a seismograph and then test how it works as you create your own small "earthquake."

MATERIALS

- string
- chair
- metric ruler
- 2 heavy books
- masking tape
- fine-point marker
- table
- shelf paper (2 m long)
- *Science Notebook*

SAFETY //////

Be careful not to push or shake the chair off the tabletop while doing this activity.

Procedure

1. Tightly wrap several lengths of string around the seat of a chair in two places (about 10 cm apart), as shown on page B69.

2. Tightly wrap string around two heavy books in two places (about 6 cm from each end of the books).

3. Tape a fine-point marker to one of the short edges of the books. The tip of the marker should hang about 3–4 cm below the edges of the books.

B68

👤 Responding to Individual Needs

Kinesthetic Activity Be sure students understand that both the model and a real seismograph work by vibrating the base and holding the pen still. To model this concept, let students draw a wave pattern, holding a marker against paper and moving only the paper. What would happen if the paper and pen both moved? Let them try it. If the paper and pen move together, there are no waves and no record of movement. If the pen and paper move in different ways and at different times, there are waves but no accurate, analyzable record of only the paper's movement.

4. Place a length of shelf paper on the top of a table. Place the chair with the string wrapped around the seat on the table, above the shelf paper. Make sure the legs of the chair don't touch the shelf paper.

5. Using string, suspend the books from the chair so that the tip of the marker just touches the surface of the shelf paper. Make sure that the books are parallel to the paper.

6. You have just built a simple seismograph. You'll use it to measure an "earthquake" that you'll create by gently shaking the table from side to side. The shelf paper will become the seismogram, or record of the earthquake.

Steps 1–4

7. Predict what will be shown on the seismogram if you shake the table gently. Record your predictions in your *Science Notebook*.

8. Place your hands against the side of the table and gently shake it as another member of your group slowly pulls the paper under the pen.

9. Repeat step 8. This time, shake the table a little harder (move the table farther but not faster).

Analyze and Conclude

1. How did your prediction in step 7 compare with what actually happened?

2. How did changing the energy with which you shook the table change the seismogram? How did the record on the seismogram for the first "earthquake" differ from that for the second "earthquake"?

3. How do you think a real seismograph is like the one you built? How might it be different?

INVESTIGATE FURTHER!

EXPERIMENT

Does the seismograph work as well if you shake the table in the same direction in which the paper is being pulled? What would this mean with a real seismograph? Is there any connection between the length of the strings and the working of the seismograph?

B69

Investigate Further

Experiment

Using the model from the activity, students should find that the strings are arranged to permit the books to remain stationary with vibrations in one direction only, across the paper. The model does not serve its purpose when the vibration comes from the direction of the length of the paper. The pen makes marks, but they generally overlap and do not measure the amount of shaking over time. Longer strings make a more stable pendulum that is less likely to move. Remind students to record their notes and observations in their *Science Notebooks* on p. 90.

Materials Hints The books and strings form a pendulum that should not move. Keep in mind that this is a crude model; the pendulum might move slightly when the table is shaken. To minimize the pendulum's motion, make the strings as long as possible.

Safety Review safety precautions with students.

2. Guide the Procedure

- Be sure students have set up the model properly. The books should be parallel to the tabletop, with the tip of the marker barely touching the paper.
- Tell students to pull the paper slowly and smoothly, not to jerk it.
- Caution students to shake the table across the paper's width, not along its length. In other words, the push needs to be perpendicular to the motion of the paper for the model to clearly record the shaking.

 Have students record their predictions and observations and answer questions on *Science Notebook* p. 89.

 Students can use the CD-ROM Spreadsheet and the Painter to organize and display their data.

3. Assess Performance

Process Skills Checklist

- Did students **make the model** correctly? Does the pen barely touch the paper?
- Did they **use the model** correctly by pushing in the right direction while slowly pulling the paper? Did the resulting seismogram clearly show a **record** of the shaking?
- Were the **predictions** reasonable? Did the predictions show an understanding of what a seismograph is?

Analyze and Conclude

1. The more energy that is applied to the desk, the greater the height of the wave recorded on the paper. The waves on the seismograms will have greater height for the second "earthquake" than for the first.

2. Student responses will depend on their predictions and their actual results. They should find that the seismogram showed small wave heights when the desk was shaken gently.

3. The model is like a real seismograph because it records vibrations. It is different because it is much cruder in structure. For example, the pendulum in the model might shake slightly, whereas this component in a real seismograph remains still.

Activity Locating Earthquakes

Preview *Students make calculations and use data to locate the epicenter of an earthquake.*

1. Get Ready

Time about 30 minutes

Grouping groups of 4–6

Collaborative Strategy Each group member should make the calculations and measurements and then check each other's work.

Materials Hints Use Activity Support Masters B7 and B8 (TRB pp. 48 and 49).

Safety Review safety precautions with students.

2. Guide the Procedure

- Some students may need help calculating the differences in arrival times in step 1.

- The success of this activity depends on students' making accurate calculations and careful measurements. Use Activity Support Master B7, *Earthquake Travel Time Graph,* for this activity and guide students through steps 2–4 of the procedure.

- The motor skills necessary to use the graph and draw the circles are likely to vary among the students. To accomodate this diversity, focus on the reasoning behind drawing the three circles (to find that intersection representing the epicenter) rather than on the accuracy of the intersecting point.

If you drew only two circles instead of three, how many possibilities would there be for the location of the epicenter? Two—where the circles intersect

Have students record their data and answer questions on *Science Notebook* p. 91.

Students can use the CD-ROM Spreadsheet to organize their data.

Activity
Locating Earthquakes

The point on Earth's surface directly above the origin of an earthquake is called the epicenter. The location of the epicenter can be found by comparing the travel times of two kinds of energy waves (called P waves and S waves) at different locations.

Data
The table below shows the times (in Pacific Daylight Saving Time) at which shock waves reached three cities in the United States after the earthquake in California on October 17–18, 1989. You'll use this information to find the exact location of the epicenter of that earthquake.

Procedure
1. In your *Science Notebook*, set up a table like the one shown. For each city, calculate the difference in arrival time between the P wave and the S wave. Record your results.

ARRIVAL TIMES OF P WAVES AND S WAVES			
City	P Wave Arrival Time (hr: min: sec)	S Wave Arrival Time (hr: min: sec)	Difference in Arrival Time (hr: min: sec)
Tucson, AZ	5:06:35	5:08:50	
Billings, MT	5:07:10	5:10:00	
Houston, TX	5:09:10	5:13:35	

2. Place a sheet of paper along the *y*-axis of the Earthquake Travel Time graph provided by your teacher. On the sheet of paper, mark the time interval between the arrival of the P wave and the S wave in Tucson. For example, if the time difference was 4 minutes, you would make a mark next to "0" and a mark next to "4."

 Responding to Individual Needs

Visual/Spatial Activity Obtain a world globe that shows the topography of the world in relief. Have students run their fingers over the mountains and valleys of the western United States. This experience will help students to get a better understanding of the three-dimensional nature of Earth's crust and its changes.

3. Keep the edge of the paper parallel to the *y*-axis. Move the paper to the right until the space between the marks matches the space between the S-wave curve and the P-wave curve.

4. The point on the *x*-axis directly below (or along) the edge of the paper is the distance from Tucson to the epicenter of the quake. **Record** this distance.

5. Repeat steps 2 through 4 for Billings and Houston.

6. On a United States map, use a drawing compass to draw a circle around each city in the chart. Use the calculated distance from the quake as the radius of each circle. The point at which the circles intersect is the epicenter of the October 1989 earthquake.

Step 6

Analyze and Conclude

1. What is the distance from each of the cities to the epicenter?

2. Where was the epicenter of the October 1989 earthquake?

3. What is the lowest number of reporting locations necessary to locate an epicenter? Explain your answer.

4. Compare your results with those of other members of your class. Account for any differences you find.

INVESTIGATE FURTHER!

TAKE ACTION

Contact or visit an office of the U.S. Geological Survey for more information about locating earthquakes. You may write to the U.S. Geological Survey at Distribution Branch, Box 25286, Federal Center, Denver, CO 80225.

B71

3. Assess Performance

Process Skills Checklist

- Were students' **calculations** correct? Did they know how to subtract like units?

- Did students **interpret data** properly when using the graph to find the distances to the epicenter? Did they manipulate the paper with the time intervals correctly against the graph?

- How carefully did they **record data** when drawing the intersecting circles? Did the circles intersect at one point?

Analyze and Conclude

1. Tucson: about 1,200 km (744 mi) to epicenter; Billings: about 1,600 km (992 mi) to epicenter; Houston: about 2,800 km (1,736 mi) to epicenter

2. The epicenter was just south of San Francisco.

3. At least three reporting locations are needed to locate the epicenter, because that is the minimum number needed to intersect at one point.

4. Differences may depend on calculating correctly, measuring on the graph accurately, and marking distances accurately on the map when making the circles.

Investigate Further

Take Action

If students telephone or visit employees of the U.S. Geological Survey, be sure they prepare questions in advance. Remind students to record in their *Science Notebooks* on p. 92 any information they receive. They might also include any impressions about their visit or phone conversations.

Activity   Be an Architect

Preview *Students build and test an earthquake-proof structure and may find that buildings in the shape of a pyramid, buildings that are short, and buildings that allow for some movement will be least likely to fall.*

Advance Preparation *See p. B52b.*

1. Get Ready

Time 45 minutes. You may want to allow more time during or after school if students want to try different designs or make them more complex.

Grouping groups of 4–6

Collaborative Strategy All students in the group should discuss and agree on the design. One group member might draw the design, but each member should help build and test the structure.

2. Guide the Procedure

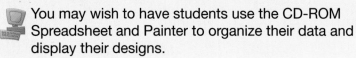 How can you use the clay, sand, and soil to make your building? If students have trouble thinking of uses on their own, suggest that they use them for weighing down the boxes used in the structures, for mortar, or as shock absorbers.

- If students have a hard time simulating an earthquake, they should shake the desktop a distance of about 2 cm (about 1 in.) four times in quick succession.

Students can record predictions, their observations, and answers on *Science Notebook* p. 93.

You may wish to have students use the CD-ROM Spreadsheet and Painter to organize their data and display their designs.

Activity
Be an Architect

The competition is stiff! You and your teammates will build an "earthquake-proof" building. Then you will create a mini-earthquake and test your building. Will it remain standing? Which team will have the most earthquake-proof building?

Procedure

1. With other members of your team, design a high-rise "building" that will not tip over in an earthquake. The building must be made of cardboard boxes and any other materials, such as clay, sand, soil, and dowels, that your teacher provides for you. You will subject this building to an "earthquake" that you create by shaking your desk or table. Draw your design in your *Science Notebook*.

2. With the rest of your class, design a standard that describes when a building is considered earthquake-proof. Make sure the standard will clearly separate good designs from poor designs following an earthquake.

3. Construct your building on top of your desk or table.

4. Predict how well your building will withstand an earthquake. Discuss your prediction with other members of your group.

Step 1

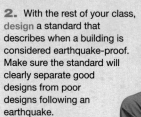

B72

Responding to Individual Needs

Students Acquiring English Encourage clarification of the standards students develop for testing their buildings. Write the standards on the chalkboard. Underline key words and demonstrate each standard, if possible. For example, if the standard says the building has to remain standing for 10 seconds following the earthquake, demonstrate this with a very simple model of a building and a mini-earthquake.

5. With the rest of your class, determine how long the earthquake will last and how strongly you'll shake the table. Note the length of time the building remains standing during the earthquake. Note whether the building undergoes any kind of damage during the earthquake. Use the standard to determine if your building is earthquake-proof. Record all observations.

6. Compare your results with those of other groups of students in your class.

Analyze and Conclude

1. How closely did your results agree with your prediction of how well your building could withstand an earthquake?

2. How did your design compare with those of other teams of students?

3. Which design best stood up to the earthquake? What was important about that design?

> ## INVESTIGATE FURTHER!
> ### EXPERIMENT
> After you've had your classroom competition, decide how to improve your design. Redesign, reconstruct, and retest your building. How can you make a tall building earthquake-proof?

B73

Investigate Further

Experiment

After the competition, discuss experimental designs with an emphasis on variables. Encourage students to discuss mistakes in design constructively so that everyone can learn from them. Then challenge students to try again. Remind them to record their observations in their *Science Notebooks* on p. 95.

3. Assess Performance

Process Skills Checklist
- Did students **draw** designs that show an understanding of how an earthquake affects buildings? Did students attempt to design a building that was truly earthquake-proof?
- Was the **prediction** about the stability of the structure reasonable? Did the prediction show an understanding of the effects of earthquakes?
- Were students able to **compare** designs and judge the quality of the better designs? Could students pick out the most important features of each design?

Analyze and Conclude
1. Students should point out specific variables when comparing their results to their predictions.

2. Students should analyze specific variables, such as height, shape, overall weight, distribution of weight, and materials used, to compare designs.

3. Buildings that are shorter, that are shaped like a pyramid, and that allow some movement will probably suffer the least damage in this activity.

The Seismograph

Preview *Students focus on different kinds of seismographs and how they work.*

1. Get Ready

Science Terms seismograph

Background

• Seismographs have other uses besides detecting and measuring earthquakes. One of their most important uses is for finding out what the interior of Earth is like, since seismic waves travel at different speeds and directions through different materials. But scientists do not have to wait for an earthquake to study seismic waves. They create waves by setting off small explosions. Scientists and engineers use data on these waves to search for oil and natural gas.

Discussion Starter

What can scientists find out about an earthquake by making measurements? Encourage speculation about what aspects of an earthquake can be measured and which are useful to scientists. You might discuss what kinds of information can be quantified (time, location, and magnitude of quakes) and what cannot (some descriptions of effects of quakes).

Why is it important for scientists to have the precise measurements of an earthquake? Accurate information helps scientists predict earthquakes and learn about the effects of different kinds of earthquakes. Such information also helps engineers understand which designs are most effective for earthquake-proof buildings.

The Seismograph

Energy from an earthquake travels outward from the focus in all directions, much in the way that energy is released when a pebble is dropped into a pond. Seismic waves travel at different speeds through Earth's crust and upper mantle. P waves are the fastest; S waves are the slowest. These waves are recorded by an instrument called a **seismograph** (sīz′ mə graf).

One of the earliest seismographs used bronze balls to detect earthquake waves.

This Chinese earthquake detector is known as Chang Heng's seismoscope. This early version of a seismograph was used to detect earthquakes. ▼

The dragons on this Chinese earthquake detector clenched the bronze balls in their mouths. When the ground vibrated, one or more balls fell from the dragons' mouths. The balls landed in the mouths of waiting metal toads around the base of the instrument. The noise the balls made when they reached the toads' mouths alerted people that the ground had shaken. The direction from which the waves came was determined by the direction in which the dragons' empty mouths pointed.

A modern seismograph is a device that generally includes a frame (mounted to bedrock), a weight, a pen, and a rotating drum. You built a model of a seismograph on pages B68 and B69. With seismographs, either up-and-down or side-to-side Earth movements can be measured.

A pendulum seismograph consists of a support frame, a heavy weight to which a pen is attached, and a rotating drum. This type of seismograph measures side-to-side Earth movements. A spring seismograph measures up-and-down Earth movements. The drawings on the facing page show you all the parts of these earthquake-recording devices.

B74

Integrating the Curriculum

Science & the Arts

DESIGNING

What to Do Challenge students to design and draw a seismograph that is different from those shown on these pages. The design can be decorative, as with the Chinese seismoscope. Some students may choose to design and draw a spring- or pendulum-style instrument. Encourage imagination. The designs should show how the seismograph would work. Students may wish to build models of their instruments to test them. If so, provide various building materials.

What's the Result? How well do you think your seismograph would work? Why? Responses should show knowledge of how a real seismograph works.

Parts of the Seismograph

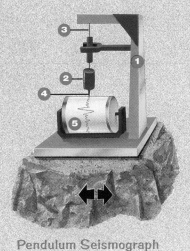

Spring Seismograph

Pendulum Seismograph

1 SUPPORT FRAME
The frame is anchored to solid rock, deep beneath the soil.

2 WEIGHT
The weight of a seismograph is essentially motionless. The magnet reduces the motion of the weight.

3 WIRE OR SPRING
In the spring seismograph, the spring supports the weight. In the pendulum seismograph, the metal wire keeps the weight suspended above the rotating drum.

4 PEN
The pen, which touches the rotating drum, records movements caused by seismic waves.

5 ROTATING DRUM
The drum rotates, or turns, all the time. If there are any movements of Earth, the pen touching the drum records these movements.

INVESTIGATE FURTHER!

RESEARCH

Find out about early seismographs. How are they like modern ones? How are they different from modern ones?

B75

Investigate Further

Research

Students could find out about early seismographs from books on earthquakes and geology, such as *Earthquakes* and *Geological Discovery* by Bruce A. Bolt, Scientific American Library, 1993, or from encyclopedias. They could look up topics such as *seismograph, seismoscope, Luigi Palmieri, John Milne,* and *James Ewing.* Remind students to record their findings in their *Science Notebooks* on p. 95.

2. Guide the Discussion

Choose from the following strategies to facilitate discussion.

Connecting to the Activities

*   *Shake It Harder!, p. B68*
    Which of the two kinds of seismographs is most like the model you made in the activity?
    The pendulum seismograph is most like the model. Encourage students to compare and contrast the parts of the pendulum seismograph with the model.

*   *Locating Earthquakes, p. B70*
    How do seismographs help scientists locate the epicenter of an earthquake? The information scientists need to find the epicenter of an earthquake is provided by seismographs in different places. Students should remember from the activity that data from seismographs provide the difference in arrival times of different seismic waves. This information is needed to determine the location of the epicenter.

Making Comparisons

*   **What are the differences and similarities between the two major kinds of seismographs?**
    Let students point out differences and similarities and suggest the advantages and disadvantages of each kind of seismograph.

 **Responding to Individual Needs**

Gifted and Talented Activity Suggest that students compare and contrast a seismograph and a Foucault pendulum. Both have a mass that hangs free while Earth moves beneath it. The pendulum can tell the time on a clock face drawn on the ground, recording Earth's rotation. It hangs freely suspended from a point several stories high. Once started, the pendulum always swings in the same plane, while Earth turns under it. The pendulum points to different hours as Earth turns.

3. Assess Understanding

 Suggest that students work in groups of three or four. They can use easily available materials, such as weights, a marker, a wooden frame, and a cardboard drum (such as an oatmeal box) covered with paper to make a nonworking model of a seismograph. They can use the pictures shown on p. B75 as a guide.

Earthquakes on the Sea Floor

Preview *Students focus on the causes and effects of tsunamis, or seismic sea waves.*

1. Get Ready

Science Terms tsunami

Background

- The Tsunami Warning System consists of a network of earthquake observatories that cable, radio, or telephone to a warning center any evidence they receive of large earthquakes in the Pacific. Information is received from locations in the United States, Japan, Taiwan, Philippines, Fiji, Chile, Hong Kong, New Zealand, and other countries around the Pacific. The center decides whether to send out tsunami alerts based on the seismic evidence it receives.

  Although tsunamis travel quickly, a wave still takes 10 hours to travel to Hawaii from an earthquake off the coast of Chile and 4 hours to go from the Aleutian Islands of Alaska to southern California. Warnings can often be received in time to evacuate the shorelines and other low-lying areas.

Discussion Starter

What do you think a seismic sea wave might be and what could cause it? Let students speculate about the meaning of the term seismic sea wave from what they know of the word *seismic*. They might infer that a seismic sea wave is related to earthquakes or vibrations and is a wave in the ocean.

Earthquakes
On the Sea Floor

Tsunamis—What Are They?

You have probably heard the term *tsunami* (tsoo nä'mē). This Japanese word means "harbor wave." You may have heard such waves incorrectly called tidal waves. A **tsunami** has nothing to do with ocean tides. Rather, this seismic sea wave forms when an earthquake occurs on the ocean floor. The earthquake's energy causes the sea floor to move up and down. This movement can produce destructive waves of water. Why are these waves so dangerous?

Most tsunamis are related to the earthquakes that occur around the edges of the Pacific Plate. In these areas massive slabs of rock are being forced down into the mantle. Often, when the plates collide, they lock, allowing energy to build up. Eventually this energy is released as

---

1 TSUNAMI FORMING
In the open ocean, tsunamis are barely detectable. In deep water, where a tsunami generally forms, the wave's height is only about a meter (about 3 ft).

2 TSUNAMI TRAVELING
In the open ocean, the distance between two crests or troughs can be about 100 km (62.1 mi). A tsunami is often unnoticed in the open ocean, even though it can be traveling close to 800 km/h (496 mph)!

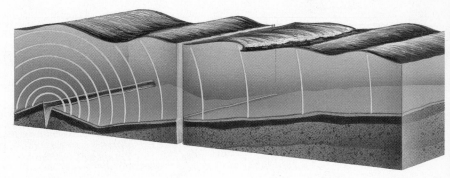

▲ A tsunami

B76

Integrating the Curriculum

Science & Math

CALCULATING

What to Do Tsunamis often travel about 800 km per hour. Using this figure, set up a situation in which an underwater earthquake has occurred at some point around the edge of the Pacific Ocean. Students have the task of calculating how long it will be before the tsunami reaches various shores, including islands. Assign different shores to different groups.

What's the Result? How much warning will people in your area have before the tsunami hits? Answers will depend on the area for which each group is calculating. Most areas will have at least a few hours' warning.

an earthquake, which raises and lowers the nearby ocean floor. This movement sets a tsunami in motion.

Destructive Walls of Water

Most tsunamis are caused by earthquakes. But landslides on the ocean floor and volcanic eruptions can also cause tsunamis. Fortunately, tsunamis only occur about once a year. Study the table on page B78. What was the cause of the 1993 tsunami that began off the coast of Japan?

As with earthquakes, tsunamis cause destruction where they begin as well as along their paths. The tsunami that began with the 1964 Alaskan earthquake, for example, struck the Alaskan coastline and then Vancouver Island in Canada. Waves also struck California and

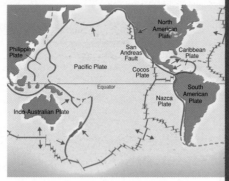

▲ Tsunamis are common along the shores close to the edges of the Pacific Plate.

the Hawaiian Islands. The seismic sea waves finally lost their energy at the Japanese coast—over 6,400 km (about 4,000 mi) from their point of origin!

③ TSUNAMI NEARING SHORE
As the wave makes its way toward shore, it slows down due to friction between the advancing water and the ocean floor. But as the water becomes shallower, the height of the wave increases.

④ TSUNAMI STRIKING SHORE
Close to shore a tsunami can reach a height of tens of meters! On March 2, 1933, a tsunami struck the Japanese island of Honshu. It reached a height of 14 m (46 ft).

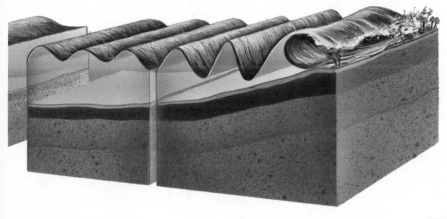

B77

Investigate Further

Integrating the Sciences

PHYSICAL SCIENCE

What to Do Challenge students to make a model of a tsunami and to explore the nature of water waves. Place a wallpaper tray on several large towels to absorb water spills. At one end of the tray, students could use sand to build up a model shoreline. The sand should start about two-thirds of the way up the side of the tray and then taper out toward the middle of the tray. Suggest they fill the tray halfway with water. Then a student can start a "tsunami" by using a hand to push the water quickly at the end of the tray toward "shore."
What's the Result? How do the waves change near the shore? They get larger.

2. Guide the Discussion

Choose from the following strategies to facilitate discussion.

Connecting to the Activities

- *Locating Earthquakes, p. B70*
How can knowing how to locate the epicenter of an earthquake help in determining where a tsunami might strike? Students should relate locating the epicenter of an earthquake with locating the source for the energy of a tsunami. Just as the earthquake's vibrations radiate out from the epicenter, the disturbance of the water caused by the earthquake can send a tsunami rushing across the ocean.

Making Comparisons

- **How are tsunamis different from regular surface waves?** Surface waves are driven by the wind and do not extend very deep into the water. Therefore they are not very strong and often dissipate after traveling a few miles. Tsunamis, however, begin on the ocean floor and result from great forces such as earthquakes or landslides. They travel across the ocean without weakening appreciably.

- Students might be unable to imagine the destructive power of a large wave such as a tsunami. To aid their comprehension, ask: **Have you ever stood along a shore in water up to your knees as a wave was breaking?** Invite students to relate their experiences with waves in the ocean or large lakes. Some students may recall being pushed over by a wave only a meter high.

- Now ask students to imagine a wave, or series of waves, 15 m (about 48 ft) high. Compare this height to a tree, telephone pole, or other object to help students visualize it. Discuss how such a wall of water, breaking on shore, would demolish and sweep away almost everything in its path.

Responding to Individual Needs

Students Acquiring English If some students have witnessed or spoken with people who have witnessed an earthquake or tsunami, let them give an account of it to the class. Encourage them to use body language, drawings on the chalkboard, their native language, and English to communicate what happened and how those involved felt.

Thinking About the Data

🔲 Direct students' attention to the table of tsunamis and their effects. **What caused the 1960 tsunami that started near Chile?** An earthquake

🔲 **Which tsunami resulted in 36,000 deaths?** The tsunami which started in the East Indies in 1883 caused these deaths. Incidentally, this tsunami was caused by the volcanic eruption of Krakatoa. The deaths occurred when a series of tsunamis crashed into Java and Sumatra.

Making Comparisons

• Again, direct students' attention to the table. Compare the height of each tsunami to an object students can visualize. For example, a 10-meter tsunami may be as tall as a two-story house from the ground to the peak of the roof.

Thinking Critically

🔲 **How is the tsunami warning center located in Hawaii useful to the people who live there? Look at a map of earth's tectonic plate boundaries on pp. B20–B21 to help you.** The warning signals pertaining to nearly any Pacific rim earthquake will reach Hawaii long before any potential tsunamis and, if necessary, allow people to evacuate the area.

3. Assess Understanding

 Students can work in groups of three or four. Invite each group to imagine that they live in a community along the coastline bordering the Pacific Ocean and are in charge of planning how the community should respond to a tsunami warning. Let each group list what preparations should be made in advance, such as

• purchasing warning sirens;
• informing people what should be done if there is a warning;
• having emergency supplies of food, water, batteries, radios, and so on;
• and putting up signs in areas where water would rise most.

Students should also list what steps should be taken after the warning comes, such as evacuating low-lying areas. The groups might want to compare their lists and compile a class list.

SELECTED TSUNAMIS AND THEIR EFFECTS

Year	Place of Origin	Cause	Height of Water (m)	Deaths
1883	East Indies	volcano	>40 m	>36,000
1896	Japan	earthquake	38 m	26,000
1946	Alaska	earthquake	>30 m	164
1960	Chile	earthquake	6 m	144
1992	Indonesia	earthquake	10 m	71,000
1993	Japan	earthquake	32 m	120

Predicting Tsunamis

Unlike earthquakes and volcanic eruptions, some tsunamis can be predicted. In 1946 the Tsunami Warning System was established to forewarn people in the areas surrounding the Pacific Ocean of these destructive events.

There are two tsunami warning centers in the United States. One center is near Honolulu, Hawaii; the other is just north of Anchorage, in Palmer, Alaska. Scientists at these centers use satellites to gather seismic data from more than 20 countries that border the Pacific Ocean. If earthquakes registering more than about 6.5 on the Richter scale are found, warnings are sent to other centers.

Recall that in the open ocean, tsunamis are hardly detectable at the surface of the water. So in addition to the warning centers, scientists with the National Oceanic and Atmospheric Administration are studying the usefulness of tsunami sensors that rest on the ocean floor. These devices look promising. In water 4,000 to 5,000 m deep, the sensors can detect a change in sea level of less than a millimeter!

Tsunami sensors are flexible metal tubes that are weighted down on the ocean floor. Each tube measures the mass of the water column above it. When a wave passes over the tube, the mass of the water column increases, causing the tube to straighten. After the wave has passed, the tube coils up again. The straightening and coiling of the tubes record changes in water pressure—and the presence of large waves. Such changes can show the presence of tsunamis. ■

Huge waves from a tsunami strike the shore. ▼

B78

Investigate Further

TSUNAMIS **What to Do** Ask students which instruments or systems that they have learned about in this investigation are directly helpful to society. They should mention tsunami sensors and the Tsunami Warning System. Discuss how these instruments and systems help people. Guide students to understand that such helpful tools could not have been developed without an understanding of tsunamis themselves. Ask for examples of other scientific instruments that directly help people. (weather satellites, medical instruments)

What's the Result? Give an example of how technology might help people in the future. Students might refer to instruments that could predict disasters.

Designing For Survival

Much of the damage done during an earthquake is caused by the earthquake's L waves. Recall that these waves move in two directions—up and down and back and forth. These destructive waves cause the foundations of most buildings to move with the passing waves. The buildings themselves, however, tend to resist the movements.

Because of the damage earthquakes can do, building codes in the western United States and in other earthquake-prone areas of the world have been

CONVENTIONAL FOUNDATION With this foundation, the ground movement is exaggerated on upper floors. The building "drifts," and a lot of damage occurs. Upper floors can collapse onto lower floors.

EARTHQUAKE-RESISTANT FOUNDATION This foundation is built of steel and rubber around columns with lead cores. Since the frame is flexible, the floors can move from side to side, and the building isn't badly damaged.

Pillars such as this one support the building and flex during an earthquake. ▶

B79

 Science, Technology & Society

ENGINEERING **What to Do** Now that students have had some experience designing earthquake-proof buildings and have read about some helpful designs, let them put their knowledge to work in designing a bridge that will withstand earthquakes. Provide them with assorted building materials. Students should work in groups and set up standards as they did in the activity "Be an Architect." Have them establish a minimum length for the bridge, the materials to use, and the "intensity" of the "quake."

What's the Result? Hold a "Build a Bridge" contest. Discuss each entry in terms of whether it crumbles with the quake or remains unscathed. Which design features work well? Which can be improved?

Designing for Survival

Preview *Students focus on how to help make buildings and other structures able to withstand damage during an earthquake.*

1. Get Ready

Background

- Besides buildings, other structures must be considered when designing for an earthquake-prone area. The trans-Alaska pipeline, for example, is built in a zigzag manner to allow it to expand and contract during temperature changes but also to protect it from breaking during an earthquake. Also, elevated highways in California are reinforced with steel to withstand quakes.

Discussion Starter

What kind of buildings might be safest in an earthquake? Some might suggest strong, rigid construction. Others might suggest flexible construction that would sway but not break.

2. Guide the Discussion

Use the following strategy to facilitate discussion.

Connecting to the Activities

- *Be an Architect, p. B72*
How could you strengthen your design using what you have learned? Students might mention reinforcing walls and foundations, or adding material that will absorb shock waves.

3. Assess Understanding

 Students should use drawings and captions to explain what could be done at their homes to improve earthquake resistance. Some students might make a poster showing a cutaway of their home and how it can be earthquake-proofed.

Close
the Investigation

Critical Thinking Skills
Synthesizing, Evaluating, Generating Ideas

1. An earthquake that begins under the ocean generates a seismic wave (a tsunami) that does most of its damage by flooding the coastline. An earthquake that begins under land causes most damage through cracking and shifting of Earth's crust, with subsequent structural damage to buildings and the rupture of electric and gas lines.

2. Some ideas might be that every location is susceptible to some kinds of catastrophes, and no place is completely safe. Other ideas might refer to the positive aspects of living in these areas.

Challenge Have students find out about your community's plans to prepare for an emergency such as an earthquake and consider whether the plans would be useful.

Following Up

Baseline Assessment Return to students' drawings of what they think would make a building earthquake-resistant. Ask if they would change their drawings in any way.

Reteaching Demonstrate how an uplift in the sea floor can cause changes in the water level. Half-fill a rectangular, 2-inch-high baking pan with water. Hold it over a sink or basin. Quickly jerk one end slightly up and back down. Let students observe the water slosh back and forth. A similar effect can take place in a lake or reservoir in response to an earthquake.

 Use *Science Notebook* p. 96.

Investigation Review ▶
Use Investigation Review p. 53 in the *Assessment Guide*.

changed. The new codes deal with the design of new buildings that will help to withstand earthquakes. The building codes also suggest ways to prevent damage in older buildings. Drawings in this resource show some ways that structures are strengthened against earthquakes. ■

Damage to the Golden Gate Freeway, following an earthquake in California in 1989. ▼

Steel rods in concrete

Spiral-wrapped steel rods in concrete

HIGHWAY SUPPORT The column at the left will probably collapse in an earthquake. The column at the right has vertical steel rods that are spiral-wrapped in steel. This kind of construction could prevent collapse during a quake. Blocks supporting the columns should be able to move with the earthquake. At the same time, they must be firmly anchored to the columns.

INVESTIGATION 3

1. Compare the effects of an earthquake in which the focus is under the ocean with one in which the focus is under the land.

2. Nearly everyone knows that earthquakes can be dangerous. Explain why some people still choose to live in earthquake-prone areas.

B80

Assessment

Investigation Review
How Are Earthquakes Located and Measured

Name _____ Date _____

1. Circle the correct answers.
  A. In the model you made in *Shake It Harder*, which of the following does the table represent?
   a. frame of seismograph   **c.** rotating drum on seismograph
   b. weight on seismograph   **d.** Earth's bedrock

  B. When a seismograph is operating, which part of it remains essentially motionless?
   a. wire or spring   **c.** rotating drum
   b. weight   **d.** pen

  C. Which of the following is not true about the model seismograph you made?
   a. The model measured side-to-side movement.
   b. The model measured up-and-down movement.
   c. The model had a suspended weight.
   d. The model measured variations in energy produced by the "earthquake."

2. Answer the following two questions.
  a. How could a large earthquake on the sea floor cause damage to coastal land?
  <u>Tsunamis, very destructive waves of water, are formed.</u>

  b. Following an earthquake, arrival times of P-waves and S-waves in three cities are used to determine distances to the earthquake. Circles are drawn on a map with the three cities as centers and the distances as radii. Where is the epicenter of the earthquake located?
  <u>In the region where the three circles intersect.</u>

Process Skills
Interpreting and Analyzing Data, Using a Model
In the activity *Be An Architect*, what characteristics helped your model buildings withstand "earthquakes"? Write your answer on a separate sheet of paper.

Students should indicate an understanding of the flexibility of materials used in the building frame and the idea of firm anchorage of foundations.

Portfolio

In My Opinion Encourage students to write a brief editorial supporting or opposing more stringent building requirements in your community to make structures earthquake-resistant. Have students give reasons for their position.

REFLECT & EVALUATE

WORD POWER

aftershock
earthquake
epicenter
fault
focus
magnitude
Richter scale
seismograph
tsunami

 On Your Own
Write a definition for each term in the list.

 With a Partner
Mix up the letters of each term in the list. Provide a clue for each term and challenge your partner to unscramble the terms.

PORTFOLIO

Draw a diagram that shows one way an earthquake is produced. Label each part of your diagram.

Analyze Information

What is shown in the drawing below? Describe what might occur at such a location.

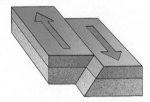

Assess Performance

Work with two or three of your classmates to design and build a model that shows how tsunamis are produced. Describe what each part of your model represents.

Problem Solving

1. Why are strong earthquakes more common on the west coast of the United States than on the east coast?

2. The 1993 earthquake near Los Angeles registered about 7.5 on the Richter scale. The 1964 earthquake near Anchorage, Alaska, registered 8.4 on the Richter scale. Compare the energy released in the two earthquakes.

3. Assume that you live in an area that experiences strong earthquakes. What could you do to protect yourself and your family during an earthquake? What could you do to prepare for an earthquake?

B81

REFLECT & EVALUATE

Word Power

 On Your Own Students can use the Glossary to check definitions.

 With a Partner Students' clues should reflect an understanding of the meanings of the terms. Remind students to check that unscrambled terms are spelled correctly.

Analyze Information

The drawing shows a model of a strike-slip fault. An earthquake can occur along this type of fault.

Assess Performance

Models should include an ocean floor that shows a region where part of a tectonic plate is being pulled down into the mantle. Ideally, the model should show waves of increasing height as they near the shoreline.

Problem Solving

1. Strong earthquakes occur more often on the west coast because it lies along a fault that is formed between the North American Plate and the Pacific Plate.

2. The Alaska earthquake released energy almost 30 times greater than that of the Los Angeles earthquake.

3. You might live in a building that is designed to be earthquake resistant. You could prepare by keeping a fresh supply of water, canned goods, first-aid kit, flashlights and batteries, a battery-operated radio, and clothing in an earthquake-safe area.

 Use *Science Notebook* pp. 96–98.

PORTFOLIO

Students could choose any one diagram that is shown on p. B64 to illustrate one way an earthquake is produced. Check students' diagrams for accuracy.

Chapter Test pp.54–55 in the Assessment Guide

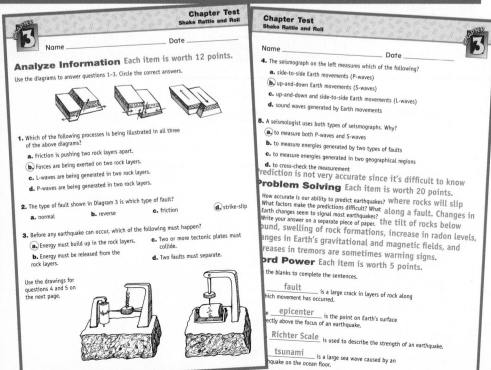

CHAPTER 3

Name _____ Date _____

Chapter Test
Shake Rattle and Roll

Analyze Information Each item is worth 12 points.

Use the diagrams to answer questions 1–3. Circle the correct answers.

1. Which of the following processes is being illustrated in all three of the above diagrams?

a. Friction is pushing two rock layers apart.

b. Forces are being exerted on two rock layers.

c. L-waves are being generated in two rock layers.

d. P-waves are being generated in two rock layers.

2. The type of fault shown in Diagram 3 is which type of fault?

a. normal   b. reverse   c. friction   d. strike-slip

3. Before any earthquake can occur, which of the following must happen?

a. Energy must build up in the rock layers.

b. Energy must be released from the rock layers.

c. Two or more tectonic plates must collide.

d. Two faults must separate.

Use the drawings for questions 4 and 5 on the next page.

Chapter Test
Shake Rattle and Roll

Name _____ Date _____

4. The seismograph on the left measures which of the following?

a. side-to-side Earth movements (P-waves)

b. up-and-down Earth movements (S-waves)

c. up-and-down and side-to-side Earth movements (L-waves)

d. sound waves generated by Earth movements

5. A seismologist uses both types of seismographs. Why?

a. to measure both P-waves and S-waves

b. to measure energies generated by two types of faults

c. to measure energies generated in two geographical regions

d. to cross-check the measurement

Problem Solving Each item is worth 20 points.

How accurate is our ability to predict earthquakes? What factors seem to signal most earthquakes? Write your answer on a separate piece of paper.

Prediction is not very accurate since it's difficult to know where rocks will slip along a fault. Changes in the tilt of rocks below ground, swelling of rock formations, increase in radon levels, changes in Earth's gravitational and magnetic fields, and increases in tremors are sometimes warning signs.

Word Power Each item is worth 5 points.

Fill in the blanks to complete the sentences.

A __fault__ is a large crack in layers of rock along which movement has occurred.

The __epicenter__ is the point on Earth's surface directly above the focus of an earthquake.

The __Richter Scale__ is used to describe the strength of an earthquake.

A __tsunami__ is a large sea wave caused by an earthquake on the ocean floor.

CHAPTER 4 VOLCANOES

Subconcepts	Activities	Materials

Investigation 1 Where Do Volcanoes Occur, and How Are They Classified?

Most volcanoes occur where one tectonic plate descends below another tectonic plate, although some volcanic activity occurs along spreading plate boundaries; volcanoes can be classified by how often they occur and by the ways they erupt.

Suggested Pacing: 3 class periods

Standards
   pp. 160, 168
Benchmarks
   p. 73

Worldwide Eruptions, p. B84
Science Processes: classify; communicate; collect, record, and interpret data; make hypotheses

wall map of the world, table of eruptions from a world almanac, red map pins*, yellow map pins*, Activity Support Master B5 (TRB p. 46), *Science Notebook* pp. 101–102

Investigation 2 How Do Volcanic Eruptions Affect Earth?

Volcanic eruptions are often preceded by changes that can be detected by various instruments; eruptions produce local and worldwide effects, some of which are long lasting.

Suggested Pacing: 2–3 class periods

Standards
   p. 160, 168, 169,
Benchmarks
   pp. 46, 73

Volcanoes You Can Eat!, p. B94
Science Processes: observe, infer, make and use models

goggles*, measuring cup*, quick oats*, saucepan*, water, hot plate*, mixing spoon*, oven mitts*, *Science Notebook* p. 105

Investigation 3 In What Other Places Can Volcanoes Occur?

Hot spots, sources of magma deep in the asthenosphere, may produce volcanic islands in the middle of tectonic plates and provide clues to the direction and speed of the movement of plates; volcanoes also occur at the margins of rifting continental plates.

Suggested Pacing: 3–4 class periods

Standards
   p. 160, 168
Benchmarks
   pp. 46, 55, 73

How Hawaii Formed, p. B100
Science Processes: measure/use numbers; infer; collect, record, and interpret data

metric ruler*, Activity Support Master B9 (TRB p. 50), calculator, *Science Notebook* p. 109

Overview
In this chapter students examine three main types of volcanoes, look at how volcanic activity can be predicted, and see how some volcanoes form as a result of hot spots.

Chapter Concept
Volcanic eruptions are most often associated with tectonic plate margins but can also occur in the middle of plates; eruptions, and their effects, can be predicted and measured.

Advance Preparation	Curriculum Connection	Assessment
Worldwide Eruptions None	Social Studies TG p. B86 Cultural Connection TG pp. B87, B92 The Arts TG p. B88 Math TG p. B89 Integrating the Sciences TG p. B90	**Chapter 4 Baseline Assessment:** *Science Notebook* pp. 99–100 --- **Investigation 1 Baseline Assessment:** TG p. B84 **Investigation 1 Review:** AG p. 56 **Think It/Write It,** p. B93; *Science Notebook* p. 104 **Following Up on Baseline Assessment:** TG p. B93 **Performance:** TG p. B93
Volcanoes You Can Eat! If you wish, arrange to work in the school kitchen or in the home economics laboratory.	Language Arts TG p. B96 Social Studies TG p. B97 Science, Technology & Society TG p. B98	**Investigation 2 Baseline Assessment:** TG p. B94 **Investigation 2 Review:** AG p. 57 **Think It/Write It,** p. B99; *Science Notebook* p. 108 **Following Up on Baseline Assessment:** TG p. B99 **Portfolio:** TG p. B99
How Hawaii Formed None	Language Arts TG pp. B102, B107 Social Studies TG p. B103 Science, Technology & Society TG pp. B104, B106 Literature TG p. B105 Math TG p. B108 Cultural Connection TG p. B109	**Investigation 3 Baseline Assessment:** TG p. B100 **Investigation 3 Review:** AG p. 58 **Think It/Write It,** p. B110; *Science Notebook* p. 112 **Following Up on Baseline Assessment:** TG p. B110 **Performance:** TG p. B110 --- **Chapter 4 Summative Assessment** Reflect and Evaluate, p. B111 Chapter 4 Review/Test: AG pp. 59–60 *Science Notebook* pp. 113–114

TG= Teaching Guide   TRB= Teacher Resource Book   AG= Assessment Guide   *Materials in the Deluxe Equipment Kit

Chapter Overview

Chapter Concept Volcanic eruptions are most often associated with tectonic plate margins but can also occur in the middle of plates; eruptions, and their effects, can be predicted and measured.

Theme: Models

Use of models is important for understanding volcanic processes, which originate deep in Earth. An active volcano provides scientists with clues and evidence to revise their models of how Earth works.

Common Misconceptions

Students may perceive volcanoes as violently explosive cones on tropical islands. In this chapter they discover that there are other types and that location of volcanoes is tied to location of Earth's plate boundaries.

Options for
Setting the Stage

Warm-Up Activity

 Shake a soda can and open it over a sink, towel, or lined wastebasket. Squeeze a toothpaste tube so that the contents ooze out the top. How do these actions model volcanic eruptions? How are they different?

Use *Science Notebook* pp. 99–100.

Discussion Starter:
Predicting Volcanic Eruptions

Use photo and text to discuss eruptions.

Merapi has erupted over 70 times in 1,000 years. Over a million people live on or near it. Why might people choose to live there? Perhaps they have nowhere else to go or accept the dangers because they make a good living and feel the risk is worth the gain.

- **Career:** Volcanologist

A volcanologist is a geologist who specializes in the study of volcanoes. Volcanologists visit eruptions to make tests and study the activity, to analyze gas and lava samples, and to measure temperature and movement of the earth in order to help predict when, where, and how other volcanoes may erupt.

VOLCANOES

Never trust a volcano! Millions of people live near active volcanoes. And over the past 20 years, sudden volcanic eruptions have killed over 28,000 people. Volcanoes have always been unpredictable and dangerous.

Predicting Eruptions

What if scientists could predict the onset of a volcanic eruption? Think of the lives that could be saved by knowing several days in advance that a volcano is about to blow! Barry Voight, a geoscientist at Pennsylvania State University, has come up with a way of making such a prediction.

Voight and his science team have placed monitoring devices on the slopes of Merapi, on the island of Java in Indonesia. Merapi is an active volcano that erupted suddenly in 1930, taking the lives of 1,300 people.

The team uses the monitoring devices and a laser to continually measure the distance to the volcano. Team members who are kilometers away can detect movements of about 2 cm on the surface of the volcano. What do you think such movement on the surface of the volcano tells geoscientists?

B82

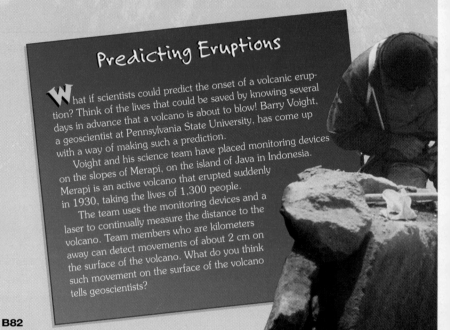

Home-School Connection

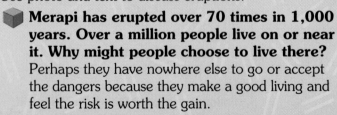

The Explore at Home activity "What If It Happened Here?" suggests that family members try to investigate how volcanoes might help preserve the record of human history. Distribute the activity (TRB p. 10) when students have completed the chapter. Discuss what archaeologists do to learn about the past.

Explore at Home

Name _____ Date _____

WHAT IF IT HAPPENED HERE?

In A.D. 79, the eruption of Mount Vesuvius sealed Pompeii in a blanket of volcanic ash. Because of that natural disaster, the town was almost perfectly preserved for 2,000 years. Volcanoes are also responsible for preserving ancient remains in Africa. By imagining the future, you and a family member can consider the ability of volcanoes to preserve the past.

Procedure

You feel Earth rumble. You may see the sky turn black. Suddenly, that dormant volcano at the end of your town erupts, spewing lava and ash throughout your neighborhood. Two thousand years from now, archaeologists find the site and begin removing the volcanic debris. What do you think they would find?

Results

Discuss the following questions. Which objects might have been destroyed? Which objects might have been preserved? What activities might the people of your community have been doing when the disaster hit? What objects or activities do you think might confuse archaeologists of the future?

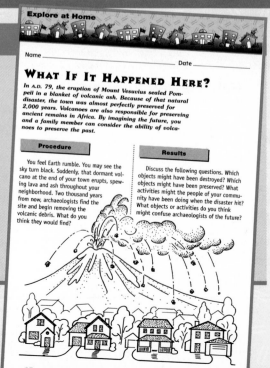

Coming Up

INVESTIGATION 1

WHERE DO VOLCANOES OCCUR, AND HOW ARE THEY CLASSIFIED? B84

INVESTIGATION 2

HOW DO VOLCANIC ERUPTIONS AFFECT EARTH? B94

INVESTIGATION 3

IN WHAT OTHER PLACES CAN VOLCANOES OCCUR? B100

◀ Barry Voight and another geoscientist installing a monitoring device on Merapi

B83

Technology Alert

CD-ROM

Thar She Blows Enhances or replaces Investigation 1

In **Thar She Blows** students watch a video of a volcanologist explaining how a volcano is formed. They view a world map that shows the locations of three major types of active volcanos. They "click" on each site to see an inset illustration and hear a narration that describes the type of volcano (stratovolcano, cinder cone, or shield), its location, and other characteristics. Finally, they examine the Volcano Super Pack and create a Spreadsheet and Bar Graph to compare different types of volcanoes worldwide.

Chapter Road Map

INVESTIGATION 1

Where Do Volcanoes Occur, and How Are They Classified?

Activities
* Worldwide Eruptions

Resources
* Volcanoes and Plate Tectonics
  Surtsey
  Mount Vesuvius

INVESTIGATION 2

How Do Volcanic Eruptions Affect Earth?

Activities
* Volcanoes You Can Eat!

Resources
* Mount Pinatubo

INVESTIGATION 3

In What Other Places Can Volcanoes Occur?

Activities
* How Hawaii Formed

Resources
* An Island in the Making
  Using Robots to Investigate Volcanoes
  Great Rift Valley of Africa

*Pressed for Time?

As you work through the upcoming investigations, focus on the activities and resources identified by the clock.

 Look for this symbol in front of questions that help develop Scientific Reasoning Skills.

WHERE DO VOLCANOES OCCUR, AND HOW ARE THEY CLASSIFIED?

Planner

Subconcept Most volcanoes occur where one tectonic plate descends below another tectonic plate, although some volcanic activity occurs along spreading plate boundaries; volcanoes can be classified by how often they occur and by the ways they erupt.

Objectives

- **Infer** the relationship between volcanism and plate tectonics. **Classify** volcanoes in different ways.

Pacing 3 class periods

Science Terms volcano, magma, lava, cinder-cone volcano, shield volcano, composite-cone volcano

Activate Prior Knowledge

Baseline Assessment Ask: **What are some words about volcanoes?** Make a list of all class responses. Save the list for use in Following Up.

Activity Worldwide Eruptions

Preview *Students research the location and characteristics of recent volcanic eruptions and should find that most volcanoes are located near plate boundaries, but some are located within a plate. The kind of eruption is related to the type of lava that is spewed from the volcanoes.*

1. Get Ready

Time about 40 minutes

Grouping groups of 4–6

Multi-Age Strategy Groups may divide the 6-month period into smaller time periods to research separately. Show students how to use an almanac to find volcanic eruptions. Encourage group members to help one another locate volcanoes on the world map.

WHERE DO VOLCANOES OCCUR, AND HOW ARE THEY CLASSIFIED?

Volcanoes form when magma erupts from an opening in Earth's surface. Where are most volcanoes found in relation to tectonic plates? In this investigation you'll locate volcanoes and find out how they are compared and classified.

Activity

Worldwide Eruptions

You can plot volcanic eruptions in the news to figure out how they relate to Earth's tectonic plates.

MATERIALS
- wall map of the world
- table of eruptions
- world almanac
- red map pins
- yellow map pins
- map of tectonic plates
- *Science Notebook*

Procedure

1. Break up into teams of researchers. Each team will research the location of active volcanoes during a six-month period in the last two years. Your teacher will make sure that no two groups are researching the same six months. The goal of all the teams is to collect news articles about active volcanoes throughout the world during the past two years.

2. In your *Science Notebook*, record the date of each eruption, the name of the volcano, and the location. Also list whether each volcano is on a spreading ridge, on a plate margin near a descending plate, on a transform fault, or in the middle of a plate. Record how each volcano erupted: Was it a quiet lava flow, did it explode, or did it belch heavy clouds of ash?

Step 3

B84

Responding to Individual Needs

Students Acquiring English As students locate each volcano on the map, they should say aloud its name, location, and what type of plate boundary it is near, if any. Help students with pronunciations. Students who speak a language other than English may be able to help other students correctly pronounce some volcano names.

SELECTED MAJOR VOLCANIC ERUPTIONS			
Date	Volcano	Area	Death Toll
79	Vesuvius	Pompeii, Italy	16,000
1169	Etna	Sicily, Italy	15,000
1669	Etna	Sicily, Italy	20,000
1793	Unzen Island	Japan	50,000
1883	Krakatoa	Java, Indonesia	36,000
1902	Pelee	St. Pierre, Martinique	28,000
1919	Kelud	Java, Indonesia	5,500
1980	Saint Helens	Washington State	62
1985	Nevado del Ruis	Armero, Colombia	22,000
1991	Pinatubo	Luzon, Philippines	200
1993	Mayon	Legazpi, Philippines	67

3. Use a world almanac to find the sites of major volcanic activity over the last 500 years.

4. Tack a large world map to your bulletin board. Using the data gathered by the teams, the data from the almanac, and the data in the table, mark the locations of volcanoes. Stick a red map pin on the map at the site of any volcanic eruption; stick a yellow map pin at the site of any active volcano.

5. Throughout the school year, keep adding to your records and to the world map. **Record** new volcanic activity and new eruptions as they occur. Note how the location of volcanoes is related to Earth's tectonic plates.

Analyze and Conclude

1. How many volcanic eruptions did you find in the news during the six months your team researched? What was the total number of eruptions found by your class during the two-year period?

2. Where on tectonic plates were the volcanoes located?

3. Were any of the volcanic eruptions on a mid-ocean spreading ridge? What kind of an eruption did they have?

4. **Hypothesize** about the relationship between volcanic eruptions and Earth's tectonic plates.

> ### INVESTIGATE FURTHER!
>
> #### RESEARCH
> Get a world atlas from the library. Look for islands that are in the same locations as mid-ocean ridges. Find out as much as possible about the islands. Are they volcanic? If they are, what kinds of volcanoes are they?

B85

Investigate Further

Research

Make several resources available for students' use. Most islands located at mid-ocean ridges are volcanic islands of either the shield volcano or composite-cone type. Students should record their findings in their *Science Notebooks* on pp. 101–102.

Materials Hints Use Activity Support Master B5 (TRB p. 46).

2. Guide the Procedure

- Provide a section of a bulletin board for students to display their articles. Some students might want to decorate the board.
- Your school media specialist may be able to help students with their research by directing them to appropriate resources.
- **Were you surprised by the number of volcanic eruptions that have occurred in the last two years?** Students will probably be surprised because they don't hear about all the eruptions that occur.

 Have students record their data and answer questions on *Science Notebook* pp. 101–102.

 Students can use the CD-ROM Spreadsheet and Grapher to organize and display their data.

3. Assess Performance

Process Skills Checklist

- Did students **collect data** from reliable sources and then **record** the data accurately? Did they use library resources such as the *Reader's Guide to Periodical Literature* as well as an almanac?
- Were students' **hypotheses** about the relationship between plate boundaries and volcanic eruption based on their findings?

Analyze and Conclude

1. Answers should correspond with the results of the class research.

2. Most volcanoes are located at or near the boundaries of tectonic plates. Some are within plates.

3. Because they are submerged, mid-ocean ridge volcanoes are rarely observed. They are found, however, on Iceland where the mid-ocean ridge reaches the surface. Most of these volcanoes have a quiet eruption.

4. Students should hypothesize that most volcanoes occur near plate boundaries and that eruptions are especially violent where plates collide.

Volcanoes and Plate Tectonics

Preview *Students focus on the formation, structure, and classification of volcanoes.*

1. Get Ready

Science Terms
volcano, magma, lava, cinder-cone volcano, shield volcano, composite-cone volcano

Background

* Magma that rises to the surface does not come from Earth's core. The outer part of the core is fluid, but it is composed of iron-rich material. Therefore, this fluid is very dense—too dense to rise through Earth's crust. Actually, magma forms relatively close to the surface—within the lower crust or upper mantle. This depth places the origin of magma between 50 and 200 km (30–120 mi) below the surface of Earth.

Discussion Starter

 What do you think causes a volcanic eruption?
Encourage students to consider a variety of explanations. Students may suggest that hot gases are involved, or that earthquakes crack the crust, making a hole through which magma flows. Encourage students to evaluate the reasonableness of their explanations.

How likely is a volcanic eruption in our area?
Most students will think of this question in terms of whether or not there are mountains nearby. Broaden the discussion to consider the whole geology of the area, especially proximity to a plate boundary. The question is not so much what can we see around us. but rather, what is happening beneath us.

Use **Transparency 8,** "Volcanic Activity Around the World," to review with students the regions where volcanic activity is likely to occur.

Volcanoes and Plate Tectonics

Volcanoes

What comes to mind when you hear the word *volcano*? Probably you think of a large mountain spewing red-hot lava and other material high into Earth's atmosphere. Some volcanoes are, in fact, towering mountains that throw rock, molten material, dust, and ash into the air. But a **volcano** is *any* opening in Earth's crust through which hot gases, rocks, and melted material erupt.

Have you ever opened a can of cold soda that has been dropped on the floor? Soda probably squirted into the air above the can. More soda bubbled out and flowed down the side of the can. Now, what do you think would happen if you opened a can of warm soda that had been dropped? The release of the warm soda from the can would be even *more* violent. Volcanoes are like cans of soda. Some erupt violently; others have more gentle eruptions.

The high temperatures and pressures deep within Earth can cause rock to melt. This melted rock is called **magma**. Because it's less dense than surrounding material, magma slowly makes its way toward Earth's surface. As it travels toward the surface, the magma melts surrounding material to form a central pipe, which is connected to the magma chamber. Eventually this hot melted material escapes through an opening in the crust called a volcanic vent. When magma reaches Earth's surface, it is called **lava**.

When a volcano erupts, different kinds of materials can be spewed out. Lava is magma that reaches Earth's surface. When lava flows from a volcano, its temperature can be higher than 1,100°C

Structure of an erupting volcano ▼

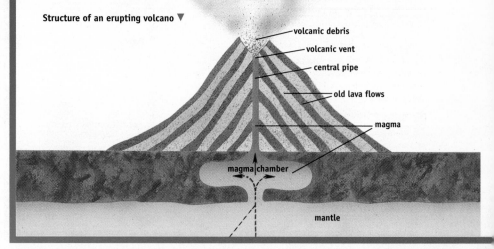

volcanic debris
volcanic vent
central pipe
old lava flows
magma
magma chamber
mantle

Integrating the Curriculum

Science & Social Studies

COORDINATES **What to Do** Using a world map, students can play a game by randomly selecting a series of latitude and longitude coordinates and then plotting them to locate places around the world. Students should then predict the likelihood of volcanic activity (high/moderate/low) occurring at each location.

What's the Result? **What volcanoes were closest to your coordinates? On which plate did the greatest number of coordinates fall?** If selected randomly, the greatest number of coordinates should fall on the larger of the plates, such as the Pacific, North American, and Eurasian Plates.

▲ Mount Tolbackik erupts in former U.S.S.R.

▲ Mount Kilauea erupts in Hawaii.

(2,012°F)! Solid volcanic debris includes bombs, cinders, ash, and dust. Bombs are volcanic rocks the size of a baseball or bigger. Large bombs can weigh nearly 100 metric tons (110 short tons). Volcanic dust and ash, on the other hand, range in size from about 0.25 mm to 0.5 mm (0.009 in. to 0.02 in.) in diameter and can be carried hundreds or thousands of kilometers from a volcano.

Volcanism and Plate Tectonics

Like earthquakes, volcanoes occur along certain plate boundaries. From the map to the right, you can see that many volcanoes occur around the edges of the Pacific Plate in an area that scientists have named the Ring of Fire. Between 500 and 600 active volcanoes make up the region called the Ring of Fire.

Volcanoes in the Ring of Fire were formed in subduction zones. In a subduction zone, plates collide and one plate

descends below the other. The descending plate melts as it descends slowly into the mantle. The magma then rises to the surface, forming a chain of volcanoes near the boundaries of the two plates.

Lava also erupts at divergent plate boundaries. Find the purple faults on the map. These indicate divergent plate boundaries, where new ocean floor is formed as magma wells up between the separating plates.

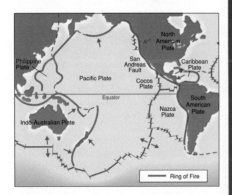

Hundreds of active volcanoes are located in a region known as the Ring of Fire. ▶

B87

Investigate Further

Cultural Connection

ANCIENT IDEAS **What to Do** Tell students that the ideas of how our world works have changed over time. For example, the Greek philosopher Aristotle thought volcanic eruptions were caused by a fire burning deep within Earth. This fire ignited now and then when air was drawn down and mixed with the central flame. The Hawaiians attributed eruptions of Kilauea to the anger of the goddess Pele. For ancient Romans, eruptions resulted from the blacksmith's forge of Vulcan, the god of fire. **What's the Result?** Have students offer reasons why ancient people developed these explanations. Help them to see it is natural for people to want to explain what they observe and to base these explanations on what they know.

Choose from the following strategies to facilitate discussion.

Making Inferences

- Imagine that you are watching a cherry pie baking in the oven. The top crust of the pie has tiny holes punched in it. The cherry filling is very hot and is in liquid form.

   Where is the cherry filling most likely to ooze out? The filling will probably come out through the holes in the crust or in places where the top and bottom crust are not completely sealed. **How is the cherry pie similar to plate tectonics and volcanoes?** The filling is like the magma within Earth. Volcanoes form at cracked regions of the crust—such as at plate boundaries.

Making Comparisons

- Compare the different sizes and shapes of volcanic debris to the different sizes and shapes of balls. Display a golf ball, baseball, softball, football, basketball, and so on. Ask: **What are volcanic rocks of these sizes called?** Bombs

Making Inferences

- Direct students' attention to the photographs of erupting volcanoes. Ask: **What do you think comes out of volcanoes?** In addition to the lava and ash students might see in the pictures, they might speculate that the lava flows and ash clouds contain rocks of various sizes.

Thinking About the Data

- **Are you surprised that there are 500 to 600 active volcanoes in the Ring of Fire?** Students will probably be surprised by these numbers. To reinforce these numbers, show the class a map of Alaska, pointing out the many volcanoes that make up the Aleutian Islands. Thirty-two of these volcanoes in the Aleutians are active.

🛈 Responding to Individual Needs

Kinesthetic Activity Acquire a relief map of an area with composite cones, such as Mount St. Helens. Let students run their fingers over the map to get a better understanding of the relative heights this kind of volcano can attain.

Connecting to the Activities

- ***Worldwide Eruptions, p. B84***

CINDER-CONE VOLCANO Paricutín, in Mexico (*left*); drawing of a cinder-cone volcano. Notice the very steep slopes (*below*).

vent
magma
layers of cinders

Of the volcanoes you investigated in the activity, which do you think had very fluid lava? Which do you think had very sticky lava? What makes you think so? The volcanoes with quiet eruptions had very fluid lava, while those with explosive eruptions had stickier lava.

Thinking Critically

Imagine that you had to live near one of the three types of volcanoes. What are the risks and benefits of living near each one? While shield volcanoes erupt quietly, they are active for a long time. Cinder-cone volcanoes erupt less frequently, but the cinders they eject can present a risk. Composite-cone volcanoes erupt the most violently and generally cause the most damage; however, they erupt very infrequently and are often dormant for hundreds of years.

Thinking About the Data

- As each volcano is mentioned in this resource, ask students to locate it on a map. Ask: **What do you notice about the locations of these volcanoes?** Except for the volcanoes located on the Hawaiian islands, the volcanoes are located near plate boundaries. Let students speculate how the Hawaiian volcanoes formed. They will learn about the origin of these volcanoes in Investigation 3.

Responding to Individual Needs

Kinesthetic Activity Instead of making posters for the Science & the Arts activity on this page, some students might prefer to make model volcanoes using clay, salt clay, modeling compound, or papier mâché. They could use pins and cards to label their models. Challenge students to find out the height and width of one volcano of each major kind. Then they can build their models to scale for a comparison of size as well as shape.

Classifying Volcanoes

Volcanoes can be classified in different ways. One classification system is based on how often eruptions occur. An *active* volcano is one that erupts constantly. Some volcanoes that make up the Hawaiian Islands are active volcanoes. *Intermittent* volcanoes are those that erupt on a regular basis. Mount Vesuvius, in Italy, is an intermittent volcano. Volcanoes that haven't erupted in a while but could erupt in the near future are called *dormant* volcanoes. Mount Lassen, in the California Cascade Range, is a dormant volcano. Volcanoes that have not erupted in recorded history are classified as *extinct* volcanoes. Mount Kenya, in Africa, is an extinct volcano. Go back to the records you have been keeping from the "Worldwide Eruptions" activity. For each of the volcanoes you have listed, classify it as active, intermittent, or dormant. Would any of the volcanoes be listed as extinct?

Volcanoes can also be classified by the way they erupt. The way they erupt depends on the type of lava that is spewed from the volcano. One kind of lava is highly fluid. Fluid lava erupts quietly. Another kind of lava is very sticky. This sticky lava erupts violently. The kind of lava that pours from the volcano affects the shape of the volcano that is formed. These two pages show the main kinds of volcanoes—cinder cone, shield, and composite-cone—which are based on their shapes.

Cinder-Cone Volcanoes

Cinders are sticky bits of volcanic material that are about the size of peas. A **cinder-cone volcano** is one made of layers of cinders. The cinder cone forms around a central vent containing magma.

These volcanoes are produced by explosive eruptions. Generally, cinder cones are small volcanoes, less than 300 m (984 ft) tall, with very steep slopes. There is usually a bowl-shaped crater. Cinder cones often form in groups. Paricutín, which is a dormant volcano just west of Mexico City, and Stromboli, a very active volcano off the coast of Italy, are cinder-cone volcanoes.

B88

Integrating the Curriculum

Science & the Arts

VOLCANO TYPES

What to Do Students can work in groups to make posters showing the three basic forms of volcanoes: cinder cones, shield, and composite cones. They might include labeled cutaway views together with photographs and captions. Encourage students to list examples of each kind of volcano in addition to those referred to in the text.

What's the Result? Encourage students to present their posters to the class. Students should describe the similarities and differences of the three volcanic forms based on their drawings. Afterwards, display their posters for the rest of the school to see.

Multi-Age Classroom Working in small groups students can make their posters of volcano types.

Shield Volcanoes

Shield volcanoes form when lava flows quietly from a crack in Earth's crust. What kind of lava do you think makes up shield volcanoes? Because of the composition of the lava, shield volcanoes are large mountains that have very gentle slopes. Mauna Loa, the largest volcano on Earth, is a shield volcano. Mauna Loa, which is a part of the island of Hawaii, towers over 4,100 m (13,448 ft) above sea level. The rest—about 5,000 m (about 16,400 ft)—of this vast volcano is below the waters of the Pacific Ocean.

COMPOSITE-CONE VOLCANO   Mount Fuji, in Japan (*top*); a drawing of a composite volcano. This type of volcano has steep slopes near its top and gentle slopes near its base (*bottom*).

Composite-Cone Volcanoes

Composite-cone volcanoes are those that form when explosive eruptions of sticky lava alternate with quieter eruptions of volcanic rock bits. Composite cones are also called stratovolcanoes. A composite cone has very steep slopes near its top but gentle slopes closer to its base.

Composite cones are the most explosive of all volcanoes. Their eruptions often occur without warning and can be very destructive. Mount Vesuvius, a once-dormant volcano in Italy, erupted in A.D. 79 and killed thousands of residents in Pompeii and nearby cities. This same volcano still erupts from time to time. You will learn more about Mount Vesuvius on page B92. ■

SHIELD VOLCANO   Mauna Loa (*top*); a drawing of a shield volcano. Notice the very gentle slopes (*bottom*).

B89

Science & Math

MEASURING LAVA

What to Do Students can carefully pour out equal amounts of various liquids (water, liquid soap, cooking oil, shampoo, honey, molasses.) They should compare differences in the flow, timing how long it takes each liquid to spread out on a plate. Then students can experiment with making the liquid runnier by placing the jar in a bowl of warm water for a few minutes. They can make some liquids thicker and stickier by mixing in some sand. Have them estimate the time it will take the liquids to spread under these conditions.

What's the Result? The students can compare what they did in the activity with how lava flows in a real volcano. Heated lava flows faster. Lava with rocky material in it slows down.

Making Inferences

- **Why are the three kinds of volcanoes on these pages named as they are?** A cinder-cone volcano is made largely of cinders. With its gentle slopes, a shield volcano looks like a shield. A composite-cone volcano is a composite, or combination, of lava and solid rock.

Identifying and Solving Problems

- **Imagine that you have discovered a new mountain in a remote region of the world. You suspect that it's a dormant volcano. How could you determine what type of volcano it is? What evidence would you look for?** Students might suggest looking at eroded sections to check for layers, looking at the size and shape, examining the type of material that makes the slope, or measuring the angle of the slope.

- **How would this evidence help you determine the type of volcano you have found?** The presence of layers, the kinds of materials that make up the volcano, and the height and shape of the cone are clues to the type of volcano.

Making Comparisons

- **What is the tallest mountain in the world on land?** Mt. Everest: 8,848 m (29,028 ft) **Which is taller—Mt. Everest or Mauna Loa?** If measured in height above sea level, Mt. Everest is taller. If the entire mountain—both above and below water—is included, Mauna Loa is slightly taller.

3. Assess Understanding

Ask students to use their hands to explain how a volcano forms where plates collide. With their hands representing plates, students should show one plate descending below the other, then the descending plate melting to form magma, which rises to form a volcano.

Surtsey

Preview *Students focus on a case study about the formation of a volcanic island.*

1. Get Ready

Background

• The eruption of Surtsey probably started weeks before the volcano broke the surface. A couple of days earlier, coastal villagers noticed that the air smelled of rotten eggs, due to hydrogen sulfide. For the first week after the volcano broke the surface, the island grew continuously. The eruption varied from short bursts lasting for minutes to huge columns of steam and ash rising several kilometers in the sky for hours at a time. At night, glowing red volcanic bombs and spectacular displays of lightning illuminated the eruption. Seawater washing into the crater resulted in explosive eruptions due to the formation of steam. After six months, seawater could no longer reach the crater. Quieter flows continued until 1967.

Discussion Starter

Ask a student to locate Iceland on a world map for the class. **What do you think Iceland is like?** Because of its name and northern location, students might picture a barren, icy world—not the kind of setting in which they might expect to find volcanoes.

• **What do you notice about Iceland in relation to plate tectonics?** By looking at the plate boundary map on pp. B20–B21, students should notice that a divergent boundary runs directly through Iceland. **What does this tell you about the island?** Students should infer that volcanic activity probably occurs on or near Iceland.

2. Guide the Discussion

Choose from the following strategies to facilitate discussion.

Connecting to the Activities

• *Worldwide Eruptions, p. B84*
During your research did you find recent eruptions around Iceland? Why would you expect volcanic activity there? Because of its location on a mid-ocean ridge

Surtsey

▲ Surtsey, a young volcanic island, begins to form.

▲ Living things begin to populate the new island of Surtsey.

In 1963 off the southern coast of Iceland, a sailor on a fishing boat observed a pillar of smoke in the distance. He ran to alert his captain that he had spotted a ship that was on fire. Soon the odor of sulfur filled the salty air. The crew of the fishing vessel measured the water's temperature. It was much warmer than usual. The captain soon informed his crew that the smoke in the distance wasn't a burning ship at all. The smoke and fire signaled that one of the youngest volcanic islands on Earth was beginning to rise from the icy waters. Named after the Norse god Surtur, a giant who bore fire from the sea, Surtsey started to form

as lava spewed from a long, narrow rift on the ocean floor.

Within a couple of weeks, an island nearly half a kilometer wide rose about 160 m (528 ft) above the water's surface. And after spewing lava, gases, and bits of rock debris from its vent for almost four years, Surtsey became inactive—geologically, that is. Scientists then had Surtsey designated as a nature preserve in order to study how living things inhabit a newly formed area. Surtsey is now home to 27 species of plants and animals. Among the first organisms to inhabit the island were plants called sea rockets. Seeds from faraway places were carried to the island by

B90

Investigate Further

Integrating the Sciences

LIFE SCIENCE **What to Do** Ask students what they think happens to plants and animals after a major eruption. Invite them to study Mount St. Helens to find out. Students will discover that many plants and animals survived the eruption. The area around the eruption zone continues to be repopulated by plants and animals and other groups of organisms.

What's the Result? Students should find out that airborne seeds were carried into the area; some plants survived the eruption and began growing; animals were attracted to the new plants; the area continued to grow and replenish itself.

Multi-Age Classroom Working in small groups, students can present diagrams, conduct a question-and-answer session, or play a video.

birds and the wind. A few varieties of grasses and mosses painted colorful splotches against the black rock of the island. In the spring, seals now crawl up the black beaches to have their young.

Few people are allowed to visit this volcanic island. The Surtsey Research Council allows only a few scientists to visit the island to study the living things growing there. The impact of the few human beings that visit the island is very small. Only natural forces, such as wind and rain, have acted upon the land and its inhabitants. Erosion has shrunk the island to about three fourths of its original size. Unless it erupts again, the effects of wind and water will eventually make Surtsey disappear. ■

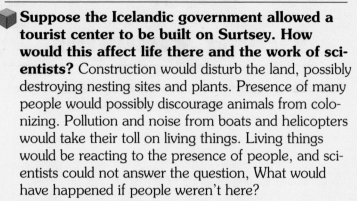

INVESTIGATE FURTHER!

RESEARCH

In 1973 a volcanic eruption occurred on Heimaey, an island off the southern coast of Iceland. Find out how much destruction was done as a result of this eruption. Look also for ways that the eruption benefited the island. Compare the eruption on Heimaey with the eruption on Surtsey.

SCIENCE IN LITERATURE

SURTSEY: THE NEWEST PLACE ON EARTH
by Kathryn Lasky
Photographs by Christopher G. Knight
Hyperion Books for Children, 1992

During the 20 years following the eruption of Surtsey, only about 100 people have been allowed to visit this laboratory of nature. Author-and-photographer team Kathryn Lasky and Christopher Knight are two of the select few who have visited Surtsey.

In the book *Surtsey: The Newest Place on Earth*, you can examine more than 40 color photographs recording Surtsey's formation. In addition to the fascinating photos, author Kathryn Lasky has paired the story of Surtsey with selections from ancient Icelandic mythology. These myths reveal that the people of Iceland have witnessed mid-ocean volcanism for thousands of years.

B91

Research

The eruption on Heimaey blanketed a nearby town with ash. No one was killed, however, and people were able to move back into their homes thanks in part to the efforts of volunteers who fought the advance of lava by spraying it with seawater. The lava that hardened near the edge of the harbor provided a barrier against waves that eroded the coast. Students may wish to communicate their findings in a variety of ways, including written reports, newspaper articles, interviews, posters, booklets, or computer multimedia presentations. Presentations might also include the benefits of geothermal energy from the volcanic activity. Remind students to record their findings, and the findings of classmates, in their *Science Notebooks* on p. 103.

Identifying and Solving Problems

Suppose the Icelandic government allowed a tourist center to be built on Surtsey. How would this affect life there and the work of scientists? Construction would disturb the land, possibly destroying nesting sites and plants. Presence of many people would possibly discourage animals from colonizing. Pollution and noise from boats and helicopters would take their toll on living things. Living things would be reacting to the presence of people, and scientists could not answer the question, What would have happened if people weren't here?

Drawing Conclusions

- **How might wind and water make Surtsey disappear eventually?** By eroding it; you may demonstrate erosion by pouring water over a pile of sand.

- **What actions could prevent Surtsey from disappearing?** Erosion could be slowed by protecting the island against waves. Eruption would add land.

Responding to Individual Needs

Students Acquiring English Ask for volunteers to "build" Surtsey by drawing on the chalkboard. The drawing should show building up from the ocean floor and emergence from the ocean surface.

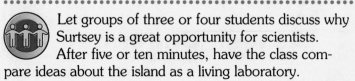

SCIENCE IN LITERATURE

Surtsey: The Newest Place on Earth
by Kathryn Lasky

Students can use information in this book for their stories or skits in Assess Understanding. In addition to the facts, students can incorporate the myths that are discussed in the book.

3. Assess Understanding

Let groups of three or four students discuss why Surtsey is a great opportunity for scientists. After five or ten minutes, have the class compare ideas about the island as a living laboratory.

Mount Vesuvius

Preview *Students focus on the archaeological records of the ancient eruption of Mount Vesuvius.*

1. Get Ready

Background

- The eruption of Mount Vesuvius displayed one of the greatest volcanic dangers: flows of hot ash and gas.

Discussion Starter

- Show pictures of casts of the victims of the Mount Vesuvius eruption of A.D. 79. Ask: **What do you think caused this?** Point out positions of the victims. Ask students to relate what they know about Vesuvius, Pompeii, or Herculaneum.

2. Guide the Discussion

Choose from the following strategies to facilitate discussion.

Making Inferences

How valid would archaeologists' conclusions about life in Pompeii be if only one house had been preserved? Conclusions drawn from one house would not be valid because the house might not have been typical.

Connecting to the Activities

- *Worldwide Eruptions, p. B84*
  How does the location of Mount Vesuvius explain its eruptions? It sits on a convergent boundary where the African and Eurasion Plates collide. Subducting crust creates magma that rises to the surface through volcanic vents.

3. Assess Understanding

Students can take the part of an observer and can write about the next eruption of Vesuvius.

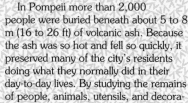

Mount Vesuvius

Over the past 2,000 years or so, Mount Vesuvius, a cinder-cone volcano in southern Italy, has erupted about 50 times. Before its eruption in A.D. 79, Vesuvius was a picturesque cone-shaped mountain, towering over 1,000 m (3,300 ft) above the Bay of Naples. Vineyards and orchards crept nearly halfway up the mountain's slopes. Most historians think that very few people knew that Vesuvius was a volcano—until the fateful morning of August 24 in the year A.D. 79.

During the early morning hours of that day, an earthquake rumbled through the area. By early afternoon loud thunder ripped through the air, and red-hot ash rained from the skies. Within

24 hours the twin Roman cities of Pompeii and Herculaneum were destroyed.

In Pompeii more than 2,000 people were buried beneath about 5 to 8 m (16 to 26 ft) of volcanic ash. Because the ash was so hot and fell so quickly, it preserved many of the city's residents doing what they normally did in their day-to-day lives. By studying the remains of people, animals, utensils, and decorations found in Pompeii, archaeologists have learned a lot about the people who lived at this time. Archaeologists are scientists who study ancient cultures by digging up the evidence of human life from the past.

The city of Herculaneum, which was several kilometers from Pompeii, met its fate not from the volcanic ash but from a mudflow. A mudflow is a mixture of wet materials that rushes down a mountainside and destroys everything in its path. Volcanologists, or scientists who study volcanoes, think that flowing hot volcanic debris swept over the city and covered it to depths of over 20 m (66 ft)!

The eruption of Mount Vesuvius in A.D. 79 is probably most famous because

Cast of man buried by the eruption of Mount Vesuvius *(far left)*; **nuts buried and preserved by the eruption** *(left)*

Investigate Further

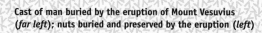

Cultural Connection

MAKING CASTS

What to Do Explain to students that the people who first excavated Pompeii kept breaking into empty holes. Archaeologist Giuseppe Fiorelli decided to fill one of the holes with plaster. When he removed the hardened cast, he found the perfect shape of a person who had been covered by the ash. The body decayed within the casing, leaving the shape. Archaeologists also found bowls of charred fruit, nuts, and eggs. Encourage students to imbed a small object in clay to produce their own mold.

What's the Result? Invite students to carefully cut down the middle of their clay to release the object and see the mold. Discuss the details preserved in the clay.

it perfectly preserved the people and customs of ancient Rome. However, it was not the last nor the worst eruption in the area. In the summer of 1631, earthquakes once again shook the area. By winter, molten rock filled the volcano. On December 16, 1631, ash was spewing from the mountain. By the next day, red-hot lava raced down the volcano's slopes. The destructive toll of this eruption

included 15 villages. At least 4,000 people and 6,000 animals died.

Since the 1631 eruption of Mount Vesuvius, the volcano has erupted every 15 to 40 years. The ash and rock fragments have made the soil very fertile. Farmers successfully grow grapes, citrus fruits, carnations, beans, and peas in this region. But the threat of losing it all to the volcano is always there. ■

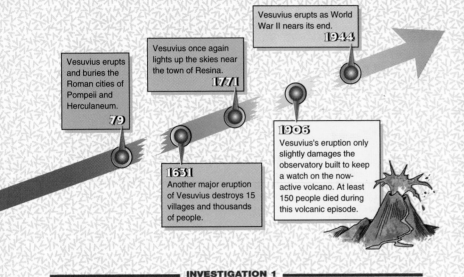

Vesuvius erupts and buries the Roman cities of Pompeii and Herculaneum.
79

Vesuvius once again lights up the skies near the town of Resina.
1771

Vesuvius erupts as World War II nears its end.
1944

1631
Another major eruption of Vesuvius destroys 15 villages and thousands of people.

1906
Vesuvius's eruption only slightly damages the observatory built to keep a watch on the now-active volcano. At least 150 people died during this volcanic episode.

INVESTIGATION 1

1. Describe how most volcanoes form.

2. Make a chart that compares and contrasts cinder cones, shield volcanoes, and composite cones. In your chart, include a sketch of each type of volcano. Label the parts of each volcano.

B93

Assessment

Performance

Models Supply students with assorted colors of modeling clay. Working in small groups, students can fashion cross-sectional clay models of the three types of volcanoes. Students should supply as much detail as possible and be able to describe a typical eruption from each volcanic type.

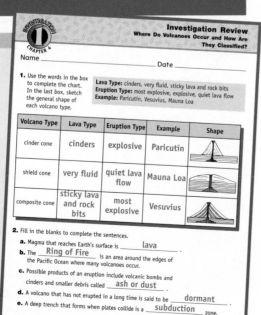

Investigation Review
Where Do Volcanoes Occur and How Are They Classified?

Name _____ Date _____

1. Use the words in the box to complete the chart. In the last box, sketch the general shape of each volcano type.

Lava Type: cinders, very fluid, sticky lava and rock bits
Eruption Type: most explosive, explosive, quiet lava flow
Example: Paricutín, Vesuvius, Mauna Loa

Volcano Type	Lava Type	Eruption Type	Example	Shape
cinder cone	cinders	explosive	Paricutín	
shield cone	very fluid	quiet lava flow	Mauna Loa	
composite cone	sticky lava and rock bits	most explosive	Vesuvius	

2. Fill in the blanks to complete the sentences.
a. Magma that reaches Earth's surface is ___lava___
b. The ___Ring of Fire___ is an area around the edges of the Pacific Ocean where many volcanoes occur.
c. Possible products of an eruption include volcanic bombs and cinders and smaller debris called ___ash or dust___
d. A volcano that has not erupted in a long time is said to be ___dormant___
e. A deep trench that forms when plates collide is a ___subduction___ zone.

Process Skills
Interpreting Data, Making a Hypothesis No; volcanoes are clustered along
Based on the data from *Worldwide Eruptions,* do volcanoes occur plate boundaries.
randomly over Earth's surface? Explain.

Critical Thinking Skills
Analyzing, Evaluating

1. Where two plates collide, one plate can descend below the other. As the plate descends, it melts to form magma. The magma rises to form a volcano.

2. Charts should show similar parts but differences in size, shape, and composition of the volcanoes.

Challenge Students can conduct research on the volcano Olympus Mons, which is located on Mars. How is it similar to volcanoes on Earth? How is it different from them?

Following Up

Baseline Assessment Return to the volcano word list the class made at the beginning of the investigation. Ask students if they would like to add to or delete anything from the list. Review how much more they know about volcanoes now than they did before they began the investigation.

Reteaching Encourage groups of students to produce a tour guide of volcanoes. Besides the main forms of volcanoes, students should include specific volcanoes, with a brief description of each one and the surrounding area.

Use *Science Notebook* p. 104.

◀ **Investigation Review**
Use Investigation Review p. 56 in the *Assessment Guide.*

HOW DO VOLCANIC ERUPTIONS AFFECT EARTH?

Planner

Subconcept Volcanic eruptions are often preceded by changes that can be detected by various instruments; eruptions produce local and worldwide effects, some of which are long-lasting.

Objectives

• **Make and use a model** of a volcano.

• **Describe** the long-term effects of an eruption.

• **Identify** some of the warning signs of an eruption.

Pacing 2–3 class periods

Science Terms island arc, seismometer

Activate Prior Knowledge

Baseline Assessment **What might be some warning signs that a volcano is going to erupt?** Record all answers on chart paper and save it for Following Up.

Activity Volcanoes You Can Eat!

Preview *Students focus on volcanic vents and should find that gases bubble through oatmeal much like gases and lava are forced through volcanic vents.*

Advance Preparation *See p. B82b.*

1. Get Ready

Time about 30 minutes

Grouping groups of 4–6

Collaborative Strategy One group member can place the ingredients in the pan while another stirs them. This activity can also be done as a whole class activity.

HOW DO VOLCANIC ERUPTIONS AFFECT EARTH?

In March 1980, a strong earthquake rocked Mount St. Helens, in the state of Washington. For the next two months steam and ash blew out. Then in May, the volcano exploded with great violence. In this investigation you'll find out what you can expect before, during, and after a volcanic eruption.

Activity

Volcanoes You Can Eat!

How is an erupting volcano like a pot of cooking oatmeal? Volcanoes erupt because liquids, solids, and gases are forced out of a hole, called a vent. Can you see a vent in a pot of oatmeal?

MATERIALS
• goggles
• measuring cup
• quick oats
• saucepan
• water
• hot plate
• mixing spoon
• oven mitt
• *Science Notebook*

SAFETY
Do this activity only under the direct supervision of your teacher. Wear goggles.

Procedure

1. Use the measuring cup to measure quick oats and water.

2. Put the oats and water into a saucepan and mix together.

3. Place the saucepan on a hot plate and set the hot plate on *Medium High*.

Responding to Individual Needs

Linguistic Activity Encourage students to say aloud any words that come to mind as they observe the boiling oatmeal. Make a list of these words as you hear them while walking around the class.

Step 4

4. After the hot plate has warmed up, stir the oats and water constantly for one minute.

5. Carefully observe the top surface of the oatmeal as it cooks. Record your observations in your *Science Notebook*.

6. After one minute, remove the oatmeal from the heat and turn off the hot plate.

Analyze and Conclude

1. What did you observe on the surface of the oatmeal as it cooked?

2. How is cooking oatmeal like an erupting volcano? How is it different?

UNIT PROJECT LINK

Have you ever dreamed of living on your own island paradise? Locate the Ring of Fire on a map and identify those islands created by volcanic activity. Predict where future volcanic islands might rise out of the ocean; indicate these areas on your map. Draw a small picture of your island paradise and describe where you think your island will emerge.

B95

Investigate Further

Unit Project Link

Students might predict that new volcanic islands will emerge near the Japanese Islands where the Pacific Plate descends below the Philippine Plate or in the South Pacific where the Pacific Plate descends below the Australian Plate. Students might also mention the Aleutian Islands as the potential site of a new volcanic island. Most students will likely associate an "island paradise" with a southern location. Have students record their predictions in their *Science Notebooks* on p. 106. Have students use Unit Project Master B3 (TRB p. 73) to help them locate the Pacific "Ring of Fire."

Safety Review safety precautions with students. Students should not put their heads directly over the cooking oatmeal. At the end of step 6, students must turn off the hot plate and remove the oatmeal from the heat. You may wish to conduct this activity in the school kitchen or home economics laboratory, where you might have more room and more than one heat source. If you prefer having only one heat source in use at a time, consider doing this activity as a class demonstration.

2. Guide the Procedure

- For best results, be sure not to cook the oatmeal too vigorously.
- **What is in the bubbles that rises to the top of the oatmeal?** Gas

 Have students record their data and answer questions on *Science Notebook* p. 105.

 Have students use the CD-ROM Spreadsheet and Grapher to organize and display their data.

3. Assess Performance

Process Skills Checklist
- Did students **measure** the ingredients correctly? Did they use 1 cup of oats and 1/2 cup of water?
- Did students understand that the cooking oatmeal was a **model** of an erupting volcano? Were they able to use the model to **make inferences** about volcanic vents?

Analyze and Conclude
1. Students should observe sputtering cavities releasing gases and some oatmeal particles.

2. The cooking oatmeal is a thick fluid, like lava and magma, that releases energy in violent spurts. The oatmeal is different in that it is not rising from the pan as lava would from a volcano. The oatmeal is not heated to the same high temperatures as magma and lava.

Mount Pinatubo

Preview *Students focus on a case study of a recent eruption of a composite cone to investigate further the effects of eruptions and methods of predicting them.*

1. Get Ready

Science Terms island arc, seismometer

Background

- Composite-cone volcanoes can erupt so explosively that millions of tons of debris are blasted high into the atmosphere. This debris can create a thin blanket that will significantly affect weather on a global scale. For example, in 1816 Mount Tambora in Indonesia exploded in one of the largest eruptions in recorded history. The volcanic debris from this eruption, as from most eruptions of this type, absorbed the Sun's shorter-length rays, causing a cooling effect. In fact, the summer of 1816 was so cool it was called "the year without a summer." That year, frost ruined crops in New England, and torrential rain ruined harvests throughout Europe.

Discussion Starter

- **What are some signs that a train is coming?** Students might mention a train whistle, sounds of the wheels on the tracks, ground vibrations, and a train schedule.

- **How might some of these signs apply to the coming of a volcanic eruption?** Students might respond that the ground might vibrate (earthquakes) before an eruption. Also, if a volcano has erupted on a somewhat regular schedule in the past, this schedule could be used to predict when the next eruption will occur.

Mount Pinatubo

THE PHILIPPINES

Mount Pinatubo, which towers over 1,900 m (6,232 ft) above sea level, is only one of about 13 active volcanoes in the Philippines. This volcano, which is located on the island of Luzon, is a composite cone. At times when it erupts, there is a sticky lava flow. At other times a combination of ash, dust, and other volcanic rock bits erupt from the volcano.

Mount Pinatubo and the other volcanoes in the Philippines formed as a result of tectonic activity. The Philippine Islands are a part of the Ring of Fire.

You already know that at some convergent plate boundaries, one oceanic plate collides with another oceanic plate. At such boundaries, one plate goes down deep into Earth's mantle. As the plate is dragged down, it bends, and a deep canyon, or ocean trench, forms. As this oceanic plate descends into the asthenosphere, parts of the plate melt, forming magma. The magma then rises and forms a chain of volcanoes called **island arcs**. The islands that make up the Philippines are a mature island arc system that formed long ago when two oceanic plates collided.

There She Blows!

After being dormant for over six centuries, Mount Pinatubo began to erupt in mid-June of 1991. As the eruption began, brilliant lightning bolts colored the skies above the volcano. Within minutes, these same skies were black because of the enormous amounts of ash, dust, and gases that spurted from the mountain. Scientists estimate that the mountain's violent eruption had a force equal to that of 2,000 to 3,000 exploding atomic bombs! The ash clouds produced by the eruption polluted the air so much that astronauts out in space in the space shuttle could not get a clear view of Earth's surface!

This period of volcanic activity lasted for several months and stopped in early September 1991. The first eruption

Two oceanic plates colliding at their boundaries ▼

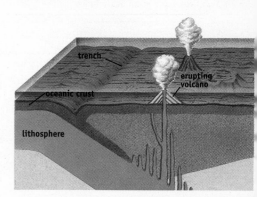

B96

Integrating the Curriculum

Science & Language Arts

Use newspapers or magazine articles about the eruption of Mount Pinatubo on June 15, 1991.

What to Do Students can work in groups to write and tell stories about Mount Pinatubo. They can develop some fictional human-interest stories, perhaps focusing on an act of heroism in the midst of the disaster.

What's the Result? Let students share their stories with the class or develop dramatic skits, which can be performed.

Multi-Age Classroom Use the abilities of all students to collaborate on ideas for their stories. Delegate responsibilities for researching, writing, illustrating, and acting.

destroyed about 42,000 houses and nearly 100,000 acres of farmland. Over 900 people died. Much of the damage and many of the deaths were caused by flowing mud and hot volcanic material. Also, masses of gas, ash, and igneous rock called pumice covered many villages at and near the base of Mount Pinatubo.

The cause of the 1991 eruption of Mount Pinatubo is not completely understood. It is likely that many months prior to the eruption, magma began forcing its way up through the lithosphere. Slowly the magma made its way toward the surface. As it snaked along its path, the magma increased temperatures and pressures beneath the mountain. In some places the magma crept into cracks in the bedrock, causing the bedrock to swell. On June 15, 1991, the mountain erupted, sending clouds of gases and tons of lava to Earth's surface.

Mount Pinatubo's Warning Signs

Earthquakes and volcanoes are more common in some parts of the world than

JUNE 19-27,1991

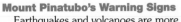
AUGUST 8-14, 1991

▲ **Effect of the eruption of Mount Pinatubo. The yellow band shows how volcanic debris travels around the globe and extends over time.**

in others. Both are closely related to the movements of tectonic plates. Scientists monitor earthquake- and volcano-prone areas for changes. But the exact time of volcanic eruptions can be difficult to predict accurately. Fortunately, in the case of Mount Pinatubo, the mountain "cooperated." There were many warnings of its explosive 1991 eruption.

First, there was an earthquake that shook the area in July 1990. There is

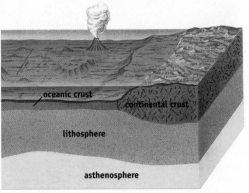
oceanic crust
continental crust
lithosphere
asthenosphere

INVESTIGATE FURTHER!

RESEARCH

Find out about another famous volcano in the Philippines called Mount Mayon. Where is it located? How do you think this volcano formed? When did it last erupt? What kind of volcano is it?

B97

Science & Social Studies

PHILIPPINES **What to Do** Show students a world map and have them locate the Philippines. Encourage interested students to form groups to research the geography, history, and culture of the islands. Suggest that they find out how the presence of volcanoes affects the lives of the islands' inhabitants.

What's the Result? Groups can then share their findings with the rest of the class. Some groups might describe a typical meal of the Philippines or share information with the class about some of the more unusual fruits found on the islands.

Multi-Age Classroom Students can decide together what they will research and develop ways of presenting their work.

2. Guide the Discussion

Choose from the following strategies to facilitate discussion.

Identifying and Solving Problems

- **How could you demonstrate that two oceanic plates form an ocean trench when they collide?** Students could simply bring their hands together with the fingertips touching and show how the fingers moved down, forming a V-shaped "trench." Students could also push together two sheets of paper, demonstrating the formation of a trench.

Connecting to the Activities

- ***Volcanoes You Can Eat!, p. B94***
  How is the description of the eruption of Mt. Pinatubo similar to the bubbling oatmeal in the activity? Students may draw a parallel between the "sputtering" of gases, ash, and dust as described in the text and the sputtering nature of the boiling oatmeal. **Based on similarities you observed, what can you infer about the kind of lava erupting from Mt. Pinatubo?** The lava is thick and sticky, much like the oatmeal.

Responding to Individual Needs

Visual/Spatial Activity Show students an aerial picture of Manhattan. Then tell them that the ash and rocks from the Mount Pinatubo eruption would have covered all of Manhattan to a depth of 305 m (about 1000 ft). Only the tops of the tallest skyscrapers would have remained visible through the debris.

Thinking Critically

 What might happen to the surface of a volcano as magma rises through the vent? Students might suggest that the volcanic mountain would shake and perhaps bulge. Point out these changes if students do not suggest them.

 Suppose these changes are too slight to feel or see. How could scientists tell if they occurred? Students might say that instruments could detect changes too slight for people to sense.

Making Inferences

 What do you think might cause an earthquake to happen shortly before a volcanic eruption? As magma forces its way up through the crust, the magma pushes against the bedrock and could cause the rock to shift, causing an earthquake.

Drawing Conclusions

• **Why didn't sulfur dioxide gas from Mount Pinatubo stay in the atmosphere only above the volcano?** Air currents in the upper atmosphere carried it around the globe.

3. Assess Understanding

Students can work in small groups to produce a fictional short story describing what a person living near a composite-cone volcano experiences as it erupts. In their stories, they can describe life before the eruption and talk about clues the volcano might have given that an eruption was about to occur.

◄ Clouds and gases rise from Mount Pinatubo.

the 1991 eruption. Its lava dome, a bulge that is produced when sticky lava is slowly squeezed from a volcano's vent, had doubled in size in a little over two months!

Because the volcano gave these warning signs, many lives were saved. For several months before the explosion, scientists explained what the mountain was doing and urged people to leave the area. Over 200,000 people had been safely evacuated before the explosion.

What Goes Up Must Come Down—But When?

Before the eruption, instruments aboard weather satellites monitored the atmosphere above the volcano. These instruments were looking for increases in the amount of sulfur dioxide in the air around the composite cone. About two weeks before the explosion, the amount of sulfur dioxide was ten times what it

often a relationship between earthquake activity and later volcanic activity. In April 1991, small clouds of smoke and ash were forced from cracks along the mountain's slopes. These clouds prompted earth scientists from the Philippines and the United States to more closely monitor the majestic Pinatubo.

Watching Pinatubo

Two kinds of measuring devices—seismometers and tiltmeters—were put into place near the mountain and then connected to computers. A **seismometer** is an instrument that detects Earth's movements. These movements can indicate that a volcano is preparing to blow its top! A tiltmeter measures any change in the slope of an area. Installing these devices allowed scientists to note any bulges in the mountain's slopes. Such bulges indicate the presence of magma and/or gases welling up into the volcano. In fact, Mount Pinatubo did bulge before

Evacuation of people before the eruption of Mount Pinatubo ▶

B98

Investigate Further

Science, Technology & Society

DISASTERS **What to Do** Encourage students to explain in their own words how so many lives were saved before the eruption of Mount Pinatubo. Stress the role that communication plays in such a disaster. Guide students to understand that the most advanced and the best scientists in the world cannot prevent the disastrous effects of a catastrophe if vital information is not communicated effectively to the public.
What's the Result? **Why might people choose to stay in their homes after being warned of a coming disaster?** Some people may think the danger has been exaggerated. Some people might be curious and want to witness the event. Others feel their home is the safest place to be.

had been the month before. This increase was another warning that Mount Pinatubo might erupt.

These same instruments measured the amount of sulfur dioxide that had been spewed out into the air during the eruption. About 15 to 20 million tons of this gas blew nearly 40 km (about 25 mi) into the air! This gas combined with other gases in the air and formed a thin layer of sulfuric acid droplets that circled the globe within about three weeks.

Mount Pinatubo, like other active volcanoes, is a source of pollution. The dust, gases, and ash spewed out in 1991 had several effects on Earth and its atmosphere. First, vivid sunsets colored the skies in many places far removed from the Philippines.

Second, the sulfuric acid droplets remained above the planet for a few years following the eruption. The droplets reflected back into space about 2 percent of the Sun's energy that normally reached Earth's surface. This in turn led to a global cooling of about 1°C (1.2°F). This short period of cooling reversed a global warming trend for a short time. The warming

▲ Sunset after the 1991 eruption of Mount Pinatubo

trend is caused by the collection of gases that trap the Sun's heat. This effect, called the greenhouse effect, is the result of natural climatic changes and human activities, such as burning fossil fuels and cutting down forests.

Another effect of the 1991 eruption of Mount Pinatubo is that the 30 to 40 million tons of sulfuric acid added to the air may speed up the breakdown of Earth's ozone layer. The ozone layer in the upper atmosphere protects you and Earth's other inhabitants from harmful solar rays. ■

─── INVESTIGATION 2 ───

1. Using Mount Pinatubo as your example, explain how volcanic eruptions can have long-term effects on the planet.

2. Describe some of the events that may occur and some measurements that may be taken to alert scientists to a coming volcanic eruption.

B99

Assessment

Portfolio

Defend Your Position Invite students to pretend they are scientists trying to convince government officials that a volcanic eruption will occur in the near future. They must write a letter to a mayor, governor, or president stating facts and professional opinions.

Investigation Review
How Do Volcanic Eruptions Affect Earth?

Name _____ Date _____

INVESTIGATION 2 CHAPTER 4

1. Circle the letter of the correct answer for each of the following questions.
   A. Chains of volcanoes, such as those forming the Philippine Islands, were formed when two plates collided and one was dragged under the other. These chains are called ____.
   a. subduction volcanoes   **c.** island arcs
   b. intermittent volcanoes   **d.** rifts

   B. Before its 1991 eruption, Mount Pinatubo gave certain warning signs. Which of the following was not a warning sign?
   a. The lava dome doubled in size.
   b. An earthquake preceded the eruption.
   c. Smoke and ash were forced from cracks on the slopes.
   d. The air temperature increased by about 10°C throughout the area.

2. Circle the letter of each statement that describes how the eruption of Mt. Pinatubo affected Earth.
   a. Dust blown into the atmosphere produced vivid sunsets.
   b. Tsunamis were produced throughout the Pacific Ocean.
   c. Sulfuric acid droplets from the eruption reflected solar energy into space, lowering Earth's temperature by 1°C.
   d. Movement of the Pacific Plate was reversed.

Process Skills
Making and Using a Model, Analyzing
Compare the eruption of a volcano to the boiling process used in *Volcanoes You Can Eat!*. Write your answer on a separate sheet of paper.

Heated oatmeal moves upward to the surface just as magma moves up through a volcano. "Eruptions" of vapor occur throughout the oatmeal, just as gases escape from the volcanic lava.

Close
the Investigation

Critical Thinking Skills
Analyzing, Evaluating, Solving Problems

1. Gases from the volcano form sulfuric acid droplets that stay in the atmosphere for years and block some of the Sun's energy, lowering the global temperature. The sulfuric acid also speeds up the breakdown of the ozone layer.

2. Earthquakes, changes in the volcano's slopes, and an increase in sulfur dioxide gas released from the volcano could indicate a future eruption. Seismometers measure earthquakes by measuring earth movements. Tiltmeters measure changes in a volcano's slopes. Instruments on weather satellites measure the amount of gases in the atmosphere.

Challenge Have students find out more about major composite-cone volcano eruptions. How have they affected the environment? How were humans affected by the eruption?

Following Up

Baseline Assessment Return to the responses the class gave about possible warning signs of an eruption. Give students an opportunity to revise their responses based on their new knowledge.

Reteaching Encourage students to compare and contrast the eruptions of Mount Pinatubo and Surtsey. Students may wish to make a table that compares causes and characteristics of the two volcanoes.

Use *Science Notebook* p.108.

◄ **Investigation Review**
Use Investigation Review p. 57 in the *Assessment Guide*.

IN WHAT OTHER PLACES CAN VOLCANOES OCCUR?

Planner

Subconcept Hot spots, sources of magma deep in the asthenosphere, may produce volcanic islands in the middle of tectonic plates and provide clues to the direction and speed of the movement of plates; volcanoes also occur at the margins of rifting continental plates.

Objectives

- **Infer** the existence of a hot spot forming the volcanoes that built the Hawaiian Islands.
- **Describe** how robots can explore volcanoes.
- **Explain** what is happening in the Great Rift Valley.

Pacing 3–4 class periods

Science Terms hot spot, caldera, rifting

Activate Prior Knowledge

Baseline Assessment Let students draw a diagram of a volcanic island underwater and how it formed. Save for Following Up.

Activity How Hawaii Formed

Preview *Students focus on the formation of the volcanic Hawaiian Islands by the progressive movement of a tectonic plate over a hot spot. They should find that the Pacific Plate is moving toward the northwest, making the islands on the southeast end of the chain the youngest.*

1. Get Ready

Time about 40 minutes

Grouping groups of 4–6

Multi-Age Strategy Group members can take turns measuring and calculating. Encourage all students to check their partner's calculations. Some students may need help subtracting to find the age differences between the islands.

IN WHAT OTHER PLACES CAN VOLCANOES OCCUR?

So far, you have learned that volcanoes can occur along mid-ocean ridges and where one tectonic plate is descending under another. In this investigation you'll explore two other kinds of places where volcanoes can occur.

Activity

How Hawaii Formed

MATERIALS
- metric ruler
- map of the Hawaiian Islands, showing volcanoes
- calculator
- *Science Notebook*

Geologists have a hypothesis that magma rising from a large chamber of molten rock—called a hot spot—deep below the Pacific Plate has built the volcanic islands that make up the state of Hawaii. In this activity you'll examine some of their evidence.

Procedure

1. Measure the distance between the center of the island of Hawaii and the center of each of the other islands. Record this information in your *Science Notebook*. Use the map scale to find out how far apart the centers are.

2. The table on this page tells you the estimated age of the rock on each island. Record the youngest island and the oldest island.

3. Make a chart that shows the age difference between Hawaii and each of the other islands.

B100

THE HAWAIIAN ISLANDS	
Island	**Estimated Age of Rock**
Maui	1.63 million years
Molokai	1.84 million years
Oahu	2.9 million years
Kauai	5.1 million years
Hawaii	375,000 years
Lanai	1.28 million years
Niihau	5.5 million years
Kahoolawe	1.03 million years

Responding to Individual Needs

Students Acquiring English Say and write the names of the compass directions while pointing them out on the map. Include not only the four main directions, but also combinations such as northeast and southwest. Give some practical uses of such directions. Students from the Pacific Islands might help others with the names of the Hawaiian Islands.

Kauai

Mount
Waialeale

Niihau

Oahu

*Diamond
Head*

Molokai

Maui

Lanai

Kahoolawe

Haleakala

HAWAIIAN
ISLANDS

0   30 mi
0   50 km

*Pacific
Ocean*

N

Hawaii

*Mauna
Loa*

▲ The Hawaiian Islands

Analyze and Conclude

1. Based on your measurements, how far apart are the Hawaiian Islands?

2. Which island is the youngest? Which is the oldest?

3. If the hot spot under the islands stayed in the same place and the Pacific Plate moved over it, the hot spot may have created one island after another. In which direction does this show the Pacific Plate moving?

4. Based on the dates of formation of Hawaii and Kauai, what was the speed of the plate's movement?

5. Would you say that the Pacific Plate moves at a nearly constant speed, or does its speed change from time to time? What evidence supports your conclusion?

> **INVESTIGATE FURTHER!**
>
> **RESEARCH**
>
> Look at a map of Earth's surface features. Observe the northwestward underwater extension of the Hawaiian Islands. Notice that there is an abrupt northward bend where the Hawaiian chain meets the Emperor Seamount chain. What do you think this bend means?

B101

Investigate Further

Research

Students may suggest that when the Emperor Seamount chain was being formed, the Pacific Plate was moving in a more northerly direction. Students should record their ideas in their *Science Notebooks* on p. 111.

Materials Hint Use Activity Support Master B9 (TRB p. 50).

Safety Review safety precautions with students.

2. Guide the Procedure

• For step 3, students should start with the island of Hawaii and compute the age differences between Hawaii and each of the other islands.

Have students record their data and answer questions on *Science Notebook* pp. 109–110.

Students can use the CD-ROM Spreadsheet and Grapher to organize and display their data.

3. Assess Performance

Process Skills Checklist

• Did students **measure** the distances between the islands correctly and consistently? Did they measure from the center of each island?

• Were the **calculations** done carefully and correctly? Did students convert numbers to like units when subtracting thousands from millions?

• Were students' **inferences** reasonable? Were they based on students' calculations?

Analyze and Conclude

1. Hawaii to Maui—155 km (about 96 mi); Hawaii to Kahoolawe—about 155 km (about 96 mi); Hawaii to Lanai—about 200 km (about 124 mi); Hawaii to Molokai—about 225 km (about 140 mi); Hawaii to Oahu—about 330 km (about 205 mi); Hawaii to Kauai—about 505 km (about 314 mi); Hawaii to Niihau—about 550 km (about 342 mi). Distances will vary based on the accuracy of students' measurements and their estimate of the "center" of each island.

2. Hawaii is the youngest. Niihau is the oldest.

3. Northwest

4. About 11 cm/yr (about 4 1/2 in.)

5. The plate has slightly changed speed from time to time, based on the ages of the islands and the distances between them.

An Island in the Making

Preview *Students focus on the formation of volcanic islands at hot spots.*

1. Get Ready

Science Terms   hot spot, caldera

Background

• Most of Earth's volcanoes occur along the boundaries of tectonic plates. A few, such as those forming the chain of Hawaiian Islands, occur over so-called "hot spots." A hot spot is a plume of magma that originates in Earth's mantle and burns through the crust like a blowtorch burning through metal. The hot spot remains fixed, while the tectonic plate over it moves. Hot spots may originate near the boundary between the core and the mantle. When the plumes of the hot spot reach the surface, lower pressure causes the rock to melt, creating the magma that forms volcanoes.

Discussion Starter

• **How do you think volcanoes might form where there are no plate boundaries?** Students may speculate that the crust is thinner and/or weaker in these places.

 Look at a map of the Hawaiian Islands and the Emperor Seamounts. What do you notice about them? Students might notice the linear nature between the Hawaiian Islands and Emperor Seamounts. They might speculate that the seamounts were once islands and that they and the Hawaiian Islands had the same origin.

An Island in the Making

Hot Spots

Recall that the theory of plate tectonics states that slabs of Earth's crust and upper mantle move slowly over the planet's surface. Convection currents in the partly melted mantle, or asthenosphere, are thought to drive plate motion.

Most of Earth's volcanoes are found along convergent and divergent plate boundaries. But recently, scientists discovered that volcanoes can also form in the middle of a tectonic plate. **Hot spots** are extremely hot places deep within Earth's mantle. The magma that forms at these spots slowly rises toward the surface because the magma is less dense than the surrounding material. Scientists have evidence that most of the 120 known hot spots don't move. Rather, as a plate moves over a hot spot, the magma wells up and breaks through the crust to form a volcano, as shown in the drawings on this page.

Formation of the Hawaiian Islands

Pele is the mythical goddess of Hawaiian volcanoes. Native legends state that volcanic eruptions along the island chain are caused when the goddess is angry. She supposedly takes her Pa'oa, a magic stick, and pokes it into the ground, unearthing the fires below. The

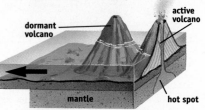

① As a plate passes over a hot spot, a volcano is formed.

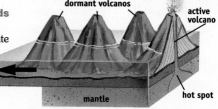

② When the plate moves, the old volcano becomes inactive and a new volcano forms over the hot spot and becomes active.

③ The plate keeps moving and the process continues.

B102

Integrating the Curriculum

Science & Language Arts

LEGENDS

What to Do Legends of the goddess Pele offer interesting explanations for the formation of the Hawaiian volcanoes. Although people know the scientific explanations, the stories still occupy an important place in Hawaiian culture. Encourage students to investigate the Hawaiian legends and to write one of their own that explains the formation of the Hawaiian Island chain. Challenge students to write a moral into their legends.

What's the Result? Let students share their legends.

Multi-Age Classroom Working in small groups, students can collaborate on researching Hawaiian legends and share the task of writing and presenting their stories.

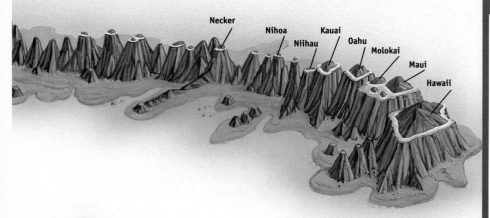

Necker Nihoa Kauai
Niihau Oahu
Molokai
Maui
Hawaii

▲ The chain of Hawaiian islands. The islands are the tips of volcanoes that have slowly built up from underwater eruptions.

▲ Pele

islands are said to have been formed when Pele and her sister, Namakaokahai, had a bitter argument. As the sisters quarreled, Pele moved from island to island and dug fire pits—the Hawaiian volcanoes themselves. Pele is said to have first used her Pa'oa on Kauai. Then she fled to Oahu, Molokai, Maui, and finally to the "Big Island," Hawaii. Legend says that Pele now lives at the summit of Kilauea on Hawaii. How is this legend similar to the data you worked with in the activity "How Hawaii Formed"?

Scientists have evidence that the Hawaiian Islands formed as the Pacific Plate slowly moved northwestward over a hot spot beneath the Pacific Ocean. A chain of volcanic islands, each developing as the plate moved over the hot spot on the ocean floor, formed over millions of years. This chain of islands, which is made up of over 80 large volcanoes, is

called the Hawaiian Ridge–Emperor Seamount Chain. A seamount is a volcanic peak that rises at least 1,000 m (3,300 ft) above the ocean floor. The Emperor Seamounts, which now lie beneath the ocean's surface, were once islands. They have been eroded by wind and waves. The oldest seamount in the chain is 74 million years old.

The Hawaiian Ridge–Emperor Seamount Chain stretches northwest from the island of Hawaii and then north to the Aleutian Trench, off the coast of Kamchatka. The Hawaiian Ridge segment alone, which includes the Hawaiian Islands, is about 2,560 km (1,590 mi) long! Scientists estimate that the amount of lava thrust out to form this volcanic ridge was enough to cover the entire state of California with a blanket of lava 1.6 km (1 mi) thick!

B103

Science & Social Studies

YELLOWSTONE **What to Do** A hot spot exists under Yellowstone National Park. Students who have visited the park or who know of it might share their knowledge of the volcanic features there. Have the students find resource books about Yellowstone National Park. Invite students to put together a multimedia presentation of what causes the geysers, hot springs, mudpots, and other volcanic features at Yellowstone. They should include a map and photographs, if possible.

What's the Result? How might people use the heat energy that lies below Yellowstone? People could extract the steam to turn the turbines of electric generators or to heat water.

2. Guide the Discussion

Choose from the following strategies to facilitate discussion.

Thinking About the Data

• **Look at the drawings on p. B102. In the second and third drawings, point out the island that is in the first drawing.** Students should point out the farthest island on the left in the second and third drawings.

Thinking Critically

Why can volcanoes be called "windows to Earth?" Since the magma that forms volcanoes is generated deep within the mantle, scientists are able to infer the temperatures, pressures, and composition of these areas within Earth.

Making Inferences

If the Emperor Seamounts and the Hawaiian Islands are all part of a continuous chain, why do you think the Emperors are below the ocean's surface, while the Hawaiian Islands are above it? Encourage students to examine the chain from Hawaii to Koko Seamount. They may suggest that the Emperor Seamounts have been exposed to erosion from waves and currents for a longer time, and volcanism no longer replaces the eroded material.

Responding to Individual Needs

Visual/Spatial Activity Guide students to use their arms to visualize the process of a plate moving over a hot spot. With one hand pointing up (hot spot), have them sweep their other arm over it slowly (moving plate).

Connecting to the Activities

- *How Hawaii Formed, p. B100*

 In the activity, you discovered that the **Hawaiian Islands were formed one after the other as the Pacific Plate moved toward the northwest. What do you think will happen in the future on the island of Hawaii and just southeast of Hawaii?** Students may suggest that the volcanoes on the island of Hawaii will become extinct, and a new island will form to the southeast with its own active volcanoes.

Thinking Critically

- **Why are the Hawaiian Islands a perfect place for studying volcanoes?** The nonviolent flows allow scientists to get very close to a volcano with far less risk than they could during the eruption of a stickier lava flow. Therefore, they can monitor the temperature, composition, and behavior of the flow. It's also a convenient place because of the ample opportunities to study an active volcano.

Thinking About the Data

- **How deep is the ocean at Loihi?** Students should add the height of Loihi (3,300 m) to the depth of water above Loihi (1,000 m) for a total depth of about 4,300 m, or 14,100 ft.

Making Judgments

 Would you like to explore Loihi in the *Sea Cliff* if you had the chance? Why or why not? Students may be drawn by the technology, adventure, and curiosity of exploring a new feature in the ocean. Others may be concerned about the dangers of exploring an underwater volcano.

◀ DSV *Sea Cliff*, used to study underwater volcanoes

Loihi—A New Island in the Making

The Hawaiian hot spot, which lies deep beneath the Pacific Ocean floor, currently feeds the volcanoes Mauna Loa and Kilauea on the island of Hawaii.

Recently a new seamount was discovered, forming off the southern coast of Hawaii. This underwater volcano, or seamount, is called Loihi (lō ē′hē).

Loihi towers about 3,300 m (10,820 ft) above the ocean floor. Only about 1,000 m (3,280 ft) of salty water covers this young volcano. Scientists don't expect Loihi to poke above the water's surface for at least another 50,000 years. To study the newly emerging member of the Hawaiian volcanic chain, scientists have used a submarine, the DSV *Sea Cliff*, to take pictures of the events as they unfold.

Photographs of Loihi taken by cameras aboard the submarine show fresh pillow lavas and talus blocks. Pillow lava is lava formed when there is an undersea eruption. The rock formed is rounded, looking somewhat like piles of pillows. Pillow lavas form when the extremely hot lava erupts into the cold ocean waters, which quickly cool the lava. Talus blocks, which are also linked with "fresh" eruptions, are large angular pieces of rock that slide down a mountain's slope and pile up at the base of the structure.

Maps made of the area surrounding the new volcano show that Loihi is similar to some of its sister volcanoes—Mauna Loa and Kilauea. It is gently sloping and has a flat top. A **caldera**, or large circular depression, with a diameter of about 5 km (3 mi) lies within the volcano's summit. Cracking, followed by the formation of new ocean crust, is occurring along the sides of the volcano. The exact age of this new volcano is not yet known. Scientists have hypothesized, though, that the volcano is only a few hundred years old.

Within a few years, scientists are hoping to get an even better view of Loihi. They plan to use optical cables to monitor the eruptions taking place as they happen. These cables will connect an underwater observatory with an onshore observatory. The cables will then transmit

The caldera of a volcano ▶

Investigate Further

STS Science, Technology & Society

MONITORING **What to Do** Encourage students to work in groups to locate resource material on Hawaii and to find out more about the monitoring stations at the Hawaiian volcanoes. They might want to use their information to make plaster of Paris models of the volcanoes indicating the locations of the monitoring stations.

What's the Result? **What might you like about being a volcanologist? What might you dislike about it?** Students might enjoy working outdoors and on site in different places, exploring the unknown, using the various instruments, developing new ones, and helping society by working to predict eruptions. Students might not like working outdoors in harsh or potentially dangerous—even life-threatening—conditions.

information from the various instruments monitoring the volcano. Seismometers will also be put in place near the volcano. Perhaps even a small submarine rover will crawl around the ocean floor to witness history in the making!

Risk of Eruptions

Because the eruptions of the Hawaiian volcanoes are quiet flows, scientists have been able to study these volcanoes at close range without much danger. In fact, the volcanoes that make up the islands of Hawaii are probably some of the most closely studied volcanoes in the world. Look at the map showing the risk of volcanic eruptions in Hawaii. Which part of the Big Island seems to be the most dangerous? Why?

Perhaps because they are two of the youngest and most active volcanoes in the Hawaiian Ridge chain, Mauna Loa and Kilauea are closely watched. Study the bar graphs below. Which of the two volcanoes has erupted more often? ■

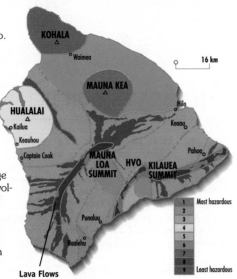

▲ Map of Hawaii, showing risk of volcanic eruptions

Eruptions of Mauna Loa and Kilauea compared ▼

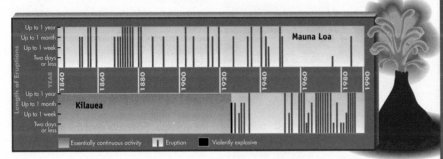

B105

Using the Trade Book

What to Do Cropland on Hawaii is periodically destroyed by lava flows from volcanic eruptions. Find out more about volcanic hazards by reading *Volcanoes and Earthquakes* by Basil Booth. After students read about the various short-term and long-term hazards from volcanoes, suggest that they create their own stories about living near volcanoes. Have students focus on a particular eruption mentioned in the book, providing information about the episode.

What's the Result? Let students present their stories to the class. Encourage them to comment on whether loss of life and property could have been prevented if people had been forewarned of the dangers.

Multi-Age Classroom Have students brainstorm ideas for elements to be included in their stories.

Drawing Conclusions

▪ Direct students' attention to the graphs of Mauna Loa's and Kilauea's eruptions and ask: **Why does Kilauea seem to be more active in recent years than Mauna Loa?** Students might hypothesize that the plate has moved enough to remove Mauna Loa from the main source of magma over the hot spot.

▪ **Does this graph provide enough information to confirm your hypothesis?** Probably not **What makes you say so?** More time is needed to determine whether Mauna Loa is definitely showing a pattern of less activity.

Responding to Individual Needs

Students Acquiring English Have students make a list of resource key terms, such as *hot spots, volcanoes, dormant, active,* and *plate tectonics.* Then encourage them to organize the terms by linking related terms together. It may help students to write a brief description of each term to clarify their meanings.

3. Assess Understanding

Working in pairs, let students explain to each other how the Hawaiian Islands formed. Students could use diagrams, maps, hand motions, and any other materials to facilitate their explanations.

Using Robots to Investigate Volcanoes

Preview *Students focus on recent technology used to study volcanoes.*

1. Get Ready

Background

- One of the toughest design problems in making mobile robots like Dante is how to move it over rough terrain. One approach to this problem is to use wheels, but they're difficult to maneuver in extremely rocky areas. Treads, such as those on a tank, work better over rough terrain, but they're difficult to maneuver in tight spaces. Another option is to mimic the Animal Kingdom and design legs. While fulfilling all of the requirements for maneuverability, scientists found it is extremely difficult to coordinate the complex movements of the different legs. The research team at Carnegie-Mellon was successful, thanks to sophisticated software and years of research by people around the world.

Discussion Starter

- **How could a robot be useful in studying volcanoes?** Students will probably suggest that robots can withstand the extreme heat near lava flows and in volcanic craters. Using robots eliminates the risk to human life in the event of a sudden eruption.

Using Robots to Investigate Volcanoes

 What has eight legs and a "nerve cord" that sends and receives messages, is over 3 m (9.84 ft) tall, weighs about 772 kg (1,698 lb), and costs nearly $2 million? Give up? It's Dante, a series of robots designed by computer scientists at Carnegie-Mellon University, in Pittsburgh, Pennsylvania.

Dante II exploring a volcano in Anchorage, Alaska ▼

B106

Dante was named after a fourteenth-century poet who wrote a poem in which he spends some time traveling through fiery regions deep within Earth. During a part of his mythical journey, Dante is led by a ghost named Virgil. Because the scientists send their robots into the fiery depths of volcanoes, they thought it appropriate to name the robots Dante. A transporter robot called Virgil carries Dante along some stretches of its journeys.

The first version of Dante was designed to help volcanologists explore one of the most active volcanoes on Earth—Mount Erebus, a smoldering 3,790-m (12,431-ft) volcano on Antarctica. A kink in one of the robot's cables, however, stopped the robot from going deeper than 6 m (about 20 ft) into the volcano. Although it couldn't complete its mission, Dante proved that it could tackle similar future assignments.

Dante II made its debut in Anchorage, Alaska, where scientists used this improved robot to explore Alaska's active Mount Spurr. The robot could descend slowly but surely 100 m (330 ft) into the volcano. It was able to produce a three-dimensional map of the rugged terrain of the crater's floor. Dante II could also collect and analyze gases being emitted from the volcano. Scientists used the information to infer that Mount Spurr will probably remain dormant for some time.

Investigate Further

Science, Technology & Society

 ROBOT FAIR **What to Do** Challenge students to design their own robots by using clay, pipe cleaners, glue, construction paper, and similar materials. They can work in groups to design and build a model of a robot. Students should think about what they want the robot to do and then design it to accomplish those tasks. Hold a robot fair so that groups can share their creations. They should demonstrate what the robots do and explain how they can be of benefit.

What's the Result? Ask: **Which robot did you like best? Why?** Elicit responses other than those having to do with aesthetics. Students might be impressed with a robot that is designed to handle delicate objects as well as to be powerful.

The Amazing Dante II, A Volcano-Exploring Robot

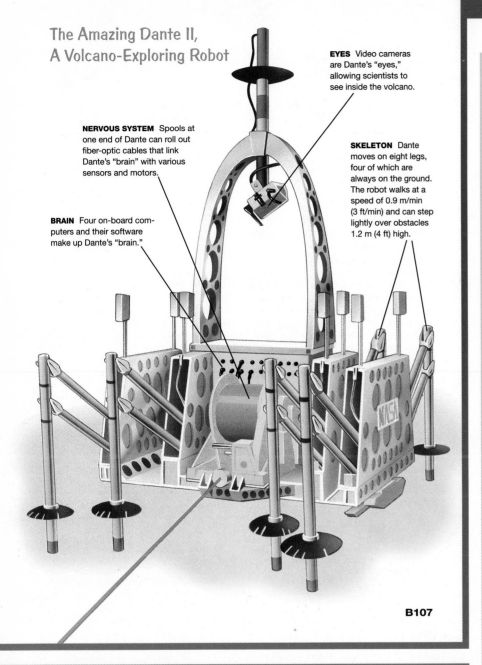

EYES Video cameras are Dante's "eyes," allowing scientists to see inside the volcano.

NERVOUS SYSTEM Spools at one end of Dante can roll out fiber-optic cables that link Dante's "brain" with various sensors and motors.

SKELETON Dante moves on eight legs, four of which are always on the ground. The robot walks at a speed of 0.9 m/min (3 ft/min) and can step lightly over obstacles 1.2 m (4 ft) high.

BRAIN Four on-board computers and their software make up Dante's "brain."

B107

Integrating the Curriculum

Science & Language Arts

ROBOT

What to Do Students might enjoy writing poems about Dante. Poems could focus on the robot itself, what Dante does, where it goes, how it might help society, or a combination of these elements. Encourage a variety of poetic styles.

What's the Result? Encourage students to read their poems aloud for the class. Compile the poems in a booklet or display them for the rest of the school to see.

Multi-Age Classroom Students can pool their poems and make a booklet of robot poems. The students can read their poems to each other and talk about what they have created.

2. Guide the Discussion

Choose from the following strategies to facilitate discussion.

Making Comparisons

- **What does Dante remind you of?** Most students will probably say Dante reminds them of a spider because of its eight legs.

Responding to Individual Needs

Kinesthetic Activity Students can demonstrate the stability that Dante's eight-legged design provides. Imitating a spider, students can "walk their hands" across the desktop, lifting one or two fingers at a time. They should observe how having some fingers on the desktop at all times provides stability as their hands walk across the surface.

Making Inferences

What are some of the problems with extremely complicated machines like Dante? Students may suggest high cost and a likelihood of mechanical failure, as in the first Dante mission. Coordinating all of the robot's systems becomes very difficult.

Connecting to the Activities

- *How Hawaii Formed, p. B100*
  How could Dante or another robot be used to investigate the Loihi Seamount in Hawaii? Students may have a variety of ideas, but they will probably include going to the sea floor and sampling lava and rocks.

3. Assess Understanding

Pairs of students can make a list of the advantages and disadvantages of using robots instead of humans to explore volcanoes.

Great Rift Valley of Africa

Preview *Students focus on the concept of rifting as a tectonic process that forms volcanoes.*

1. Get Ready

Science Terms rifting

Background

- The African Great Rift Valley is a region of special interest to anthropologists. The remains of a female hominid (an ancester of *Homo sapiens*) was found on November 30, 1974, in this region. She is speculated to have lived 3 million years ago. Anthropologist Donald Johanson named his find "Lucy." She is thought to have stood erect, walked on two legs, and was a little over a meter tall.

Discussion Starter

🔲 **The Red Sea is the beginning of an ocean. How can that be?** Direct students' attention to a map of plate boundaries as a clue. They should be able to recognize that a spreading boundary goes through the Red Sea, where new crust is forming and the Red Sea is widening.

2. Guide the Discussion

Choose from the following strategies to facilitate discussion.

Connecting to the Activities

- *How Hawaii Formed, p. B100*
  Compare and contrast formation of the Hawaiian Islands with formation of new crust at rift valleys and mid-ocean ridges. Hot spots are unusually hot regions of the mantle that cause volcano formation. As moving tectonic plates slide over them, island chains form, but only one small area of growth occurs at a time. Divergent boundaries are places where plates separate. Volcanoes emerge through cracks, forming new crust along an extended area as the plates move apart.

Great Rift Valley of Africa

Rifting

What happens if you slowly pull on some silicon putty? The putty stretches, sags, and often breaks. The process of rifting is similar to your stretching the putty.

Rifting is a process that occurs at divergent plate boundaries. As two plates separate, hot magma in the asthenosphere oozes upward to fill the newly formed gap. In general, rifting occurs along mid-ocean ridges deep beneath the oceans. Rifting along mid-ocean ridges leads to the process of sea-floor spreading. Some rifting, however, occurs where two continental plates are moving apart. When rifting occurs on land, the continental crust breaks up, or splits. Study the drawings on these two pages. What eventually forms when rifting occurs in continental crust?

The Great African Rift System

Over the past 25 million to 30 million years, continental rifting has been pulling eastern Africa apart—at the rate of several centimeters per decade. Jokes a Djibouti geologist, "[We are] Africa's fastest-growing nation!" Three rifts—the East African Rift, one in the Gulf of Aden, and a third in the Red Sea—form a 5,600-km-long (3,472-mi-long) system known as the Great Rift Valley. The place where the three rift systems meet is called the Afar Triangle, named after the people who live in the region.

The Great Rift Valley is the place

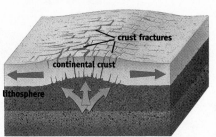

1 Magma produced by Earth's mantle rises through the crust, lifts it up, and causes fractures in the crust.

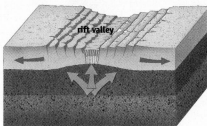

2 The crust pulls apart, faults open, and blocks of crust fall inward. Volcanoes begin to erupt. A rift valley forms.

B108

Integrating the Curriculum

Science & Math

RIFTING RATES **What to Do** Graphing is an important way to understand the relationships between numbers. Have students make a graph of the rifting rate of the Red Sea versus time. Assume that the Red Sea is growing at a constant 0.3 cm/year. Students should start at 30 million years ago and continue the graph to 30 million years from now. Encourage students to choose a scale that will easily show the growth rate of the valley. Students could use the CD-ROM Grapher for this activity. **What's the Result? According to your model, how wide will the Red Sea be 30 million years from now?** The Red Sea will be about 250 km (156 mi) wide—that is, 90 km (56 mi) wider than it is now.

where humans had their first encounters with volcanoes. In fact, it is because of volcanic eruptions that anthropologists today are finding very old human remains. Some human ancestors living in the Afar region of Africa were buried under the volcanic debris of an eruption that occurred millions of years ago! Their fossil remains continue to be unearthed and provide important information about where early humans lived.

Found along the Great Rift Valley are some of the world's oldest volcanoes—including Mount Kenya and Mount Kilimanjaro. Mount Kilimanjaro, a volcano that towers nearly 5,900 m (19,352 ft) above the surrounding land, is Africa's highest peak.

Rifting along the Great Rift Valley—which runs through Mozambique, Zambia, Zaire, Tanzania, Uganda, Kenya, and Sudan, up into the Ethiopian highlands and down into the Djibouti coastal plains—has produced some of Earth's deepest lakes as well as some of the high-

▲ **Mount Kilimanjaro, one of Earth's oldest volcanoes**

est volcanic mountains. Lake Tanganyika, the longest freshwater lake on Earth, is the second deepest lake in the world. It formed millions of years ago when two tectonic plates shifted horizontally.

All along the Great Rift Valley, as with any rift zone, earthquakes and volcanoes are common. Study the map on page B110. Notice that along the East African Rift, the Somali Plate is moving away from

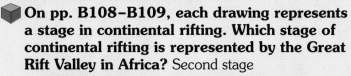

④ A new rift begins in the middle of the ocean basin that was formed. This rift is known as a mid-ocean ridge.

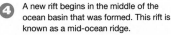

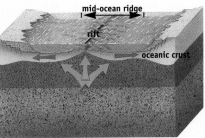

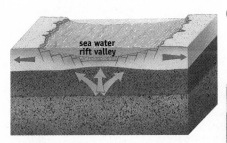

③ The rift valley widens, allowing sea water to fill the basin that has formed.

B109

Investigate Further

Cultural Connection

A VALLEY VISIT

What to Do Share with students that several cultures live along the Great Rift Valley. In the northern deserts live the Afar, who are herders. In Kenya, Tanzania, and Uganda live other groups of herders, such as the Masai. Encourage small groups to select a culture that lives in the valley. Then, using books on Africa and its many cultures, find out more about them, including how they make their living, types of houses and clothing, and the food they eat. Request that students write questions to ask other groups to learn more about their research.

What's the Result? Invite groups to interview each other. Students can role-play the people they have researched and answer questions about their lives.

Making Comparisons

- **What are the similarities and differences between rift valleys and mid-ocean ridges?** Rift valleys occur at divergent plate boundaries and are in the early stages of rifting. They are on land and are steep-walled valleys. Mid-ocean ridges occur at divergent plate boundaries and are forming oceanic crust.

Making Inferences

- **On pp. B108–B109, each drawing represents a stage in continental rifting. Which stage of continental rifting is represented by the Great Rift Valley in Africa?** Second stage
- **In which stage is the Red Sea?** Third stage
- **What is an example of an Earth feature that is in the fourth stage of rifting?** Atlantic Ocean

Thinking Critically

- **If the tectonic plates are spreading apart at rifts and new crust is being formed, why isn't Earth getting larger?** While there are places where the plates spread apart, there are also places where the plates collide, and crust subducts into the mantle. This balance keeps the same amount of crust on the planet.

Responding to Individual Needs

Visual/Spatial Activity The size of a spreading boundary is often underestimated. The active area of mid-ocean ridges is similar in width to the Appalachian Mountain system in North America. Show students a map of the eastern United States so that students can compare the width of this mountain range with the mid-ocean ridge.

3. Assess Understanding

Students can work in groups of three or four to create a model of one stage in the formation of a rift zone. Assign a different stage to each group. Students may want to use modeling clay, or they may have other ideas for materials to use in their models. Groups should present their models to the class and describe what is happening at that stage.

Close the Investigation

Critical Thinking Skills
Synthesizing, Applying, Solving Problems

WRITE IT 1. Magma rises from the upper mantle to form volcanoes. Therefore, volcanoes provide material that comes from the mantle. Studying volcanoes provides information about Earth's mantle.

2. At places within the mantle, plumes of magma, or hot spots, rise up to Earth's surface. These hot spots are often located far from plate boundaries. As the plates move, the hot spot stays in place and its magma wells up through the crust, often forming chains of volcanic islands, such as the Hawaiian Islands.

Challenge
Have students make a map of what Earth's surface might look like millions of years from now. Encourage students to consider the effects of volcanoes and rifting. Will the Hawaiian Islands keep growing? What will happen to Africa's rift valleys?

Following Up

Baseline Assessment Return to students' diagrams and sentences about what a volcanic island looks like beneath the water and how the island forms. Ask if they want to add anything to the diagrams or sentences.

Reteaching Use hand and arm gestures to model the processes of a plate moving over a hot spot and spreading plates. In each case, ask students to describe what you are showing.

Use *Science Notebook* p. 112.

Investigation Review ▶
Use Investigation Review p. 58 in the *Assessment Guide*.

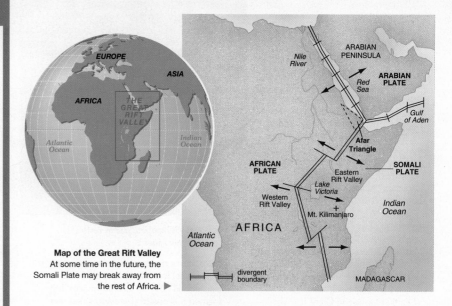

Map of the Great Rift Valley
At some time in the future, the Somali Plate may break away from the rest of Africa. ▶

divergent boundary

the African Plate. Along the Gulf of Aden arm of the rift, the Somali Plate is moving southwestward relative to the Arabian Plate. How might this area look 30 million years from now if rifting continues?

As with most volcanic areas, fertile soils cover much of the land in the Great Rift Valley. In Kenya, for example, rich red soils blanket the land. Trona, a mineral in the local volcanic ash, is used to make glass and detergents.

Near the Afar Triangle, where Earth's crust is only 25 km (15.5 mi) thick, steam from the many volcanoes spouts into the air. Someday, perhaps, the volcanoes of the rift system will provide electricity from geothermal energy to Africa's millions of residents. ■

INVESTIGATION 3

1. Volcanoes occur on Earth's surface—the crust. Yet scientists study volcanoes to find out about the planet's mantle. Explain why.

2. Using the Hawaiian Islands as an example, describe how volcanic islands can occur in places other than at the boundaries of tectonic plates.

B110

Assessment

Investigation Review
In What Other Places Can Volcanoes Occur?

CHAPTER 4

Name _____ Date _____

1. Draw a line to match each word with its definition or description.

a. hot spot — a large circular depression formed when part of a volcano collapses

b. caldera — a place where a large chamber of molten rock underlies a plate

c. rifting — a robot that can produce three-dimensional maps and analyze gases inside volcanoes

d. Dante II — process that occurs at divergent plate boundaries

e. Afar Triangle — region where three rift systems meet here

2. Fill in the chart. Write the letters of the characteristics in the appropriate columns.

a. Formed as 3 plates separated
b. Kenya and Kilimanjaro
c. Mauna Loa and Kilauea
d. Formed as a plate moved over a hot spot
e. quiet eruptions
f. some of Earth's oldest volcanoes and deepest lakes are here
g. ancient human remains found here
h. active volcano currently forming an island

Hawaiian Islands	Great Rift Valley
c	a
d	b
e	f
h	g

Process Skills
Measuring, and Collecting, Recording, and Interpreting Data

In the activity, *How Hawaii Formed*, you measured the distance between the islands and were given the age of the rocks on each island. How did these two pieces of information help you to interpret the direction the Pacific Plate is moving?
The plate is moving in the direction you would go from the youngest to the oldest island, which is northwest.

Performance

Debate Students can debate whether or not a certain amount of money should be spent on volcano research. If students oppose spending money on volcano research, have them explain why the benefits of such research do not justify the cost. If they agree with the expenditure, have them argue why the benefits do justify the cost.

REFLECT & EVALUATE

WORD POWER

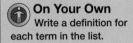

caldera
cinder-cone volcano
composite-cone volcano
hot spot
island arc
lava
magma
rifting
seismometer
shield volcano
volcano

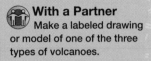 **On Your Own**
Write a definition for each term in the list.

 With a Partner
Make a labeled drawing or model of one of the three types of volcanoes.

BUILD YOUR PORTFOLIO

Search through magazines and newspapers. Make photocopies of pictures of each of the three kinds of volcanoes.

Analyze Information

Use the drawing below to help explain how the Hawaiian Islands show the direction in which the Pacific Plate is moving.

Assess Performance

Locate the Hawaiian Islands on a world map. Then locate them on a tectonic-plates map. Name the plate on which they are located and the direction in which the plate is moving.

Problem Solving

1. How are volcanoes on spreading ridges and rift zones different from those above descending edges of ocean plates?

2. On a map of Earth's tectonic plates, show where volcanoes are most likely to occur. Identify five active volcanoes throughout the world.

3. Explain how a satellite map could demonstrate that a volcano has erupted. How might that map change in a couple of months?

B111

REFLECT & EVALUATE

Word Power

On Your Own Students can use the Glossary to check definitions.

With a Partner Students' drawings or models should be similar to the ones found on pp. B88 and B89.

Analyze Information

The oldest volcanic island is shown farthest to the left. The youngest island, representing Hawaii, is at the far right. Therefore, the Pacific Plate is moving northwest.

Assess Performance

The Hawaiian Islands are located on the Pacific Plate. This plate is slowly moving northwest.

Problem Solving

1. Lava from volcanoes on ridges or rift zones is forming new crust. Lava of volcanoes found above descending edges of ocean plates is made of old crust that was remelted and pushed through the central pipe.

2. Volcanoes would most likely occur at the edges of tectonic plates. Some occur within plates, over hot spots. Examples of active volcanoes include Mount St. Helens, Nevado del Ruis, Pinatubo, and Mayon.

3. The satellite map would show a high concentration of dust, ash, and sulfuric dioxide gases in the atmosphere over a newly-erupted volcano. In a few months the volcano's airborne pollutants will have circled the Earth.

Use *Science Notebook* pp. 113–114.

BUILD YOUR PORTFOLIO

Be sure that students have examples of a cinder-cone volcano, a shield volcano, and a composite-cone volcano.

Chapter Test pp. 59–60 in the Assessment Guide

CHAPTER 4 — Chapter Test — Volcanoes

Name _____ Date _____

Analyze Information Each item is worth 10 points.

For items 1 and 4–6, circle the letter of the correct answer.

1. A _____ is a large volcano with gentle slopes.
a. lahar   b. composite cone   **c.** shield volcano   d. cinder cone

Study the drawing of a volcano that has developed a lava dome. Use the drawing to answer questions 2 and 3.

2. What feature might indicate that the volcano is about to erupt?
The bulge on the right side is an indication that pressure is building up forcing lava and gases to collect just below the surface.

3. What is the purpose of the tiltmeter?
The tiltmeter measures change in the slope of an area. Changes in slope indicate increasing pressure inside the mountain.

Problem Solving Each item is worth 15 points.

4. A certain volcano has not erupted during recorded history, but ancient legends tell of a catastrophic eruption in the past. The mountain has experienced several tremors and shows signs that it will soon erupt violently. Based on this evidence, how would you classify the volcano?
a. an active volcano with liquid lava   c. an intermittent volcano with liquid lava
b. an active volcano with sticky lava   **d.** a dormant volcano with sticky lava

CHAPTER 4 — Chapter Test — Volcanoes

Name _____ Date _____

5. A volcano has erupted violently several times in recorded history. No one can predict exactly when the next eruption will occur, but scientists expect that it will erupt again soon. How would you classify this volcano?
a. an active volcano with liquid lava
b. an active volcano with sticky lava
c. an intermittent volcano with sticky lava
d. a dormant volcano with sticky lava

6. A volcano erupts quietly. Its flow is smooth and almost constant. Scientists gather around this volcano regularly to safely study the composition of the lava. How would you classify this volcano?
a. an active volcano with liquid lava
b. an active volcano with sticky lava
c. an intermittent volcano with sticky lava
d. a dormant volcano with sticky lava

Word Power Each item is worth 6 points.

Use the clues to help you unscramble the vocabulary words from the chapter.

melted rock-like material within Earth
a m a m   magma

volcano made of debris and fairly sticky lava
c r n e n o c e   cinder cone

instrument that detects Earth movements
m s o r e m t e   seismometer

region within a plate where magma occurs in a chamber near Earth's surface
p t o s   hot spot

INVESTIGATE FURTHER!

UNIT PROJECT:
The Big Event

Students can begin their final preparations for the sharing of their guides by deciding on a guest list and then designing and making special invitations, perhaps in a form that draws attention to the theme of preparing people for emergency measures. On the day before the event, have students work in groups to prepare and decorate the classroom. For example, groups can set up tables and display the guides, mount maps on the wall, make a welcoming sign, prepare a refreshments table if you plan to serve snacks, and make programs to distribute to the guests. You might also want to assign students to take pictures of the event and have them prepare by locating and obtaining camera equipment and film. For more information on the Big Event, see Wrapping Up the Project p. B1l. For assessment use Unit Project Scoring Rubric Master B4 (TRB p. 74).

 Have students use *Science Notebook* p. 115.

Experiment

Before students begin work on their long-term projects, have them develop plans to aid in recording their observations and in identifying patterns in the incidents that occur. Allow time for students to share with the class their predictions and conclusions about geographically active areas.

Take Action

In addition to plans to express views about the quality of safety standards at nearby industrial sites and structures, invite students to investigate school safety standards and emergency measures. Students might create role-plays in which they act out the best ways for students and staff to respond during emergency situations. The scenes could be videotaped to be shown to other classes, or students might perform them live.

INVESTIGATE FURTHER!

Throughout this unit you've investigated questions related to the changing Earth. How will you use what you've learned and share that information with others? Here are some ideas…

Hold a Big Event
to Share Your Unit Project

Imagine that you live in a part of the world where earthquakes occur frequently or where a volcano erupts from time to time. You are part of a team that is developing a guide—Preparing for an Earthquake and for Volcanic Activity. Your guide should give people information on protecting themselves against earthquakes and volcanic eruptions. It should prepare people for emergency measures, such as evacuation procedures. Be sure to include maps, tables, and other ways to communicate ideas clearly.

Experiment

Plan a long-term project based on this unit. Monitor newspapers and/or news broadcasts for at least two months. Record reported incidents of earthquakes and volcanoes. On a world map, place colored labels at those sites that experience seismic or volcanic activity. Note any patterns in the incidents: on fault lines, near the Ring of Fire, and so on. What conclusions can you draw about geologically active areas? What predictions would you make on the basis of your conclusions?

Take Action

If areas in your state are geologically active, find out what kinds of structures and industries are nearby. What safety precautions are in place in the event of earthquakes or volcanic activity? Write your local newspaper or government officials. Express your views about the quality of safety standards at these sites. Report your recommendations and any responses to your class.

B112

Home-School Connection

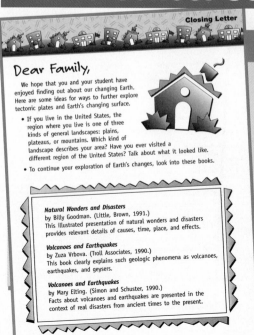

Closing Letter

Dear Family,

We hope that you and your student have enjoyed finding out about our changing Earth. Here are some ideas for ways to further explore tectonic plates and Earth's changing surface.

• If you live in the United States, the region where you live is one of three kinds of general landscapes: plains, plateaus, or mountains. Which kind of landscape describes your area? Have you ever visited a different region of the United States? Talk about what it looked like.

• To continue your exploration of Earth's changes, look into these books.

Natural Wonders and Disasters
by Billy Goodman. (Little, Brown, 1991.)
This illustrated presentation of natural wonders and disasters provides relevant details of causes, time, place, and effects.

Volcanoes and Earthquakes
by Zuza Vrbova. (Troll Associates, 1990.)
This book clearly explains such geologic phenomena as volcanoes, earthquakes, and geysers.

Volcanoes and Earthquakes
by Mary Elting. (Simon and Schuster, 1990.)
Facts about volcanoes and earthquakes are presented in the context of real disasters from ancient times to the present.

The Closing Letter at the end of this unit suggests activities with a compass that students and their families can try. It also lists books that they can read together. Distribute the Closing Letter (TRB p. 11) to students at the end of this unit.

MATERIALS LIST

UNIT B

Following is a list of materials needed for activities in Unit B. Quantities are for a class of 30 students working in groups of 5. Quantities are also listed for those materials included in the Modular Deluxe Kit.

Materials	Class Quantity Needed	Modular Deluxe Kit Quantity	Activity Page
Consumable Materials			
cardboard	6 sheets	1 pkg (6)	B42
cardboard boxes, small	24 to 36		B72
coffee stirrers	6	1 pkg (6)	B24
food coloring	6 bottles	1 pkg (6)	B36
gelatin	6 pkg	6 pkg	B62
glue	6 bottles		B6
markers, fine-point	6	6	B24, B68
milk cartons (0.24 L)	6	6	B236
modeling clay	6 lb	6 lb	B23, B72
oats, quick (oatmeal)	1 box	1 pkg	B16
paper, tracing	6 sheets	1 pkg (40)	B16
pencils	12		B22, B23
pencils (sharpened)	6		B36
rubber bands	24	1 pkg (1 oz)	B54
sand	12 lb	6 bags (12 lb)	B62, B72
sandpaper, coarse	12 pieces	1 pkg (3)	B54
shelf paper	1 roll	1 roll (25 ft)	B68
shoeboxes with lids	6	1 pkg (6)	B23, B24
soil	12 lb	3 bags (12 qt)	B72
straws, plastic	2 pkg	1 pkg (50)	B24
string (twine)	1 roll	1 roll (430 ft)	B36, B68
tape, duct	1 roll	1 roll (20 yd)	B36
tape, masking	1 roll		B68, B72
tape, transparent	1 roll		B23, B24
Nonconsumable Materials			
aquariums	6	6	B36
block, small wood	6	6	B62
blocks, wood	12	12	B54
bowls, clear plastic	12	12	B62
calculators	6		B100
compasses, drawing	6	6	B70
cups, measuring	6	6	B94
dowels	4 pkg	4 pkg (24)	B72
goggles	30	6	B94
hot plate	1	1	B94
map pins, red	1 pkg	1 pkg (100)	B84
map pins, yellow	1 pkg	1 pkg (100)	B84
oven mitts	1	1	B94
pans, large aluminum	6	1 pkg (6)	B72
rulers, metric	6	1 pkg (6)	B22, B23, B24, B36, B68, B70, B100
saucepan	1	1	B94
scissors	6		B6, B22, B24, B36
sponges, cellulose	12	12	B44

MATERIALS LIST *(Continued)*

Materials	Class Quantity Needed	Modular Deluxe Kit Quantity	Activity Page
spoons, large	1	1	B94
timers (stopwatch)	6	6	B72
wall map of the world	1 shared		B84

> ***Additional kit options are available.***
> ***Contact your sales representative for details.***

CREDITS

Front Cover: Photography: Jade Albert; Photography Production: Picture It Corporation; Illustration: Marti Shohet.

TOC: Terry Boles, Barbara Cousins, Bob Radigan, Nadine Sokol, John Youssi.

Contributing Artists:

Unit 6B Chapter B1: Skip Baker: 22; Dolores Bego: 7, 30; Warren Budd: 19, 20, 31; Eldon Doty: 8, 9; Eureka Cartography: 17, 18, 20, 21; Geo Systems: 12, 13, 14, 15; Dale Glasgow & Assoc.: 10; Brad Gaber: 29; Greg Harris: 26, 27; Bill Morris: 28; Claudia Karabaic Sargent: 11; Ray Smith: 12, 13, 14, 15. **Chapter B2:** Julie Carpenter: 40, 41; Brad Gaber: 38, 39, 40, 41; Eureka Cartography: 41, 43, 51; Ben Perini 49; Bob Swanson: 45, 47, 48; Randy Verougstraete: 49. **Chapter B3:** Dolores Bego: 77; Bob Brugger: 64; Julie Carpenter: 76, 77, 78; Eldon Doty: 56, 57; Eureka Cartography: 55, 59; Patrick Gnan: 79, 80; Greg Harris: 76, 77, 102; Robert Roper: 64, 65, 67, 81; Robert Schuster: 60; Joe Spencer: 75. **Chapter B4:** Stephen Baur: 107; Dolores Bego: 87; Eldon Doty: 93; Eureka Cartography: 90, 101, 102, 110; Dale Glasgow & Assoc.: 105; Greg Harris: 102, 103, 111; Susan Johnson Carlson: 110; Laszlo Kubini: 92, 96; Bob Swanson: 86, 96, 97; John Youssi: 88, 89, 108, 109.

Glossary: Warren Budd and Assoc., Barbara Cousins, Brad Gaber, Patrick Gnan, Verlin Miller, Bob Swanson, David Uhl, John Youssi.

Handbook: Kathleen Dunne, Laurie Hamilton, Catherine Leary, Andy Meyer

Teaching Guide Front Matter: Olivia McElroy: Common Art; Patrick Gnan: T6, T7.

Table of Contents: Geo Systems

Common Art for Unit Opener pages, Tips from Teacher pages, Technology pages, Chapter Opener pages, Home School Icons, Book Icons, Videotape Icons: Nancy Tobin

Common Art for Project File pages: Jenny Campbell

Photographs:

Unit B Opener: Liaison International. 2: Peter French. Chapter 1 4: *inset* © Tom Van Sant/Geosphere Project, Santa Monica/Photo Researchers, Inc. 4–5: *bkgd.* Richard Johnston/FPG International. 9: Courtesy, Dover Publications. 31: Bob Krist. Chapter 2 34: *r. inset* Lamont-Doherty Earth Observatory. 34–35: *bkgd.* Don Blankenship-UTIG; *l.inset* Jean Miele; *m. inset* Lawrence A. Lanver. 39: Phil Degginger/Color-Pics, Inc. 40: Bob Krist. 41: © David Parker/Science Photo Library/Photo Researchers, Inc. 45: *r.* Superstock. 47: *t.* Dr. E. R. Degginger/Color-Pics, Inc.; *b.* Rich Buzzelli/Tom Stack & Associates. 48: *t.* © Emil Muench/Photo Researchers, Inc.; *m.* Ralph Perry/Tony Stone Images; *b.* Larry Nielsen/Peter Arnold. 50: *l.* Superstock; *r.* AP/Wide World Photos. Chapter 3 52–53: *bkgd.* Les Stone/Sygma; *inset* Gaylon Wampler/Sygma. 56: *t.* The Bettmann Archive; *b.* The Granger Collection. 58: © Will and Deni McIntyre/Photo Researchers, Inc. 61: © David Parker/Science Photo Library/Photo Researchers, Inc. 62: AP/Wide World Photos. 67: Shahn Kermani/Liaison International. 72–73: Grant Huntington for SBG. 74: Michael Holford. 78: Ken Biggs/Tony Stone Images. 79: James Stanfield/© National Geographic Society. 80: Mark Downey/Liaison International. Chapter 4 82–83: *bkgd.* Dean Conger/© National Geographic Society; *inset* © 1991 Discover Magazine. 87: *l.* Mikhail Zhilin/Bruce Coleman; *r.* Franco Salmoiraghi. 88: Robert Frerck/Odyssey Productions. 89: *t.* Tony Stone Images; *b.* Phil Degginger/Color-Pics, Inc. 90: *l.* Stella Snead/Bruce Coleman; *r.* K. Eriksson/Liaison International. 92: *l.* Scala/Art Resource; *r.* Alinari/Art Resource. 97: © Robert M. Carey/NOAA/Science Photo Library/Photo Researchers, Inc. 98: *t.* AP/Wide World Photos; *b.* AP/Wide World Photos. 99: Peter French. 103: Werner Forman Archive/British Museum/Art Resource. 104: *t.* Dr. Alexander Malahoff/HURL; *b.* James Cachero/Sygma. 106: NASA. 109: Rick Carson/Liaison International.

Teaching Guide Front Matter:

T2–T3: © Stephen Dalton/Photo Researchers, Inc., Geo Systems: B1E.

TEACHER NOTES

TEACHER NOTES

TEACHER NOTES

Teacher Notes

TEACHER NOTES

TEACHER NOTES

TEACHER NOTES

THINK LIKE A SCIENTIST

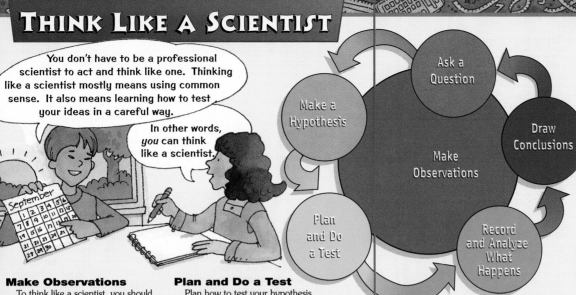

You don't have to be a professional scientist to act and think like one. Thinking like a scientist mostly means using common sense. It also means learning how to test your ideas in a careful way.

In other words, *you* can think like a scientist.

Ask a Question

Make a Hypothesis

Draw Conclusions

Make Observations

Plan and Do a Test

Record and Analyze What Happens

Make Observations

To think like a scientist, you should learn as much as you can by observing things around you. Everything you hear and see is a clue about how the natural world works.

Ask a Question

Look for patterns. You'll get ideas and ask questions like these:

- Do all birds eat the same seeds?
- How does the time that the Sun sets change from day to day?

Make a Guess Called a Hypothesis

If you have an idea about why or how something happens, make an educated guess, or *hypothesis*, that you can test. For example, let's suppose that your hypothesis about the sunset time is that it changes by one minute each day.

Plan and Do a Test

Plan how to test your hypothesis. Your plan would need to consider some of these problems:

- How will you measure the time that the Sun sets?
- Will you measure the time every day?
- For how many days or weeks do you need to measure?

Record and Analyze What Happens

When you test your idea, you need to observe carefully and write down, or record, everything that happens. When you finish collecting data, you may need to do some calculations with it. For example, you might want to calculate how much the sunset time changes in a week or a month.

Draw Conclusions

Whatever happens in a test, think about all the reasons for your results. For example, you might wonder what causes the time of sunset to change. You might also ask when the earliest and latest sunsets occur during the year. Sometimes this thinking leads to a new hypothesis.

If the time of the sunset changes by one minute each day, think about what else the data shows you. Can you predict the time that the Sun will set one month from now?

PRACTICE SCIENTIFIC REASONING SKILLS

To think like a scientist, you need to practice certain ways of thinking.

Always check for yourself.
Always ask, "How do I really know it's true?" Be willing to find out for yourself.

Be honest and careful about what you observe.
It's easy to only look for the results you expect. It's harder to see the unexpected. But unexpected results lead scientists to ask more questions. They also provide information on how things work.

Don't be afraid to be wrong.
Based on their observations, scientists make many hypotheses. Not all of these hypotheses turn out to be correct. But scientists can learn from wrong "guesses," because even wrong guesses result in information that leads to knowledge.

Keep an open mind about possible explanations.
Make sure to think about all the reasons why something might have happened. Consider all the explanations that you can think of.

How much sugar can a cup of herbal tea hold?

Can hot water dissolve more sugar than cold water can?

Nita and Mark thought the second question was more interesting because it applied to more things—like coffee and lemonade. They were not sure what the answer to this question would be. But it was the kind of question that would tell them more about the nature of solutions.

Scientific investigations usually begin with something that you have noticed or read about. As you think about what you already know, you'll discover some ideas that you're not sure about. This will help you to ask the question that you really want to answer.

"I can't believe it."

"It's true."

"It's impossible! Ten?"

"That's right."

"A cup of herbal tea can't hold ten teaspoons of sugar."

"My mother's does," replied Mark. "She likes it sweet."

"I'll bet most of the sugar just sinks to the bottom of the cup," Nita asserted. "Doesn't it?"

"No, it doesn't," Mark said. "Would I lie to you?"

"Listen," Nita said, "Ms. Cobb's been teaching us about solutions. I'll bet if I asked her she'd say it's impossible."

Ask a Question

Nita explained the issue to Ms. Cobb and the other students. She asked Ms. Cobb to give her opinion, but she wouldn't. She simply asked the class what they thought. Some students thought it was possible, others thought it was impossible. Ms. Cobb suggested that the class figure out a way to find the answer.

Ms. Cobb invited the students to come up with questions that expressed the problem they want to solve. Two of the questions were:

Make a Hypothesis

Mark and Nita talked the problem over. Mark told Nita that his mother drank her herbal tea very hot; she always waited until the water was boiling violently before pouring it into her cup. "Maybe," Nita said, "If the water wasn't so hot, it would hold less sugar." Mark agreed that this was possible. But he wasn't sure.

Mark and Nita had a hunch that the hotter water is, the more solute, such as sugar, the water will hold. They came up with a hypothesis, a statement of what they thought was true. Their hypothesis was "The hotter the water, the more sugar it will dissolve."

Nita and Mark got a few heat-proof glass beakers, a cup measure, and thermometers. Ms. Cobb got 1-teaspoon measuring spoons and a bowl of sugar from the school cafeteria. She also borrowed several hotplates. Ms. Cobb reviewed the test procedure that Mark and Nita had planned.

When you use what you have observed to suggest a possible answer to your question, you are making a hypothesis. Be sure that your hypothesis is an idea that you can test somehow. If you can't think of an experiment or a model to test your hypothesis, try changing it. Sometimes it's better to make a simpler, clearer hypothesis that answers only part of your question.

Plan and Do a Test

Mark and Nita knew they'd have to keep track of the different water temperatures in each beaker. They knew they'd have to put the same amount of water in each beaker. They would also have to keep track of how many teaspoons of sugar went into each beaker.

Nita knew that water boiled at 100 degrees Celsius (°C). So the beaker with the hottest water should be at this temperature. Another beaker could have water at 70°C; a third might have water at 40°C.

Mark suggested that they have a fourth beaker containing a cup of cold water at about 5°C—water whose temperature was close to freezing. This beaker would serve as their control. The control in this experiment would allow Mark and Nita to test the effect of heat on water's ability to dissolve sugar.

Ms. Cobb set up four water baths at the temperatures they agreed upon. Each was kept at a constant temperature. Each water bath had a thermometer in it.

One way to try out your hypothesis is to use a test called an experiment. When you plan an experiment, be sure that it helps you to answer your question. Even when you plan, things can happen that make the experiment confusing or make it not work properly. If this happens, you can change the plan for the experiment, and try again.

Record and Analyze What Happened

Mark and Nita asked two classmates to help them put teaspoons of sugar into the beakers. After each teaspoon of sugar went in, the solution was stirred with a glass stirring rod until the sugar dissolved. Each

TEMPERATURE
100°
70°
40°
5°

Spoonfuls of Sugar Dissolved

student kept track of the number of teaspoons of sugar that dissolved in it.

At the end of the experiment, each student looked at what he or she had written down. This information was organized in a graph like the one on page H6.

Mark and Nita studied the graph of the data they got during their experiment. They noticed that there was a definite relationship between water temperature and how much sugar could be dissolved in it.

Nita was surprised to see that Mark's mother's tea could really hold a lot more than 10 teaspoons of sugar. She and Mark agreed that people could drink their tea really sweet, unless, that is, they made it with cooler water.

When you do an experiment, you need to write down, or record, your observations. Some of your observations might be numbers – things that you counted or measured. Your recorded observations are called data. When you record your data, you need to organize it in a way that helps you to understand it. Graphs and tables are helpful ways to organize data. Then think about the information you have collected. Analyze what it tells you.

Draw Conclusions

Mark and Nita decided that their test results supported their hypothesis. But they had noticed something odd that had happened in the beaker containing the hottest water. At some point after the water had cooled, a small amount of sugar added to the solution caused many sugar crystals to form.

They told Ms. Cobb about this strange result. Ms. Cobb congratulated them for having created a "supersaturated" solution. She suggested that Mark and Nita might want to plan another experiment to find out more about such solutions.

After you have analyzed your data, you should use what you have learned to draw a conclusion. A conclusion is a statement that sums up what you learned. The conclusion should be about the question you asked. Think about whether the information you have gathered supports your hypothesis or not. If it does, figure out how to check out your idea more thoroughly. Also think about new questions you can ask.

SAFETY

The best way to be safe in the classroom is to use common sense. Prepare yourself for each activity before you start it. Get help from your teacher when there is a problem. Most important of all, pay attention. Here are some other ways that you can stay safe.

Stay Safe From Stains
- Wear protective clothing or an old shirt when you work with messy materials.
- If anything spills, wipe it up or ask your teacher to help you clean it up.

Stay Safe From Flames
- Keep your clothes away from open flames. If you have long or baggy sleeves, roll them up.
- Don't let your hair get close to a flame. If you have long hair, tie it back.

Stay Safe During Cleanup
- Wash up after you finish working.
- Dispose of things in the way that your teachers tells you to.

Stay Safe From Injuries
- Protect your eyes by wearing safety goggles when you are told that you need them.
- Keep your hands dry around electricity. Water is a good conductor of electricity, so you can get a shock more easily if your hands are wet.
- Be careful with sharp objects. If you have to press on them, keep the sharp side away from you.
- Cover any cuts you have that are exposed. If you spill something on a cut, be sure to wash it off immediately.
- Don't eat or drink anything unless your teacher tells you that it's okay.

MOST IMPORTANTLY

If you ever hurt yourself or one of your group members gets hurt, tell your teacher right away.

HAIR Keep it out of the way of a flame.

EYES Wear safety goggles when you are told to.

MOUTH Don't eat or drink **ANYTHING** unless your teacher tells you it's okay.

HANDS Keep your hands dry around electricity. Cover any cuts. Wear gloves when told to. Wash up after you finish.

CLOTHES Keep long sleeves rolled up. Protect yourself from stains. Stay away from open flames.

DON'T MAKE A MESS If you spill something, clean it up right away. When finished with an activity, clean up your work area. Dispose of things in the way your teacher tells you to.

Using a Microscope

A microscope makes it possible to see very small things by magnifying them. Some microscopes have a set of lenses to magnify objects different amounts.

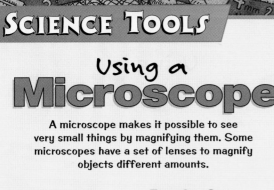

Examine Some Salt Grains

Handle a microscope carefully; it can break easily. Carry it firmly with both hands and avoid touching the lenses.

1. Turn the mirror toward a source of light. **NEVER** use the Sun as a light source.

2. Place a few grains of salt on the slide. Put the slide on the stage of the microscope.

3. While looking through the eyepiece, turn the adjustment knob on the back of the microscope to bring the salt grains into focus.

4. Raise the eyepiece tube to increase the magnification; lower it to decrease magnification.

Using a Calculator

After you've made measurements, a calculator can help you analyze your data. Some calculators have a memory key that allows you to save the result of one calculation while you do another.

Find an Average

The table shows the amount of rain that was collected using a rain gauge in each month of one year. You can use a calculator to help you find the average monthly rainfall.

1. Add the numbers. When you add a series of numbers, you don't need to press the equal sign until the last number is entered. Just press the plus sign after you enter each number (except the last one).

2. If you make a mistake while you are entering numbers, try to erase your mistake by pushing the clear entry (CE) key or the clear (C) key. Then you can continue entering the rest of the numbers you are adding. If you can't fix your mistake, you can push the (C) key once or twice until the screen shows 0. Then start over.

3. Your total should be 1,131. You can use the total to find the average. Just divide by the number of months in the year.

Rainfall	
Month	**Rain (mm)**
Jan.	214
Feb.	138
Mar.	98
Apr.	157
May	84
June	41
July	5
Aug.	23
Sept.	48
Oct.	75
Nov.	140
Dec.	108

These keys run the calculator's memory functions.

This key erases the last entry.

Using a Balance

A balance is used to measure mass. Mass is the amount of matter in an object. Place the object to be massed in the left pan. Place standard masses in the right pan.

Measure the Mass of an Orange

1. Check that the empty pans are balanced, or level with each other. The pointer at the base should be on the middle mark. If it needs to be adjusted, move the slider on the back of the balance a little to the left or right.

2. Place an orange on the left pan. Notice that the pointer moves and that the pans are no longer level with each other. Then add standard masses, one at a time, to the right pan. When the pointer is at the middle mark again, the pans are balanced. Each pan holds the same amount of mass.

3. Each standard mass is marked to show the number of grams it contains. Add the number of grams marked on the masses in the pan. The total is the mass in grams of the orange.

Using a Spring Scale

A spring scale is used to measure force. You can use a spring scale to find the weight of an object in newtons. You can also use the scale to measure other forces.

Measure the Weight of an Object

1. Place the object in a net bag, and hang it from the hook on the bottom of the spring scale. Or, if possible, hang the object directly from the hook.

2. Slowly lift the scale by the top hook. Be sure the object to be weighed continues to hang from the bottom hook.

3. Wait until the pointer on the face of the spring scale has stopped moving. Read the number next to the pointer to determine the weight of the object in newtons.

Measure Friction

1. Hook the object to the bottom of the spring scale. Use a rubber band to connect the spring scale and object if needed.

2. Gently pull the top hook of the scale parallel to the floor. When the object starts to move, read the number of newtons next to the pointer on the scale. This number is the force of friction between the floor and the object as you drag the object.

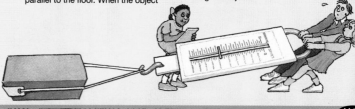

Using a
Thermometer

A thermometer is used to measure temperature. When the liquid in the tube of a thermometer gets warmer, it expands and moves farther up the tube. Different units can be used to measure temperature, but scientists usually use the Celsius scale.

Measure the Temperature of a Cold Liquid

1. Half-fill a cup with chilled liquid.

2. Hold the thermometer so that the bulb is in the center of the liquid.

3. Wait until you see the liquid in the tube stop moving. Read the scale line that is closest to the top of the liquid in the tube.

Measuring
Volume

A graduated cylinder, a measuring cup, and a beaker are used to measure volume. Volume is the amount of space something takes up. Most of the containers that scientists use to measure volume have a scale marked in milliliters (mL).

Measure the Volume of Juice

1. Pour the juice into a measuring container.

2. Move your head so that your eyes are level with the top of the juice. Read the scale line that is closest to the surface of the juice. If the surface of the juice is curved up on the sides, look at the lowest point of the curve.

3. You can estimate the value between two lines on the scale to obtain a more accurate measurement.

▲ The bottom of the curve is at 50 mL.

This graduated cylinder has marks for every 1 mL. ▶

This beaker has marks for each 25 mL. ▼

This measuring cup has marks for each 25 mL. ▼

Each container above has 50 mL of juice.

MEASUREMENTS

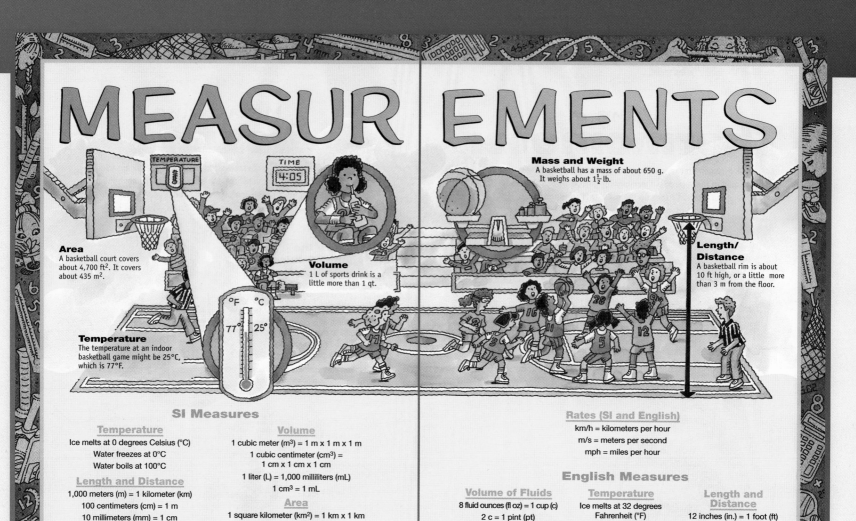

Area
A basketball court covers about 4,700 ft². It covers about 435 m².

Temperature
The temperature at an indoor basketball game might be 25°C, which is 77°F.

Volume
1 L of sports drink is a little more than 1 qt.

Mass and Weight
A basketball has a mass of about 650 g. It weighs about 1½ lb.

Length/Distance
A basketball rim is about 10 ft high, or a little more than 3 m from the floor.

SI Measures

Temperature
Ice melts at 0 degrees Celsius (°C)
Water freezes at 0°C
Water boils at 100°C

Length and Distance
1,000 meters (m) = 1 kilometer (km)
100 centimeters (cm) = 1 m
10 millimeters (mm) = 1 cm

Force
1 newton (N) =
1 kilogram x meter/second/second
(kg x m/s²)

Volume
1 cubic meter (m³) = 1 m x 1 m x 1 m
1 cubic centimeter (cm³) =
1 cm x 1 cm x 1 cm
1 liter (L) = 1,000 milliliters (mL)
1 cm³ = 1 mL

Area
1 square kilometer (km²) = 1 km x 1 km
1 hectare = 10,000 m²

Mass
1,000 grams (g) = 1 kilogram (kg)
1,000 milligrams (mg) = 1 g

Rates (SI and English)
km/h = kilometers per hour
m/s = meters per second
mph = miles per hour

English Measures

Volume of Fluids
8 fluid ounces (fl oz) = 1 cup (c)
2 c = 1 pint (pt)
2 pt = 1 quart (qt)
4 qt = 1 gallon (gal)

Temperature
Ice melts at 32 degrees Fahrenheit (°F)
Water freezes at 32°F
Water boils at 212°F

Length and Distance
12 inches (in.) = 1 foot (ft)
3 ft = 1 yard (yd)
5,280 ft = 1 mile (mi)

Weight
16 ounces (oz) = 1 pound (lb)   2,000 pounds = 1 ton (T)

GLOSSARY

Pronunciation Key

Symbol	Key Words	Symbol	Key Words
a	cat	g	get
ā	ape	h	help
ä	cot, car	j	jump
		k	kiss, call
e	ten, berry	l	leg
ē	me	m	meat
		n	nose
i	fit, here	p	put
ī	ice, fire	r	red
		s	see
ō	go	t	top
ô	fall, for	v	vat
oi	oil	w	wish
͞o	look, pull	y	yard
͞o͞o	tool, rule	z	zebra
ou	out, crowd		
		ch	chin, arch
u	up	ŋ	ring, drink
ʉ	fur, shirt	sh	she, push
		th	thin, truth
ə	a in ago	*th*	then, father
	e in agent	zh	measure
	i in pencil		
	o in atom	
	u in circus	A heavy stress mark ' is placed
		after a syllable that gets a heavy,
b	bed	or primary, stress, as in **picture**
d	dog	(pik'chər).
f	fall	

abyssal plain (ə bis'əl plān) The broad, flat ocean bottom. (E34) The *abyssal plain* covers nearly half of Earth's surface.

acceleration (ak sel er ā'shən) The rate at which velocity changes over time. (F21) The spacecraft's *acceleration* increased as it soared into the air.

acid (as'id) A compound that turns blue litmus paper to red and forms a salt when it reacts with a base. (C81) *Acids* have a sour taste.

action force The initial force exerted in a force-pair. (F92) When you push against something, you are applying an *action force*.

aftershock A less powerful shock following the principal shock of an earthquake. (B58) Many *aftershocks* shook the ground in the days after the major earthquake.

algae (al'jē) Any of various plantlike protists. (A35) Diatoms and seaweed are kinds of *algae*.

allergy (al'ər jē) An oversensitivity to a specific substance that is harmless to most people, such as pollen, dust, animal hair, or a particular food. (G42) An *allergy* may cause such symptoms as sneezing, itching, or a rash.

alloy (al'oi) A solution of two or more metals. (C59) Bronze is an *alloy* of copper and tin.

antibiotic (an tī bī ät'ik) A substance, produced by microbes or fungi, that can destroy bacteria or stop their growth. Also, a synthetic substance with these properties. (A59) Doctors prescribe *antibiotics* to treat various bacteria-caused diseases.

antibody (an'ti bäd ē) A protein produced in the blood that destroys or weakens bacteria and other pathogens. (A59, G35) *Antibodies* are produced in response to infection.

aquaculture (ak'wə kul chər) The raising of water plants and animals for human use or consumption. (E80) Raising catfish on a catfish "farm" is a form of *aquaculture*.

asexual reproduction Reproduction involving a cell or cells from one parent and resulting in offspring exactly like the parent. (D10) The division of an amoeba into two cells is an example of *asexual reproduction*.

asthenosphere (as then'ə sfir) The layer of Earth below the lithosphere; the upper part of the mantle. (B39) The *asthenosphere* contains hot, partially melted rock with plasticlike properties.

astronomical unit A unit of measurement equal to the distance from Earth to the Sun. (F9) Pluto is 39.3 *astronomical units* (A.U.) from the Sun.

atom The smallest particle of an element that has the chemical properties of that element. (C35) An *atom* of sodium differs from an *atom* of chlorine.

atomic number (ə tăm′ik num′bər)
The number of protons in the nucleus
of an atom of an element. (C73) The
atomic number of oxygen is 8.

bacteria (bak tir′ē ə) Monerans that
feed on dead organic matter or on living things. (A51, G33) Diseases such as
pneumonia and tuberculosis are caused
by *bacteria.*

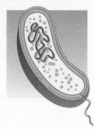

base A compound that turns red litmus paper blue and that forms a salt
when it reacts with an acid. (C81)
Bases have a slippery feel.

behavioral risk factor (bē hāv′yər əl
risk fak′tər) A health risk factor that
results from a person's choices about
his or her lifestyle. (G53) Using drugs or
alcohol is a *behavioral risk factor.*

benthos (ben′thäs) All the plants and
animals that live on the ocean bottom.
(E25) *Benthos* include oysters, crabs,
and coral.

blue-green bacteria (blōō grēn
bak tir′ē ə) Monerans that contain
chlorophyll. (A51) Like plants, *blue-
green bacteria* carry out photosynthesis
and make their own food.

budding A form of asexual reproduction in which a new individual develops
from a bump, or bud, on the body of
the parent. (D13) Some one-celled
organisms, such as yeast, reproduce by
budding.

buoyancy (boi′ən sē) The tendency
of fluids, like water, to keep objects
afloat. (F123) Objects float better in salt
water than in fresh water because salt
water has greater *buoyancy.*

caldera (kal der′ə) A large circular
depression, or basin, at the top of a volcano. (B104) The eruption formed a
caldera that later became a lake.

cast fossil (kast fäs′əl) A fossil
formed when minerals from rock
move into and harden within
the space left by a decaying
organism. (D57) *Cast fossils* of shells can provide
information about the animals from which the fossils
formed.

cell The basic unit that makes up all
living things. (A9) The human body is
made up of trillions of *cells.*

cell differentiation (sel dif ər en shē-
ā′shən) The development of cells into
different and specialized cell types. (A25)
Through *cell differentiation*, plant and
animal cells develop into tissues.

cell membrane (sel mem′brān) The
structure that surrounds and encloses a
cell and controls the movement of substances into and out of the cell. (A10)
The *cell membrane* shrank when the
cell was placed in salt water.

cell respiration (sel res pə rā′shən)
The process in cells in which oxygen is
used to release stored energy by breaking down sugar molecules. (A19) The
process of *cell respiration* provides
energy for a cell's activities.

cell theory A theory that states that
cells are the basic units of structure and
function of all living things. (A10) The
cell theory states that new cells are
produced from existing cells.

cell wall The rigid structure surrounding the cells of plants, monerans, and
some protists. (A10) The *cell wall* gives
a cell its rigid shape.

chemical bond A force, or link, that
holds atoms together in a molecule or
in a crystal. (C73) In a water molecule,
atoms of hydrogen and oxygen are held
together by *chemical bonds.*

chemical change A change in matter
that results in new substances with new
properties. (C69) A *chemical change*
occurs when wood burns and forms
gases and ash.

chemical formula A group of symbols and numbers that shows what elements make up a compound. (C40)
The *chemical formula* for carbon dioxide is CO_2.

chemical properties Characteristics
of matter that describe how it changes
when it reacts with other matter. (C34)
The ability to burn is a *chemical property* of paper.

chemical symbol One or two letters
used to stand for the name of an element. (C36) Ca is the *chemical symbol*
for calcium.

chloroplast (klôr′ə plast) A tiny
green organelle that contains chlorophyll and is found in plant cells and
some protist cells. (A10) The chlorophyll inside a *chloroplast* enables a
plant cell to capture solar energy.

cholesterol (kə les′tər ôl) A fatty
substance, found in foods, that can lead
to clogged blood vessels. (G60) A diet
that is too high in *cholesterol* can
increase the risk of heart disease.

chromosome (krō′mə sōm) A
threadlike structure in the nucleus of a
cell; it carries the genes that determine
the traits an offspring inherits from its
parent or parents. (A10, D22, G12)
Most cells in the human body contain
23 pairs of *chromosomes.*

cilia (sil′ē ə) Small, hairlike structures
lining the membranes of the respiratory
system. (G33) *Cilia* help to filter the air
that enters the body.

cinder-cone volcano (sin'dər kōn väl kā'nō) A kind of volcano, usually small and steep-sloped, that is formed from layers of cinders, which are sticky bits of volcanic material. (B88) *Cinder-cone volcanoes* result from explosive eruptions.

communicable disease (kə myōo'ni-kə bəl di zēz) A disease that can be passed from one individual to another. (A58) Bacteria, which are easily passed from organism to organism, are the cause of many *communicable diseases*.

competition The struggle among organisms for available resources. (D77) *Competition* among members of a species is a factor in evolution.

composite-cone volcano (kəm päz'it kōn väl cā'nō) A kind of volcano formed when explosive eruptions of sticky lava alternate with quieter eruptions of volcanic rock bits. (B89) Mount Vesuvius is a *composite-cone volcano* in southern Italy.

compound (käm'pound) A substance made up of two or more elements that are chemically combined. (C34) Water is a *compound* made up of hydrogen and oxygen.

condensation (kän dən sā'shən) The change of state from a gas to a liquid. (C28) The *condensation* of water vapor can form droplets of water on the outside of a cold glass.

continental edge (kän tə nent''l ej) The point at which the continental shelf, which surrounds each continent, begins to angle sharply downward. (E33) Beyond the *continental edge* the ocean increases rapidly in depth.

continental rise The lower portion of the continental slope, extending to the ocean floor. (E33) The *continental rise* usually starts angling down to the ocean floor about a mile beneath the ocean.

continental shelf The sloping shelf of land, consisting of the edges of the continents under the ocean. (E32) The *continental shelf* can extend hundreds of miles out into the ocean.

continental slope The steep clifflike drop from the continental edge to the ocean floor. (E33) The *continental slope* connects the continental shelf with the ocean bottom.

convection (kən vek'shən) The process by which heat energy is transferred through liquids or gases by the movement of particles. (B39) The pie in the oven was heated by *convection*.

convection current The path along which energy is transferred during convection. (B39) Scientists think that *convection currents* in the mantle cause Earth's tectonic plates to move.

convergent boundary (kən vʉr'jənt boun'də rē) A place where the plates that make up Earth's crust and upper mantle move together. (B40) Layers of rock may bend or break at a *convergent boundary*.

Coriolis effect (kôr ē ō'lis e fekt') The tendency of a body or fluid moving across Earth's surface to have a curving motion due to Earth's rotation. (E56) The *Coriolis effect* causes air and water currents to move to the right in the Northern Hemisphere and to the left in the Southern Hemisphere.

crest The top of a wave. (E65) The *crest* of the wave seemed to tower over the surfer.

crust The thin outer layer of Earth. (B19) Earth's *crust* varies from 5 km to 48 km in thickness.

current Great rivers of water moving through the ocean. (E55) The *current* pulled the boat away from shore.

cytoplasm (sīt'ō plaz əm) The watery gel inside a cell. (A11) Various organelles are found inside the *cytoplasm* of a cell.

D

deceleration (dē sel ər ā'shən) A decrease in speed over time. (F23) Air resistance can cause the *deceleration* of objects.

density The amount of mass in a given volume of matter. (C13) Lead has a greater *density* than aluminum.

desalination (dē sal ə nā'shən) A process for obtaining fresh water from salt water by removing the salt. (E80) A few countries operate *desalination* plants, which obtain fresh water from ocean water.

diatom (dī'ə täm) A microscopic, one-celled alga with a glasslike cell wall. (A35) A single liter of sea water may contain millions of *diatoms*.

dietary fat A nutrient in food that provides energy. (G60) A small amount of *dietary fat* is part of a healthful diet.

diffusion (di fyōo'zhən) The tendency of substances to move from an area of greater concentration to an area of lesser concentration. (A16) Substances can pass in and out of cells by *diffusion*.

divergent boundary (di vʉr'jənt boun'də rē) A place where the plates that make up Earth's crust and upper mantle move away from one another. (B40) Most *divergent boundaries* are found on the floor of the ocean.

dome mountain A mountain formed when magma lifts Earth's surface, creating a broad dome, or bulge. (B47) Pikes Peak in Colorado is a *dome mountain*.

domesticated (dō mes'ti kāt əd) Tamed and/or bred to serve people's purposes. (D70) People breed *domesticated* animals such as horses for transportation and other uses.

dominant gene (däm'ə nənt jēn) A gene that has control over how a trait is expressed. (G14) A *dominant gene* will be expressed when paired with a recessive gene.

dominant trait (däm'ə nənt trāt) A trait that if inherited, will be expressed. (D45) Gregor Mendel found that tallness was a *dominant trait* in pea plants.

drag A force that resists forward motion through a fluid; it operates in the direction opposite to thrust. (F111) The air causes *drag* on an airplane.

earthquake A shaking or movement of Earth's surface, caused by the release of stored energy along a fault. (B58) Many *earthquakes* occur near the boundaries between tectonic plates.

egg A female sex cell. (G9) In sexual reproduction an *egg* is fertilized by a sperm.

electron (ē lek'trän) A negatively charged particle in an atom. (C71) The number of *electrons* in an atom usually equals the number of protons.

element (el'ə mənt) A substance that cannot be broken down into any other substance by ordinary chemical means. (C34) Oxygen, hydrogen, copper, iron, and carbon are *elements*.

embryo (em'brē ō) An early stage in the development of an organism. (G10) A fertilized egg develops into an *embryo*.

endangered species A species of animal or plant whose number has become so small that the species is in danger of becoming extinct. (D25) The rhinoceros has become an *endangered species* because poachers slaughter the animals for their horns.

endocrine gland (en'dō krin gland) A gland that produces hormones and releases them directly into the bloodstream. (G22) The thyroid and the pituitary are *endocrine glands*.

environmental risk factor A health risk factor that results from a person's environment. (G53) Breathing smoke from other people's cigarettes is an *environmental risk factor*.

epicenter (ep'i sent ər) The point on Earth's surface directly above an earthquake's point of origin. (B65) The *epicenter* of the earthquake was 2 km north of the city.

era (er'ə) One of the major divisions of geologic time. (D59) Many kinds of mammals developed during the Cenozoic *Era*.

ethanol (eth'ə nôl) A kind of alcohol used to make medicines, food products, and various other items. (A42) *Ethanol* is a flammable liquid.

evaporation (ē vap ə rā'shən) The change of state from a liquid to a gas. (C27) Heat from the Sun caused the *evaporation* of the water.

evolution (ev ə lōō'shən) The idea that all living things are descended from earlier forms of life, with new species developing over time. (D58) According to the theory of *evolution*, the plants and animals alive today descended from organisms that lived millions of years ago.

extinct (ek stiŋkt') With reference to species, no longer in existence. (D25) Dinosaurs are *extinct*.

extinction (ek stiŋk'shən) The disappearance of species from Earth. (D62) Scientists do not agree about what caused the *extinction* of the dinosaurs.

fault A break in rock along which rock slabs have moved. (B65) The shifting of Earth's tectonic plates can produce a *fault*, along which earthquakes may occur.

fault-block mountain A mountain formed when masses of rock move up or down along a fault. (B47) Mountains in the Great Rift Valley of Africa are *fault-block mountains*.

fermentation (fur mən tā'shən) A chemical change in which an organism breaks down sugar to produce carbon dioxide and alcohol or lactic acid. (A19, A42) The chemist used yeast to cause *fermentation* in the sugary liquid.

fertilization (fur tə li zā'shən) The process by which a sperm and an egg unite to form a cell that will develop into a new individual. (D24, G9) In humans, *fertilization* produces a cell containing 46 chromosomes, half from the female and half from the male.

fetus (fēt′əs) A stage in the development of an organism that follows the embryo stage. (G10) After about eight weeks, a human embryo is called a *fetus*.

first law of motion The concept that objects at rest tend to remain at rest and objects in motion tend to remain in motion, traveling at a constant speed and in the same direction. (F59) According to the *first law of motion*, a stationary object will stay in place unless some force makes it move.

fission (fish′ən) A method of asexual reproduction in which a parent cell divides to form two new cells. (A51, D10) Many one-celled organisms, such as amoebas, reproduce by *fission*.

focus (fō′kəs) The point, or place, at which an earthquake begins. (B65) The *focus* of the earthquake was about 20 km beneath Earth's surface.

folded mountain A mountain formed when two tectonic plates collide. (B45) The Alps and the Himalayas are *folded mountains*.

food pyramid A model showing the relative amounts of different kinds of food a person should eat each day for a healthful diet. (G59) Grains, including breads, cereals, rice, and pasta, make up the base of the *food pyramid*.

force A push or a pull. (F33, F65) The *force* of friction caused the rolling wagon to slow and then stop.

fossil (fäs′əl) The remains or traces of a living thing, usually preserved in rock. (D56) *Fossils* are usually found in sedimentary rock.

freezing The change of state from a liquid to a solid. (C28) The *freezing* of water occurs at 0°C.

friction (frik′shən) The rubbing of one thing against another. The force of friction resists motion between two surfaces that are in contact with each other. (F73) *Friction* keeps a car's tires from slipping off the road.

fungus (fuŋ′gəs) Any of a large group of organisms that feed on dead organisms or that are parasitic. (A43, G40) A mushroom is a *fungus*.

gene (jēn) One of the units that make up a chromosome; genes determine the traits an offspring inherits from its parent or parents. (D35, G13) Half of your *genes* come from your mother, and half come from your father.

gene splicing (jēn splīs′iŋ) A process by which genes are manipulated to alter the function or nature of an organism, usually by being transferred from one organism to another. (D48) Through *gene splicing*, scientists have transferred a gene for making insulin from one organism to another.

genetic engineering (jə net′ik en jə-nir′iŋ) The process by which genes are manipulated to bring about biological change in species. (D47) Using *genetic engineering* techniques, scientists have successfully combined DNA from different organisms.

gravity (grav′i tē) The force that pulls objects toward Earth; also, the attractive force exerted by a body or object on other bodies or objects. (F33) *Gravity* causes a ball to fall to the ground after it is thrown into the air.

health risk factor An action or condition that increases the probability of getting a disease or becoming injured. (G52) Smoking cigarettes and living in an area with severe water pollution are two *health risk factors*.

heat Energy that flows from warmer to cooler regions of matter. (C26) *Heat* can cause matter to change from one state to another.

hereditary risk factor A health risk factor that is passed on through genes from parent to child. (G52) A family history of heart disease is a *hereditary risk factor*.

hormone (hôr′mōn) A chemical substance that acts as a messenger, causing a change in organs and tissues in the body. (G23) Growth *hormones* are released by the pituitary gland.

hot spot A place deep within Earth's mantle that is extremely hot and contains a chamber of magma. (B102) Magma rising from a *hot spot* can break through Earth's crust to form a volcano.

immune system (im myōōn′ sis′təm) The body's system that defends the body against pathogens. (A59, G33) The *immune system* produces antibodies to fight disease.

immunity (im myōōn′i tē) The body's resistance to a disease or infection. (G35) Polio vaccine gives people *immunity* to the disease.

incomplete dominance (in kəm-plēt′ däm′ə nəns) The expression of both genes (traits) in a pair, producing a blended effect. (D46) A plant with pink flowers, produced by crossing a plant having red flowers with a plant having white flowers, is an example of *incomplete dominance*.

indicator (in'di kāt ər) A substance that changes color when mixed with an acid or a base. (C81) Paper treated with an *indicator* is used to test whether a compound is an acid or a base.

inertia (in ur'shə) The tendency of matter to remain at rest if at rest, or if in motion, to remain in motion in the same direction. (F59) *Inertia* results in passengers in a car moving forward when the driver applies the brakes.

inflammation (in flə mā'shən) A defense response by a part of the body, resulting from infection, injury, or irritation and marked by such symptoms as redness, pain, and swelling. (G33) The boy developed an *inflammation* where he had scraped his knee.

inherited trait (in her'it əd trāt) A trait that is passed on from parents to offspring by means of genes. (D34) Eye color is an *inherited trait*.

ion (ī'ən) An electrically charged atom. Ions form when atoms lose or gain electrons. (C73) A negative *ion* is formed when an atom gains electrons.

island arc A chain of volcanoes formed from magma that rises as a result of an oceanic plate sinking into the mantle. (B96) The Philippine Islands are part of an *island arc*.

kinetic energy (ki net'ik en'ər jē) Energy of motion. (C25) A ball rolling down a hill has *kinetic energy*.

lava (lä'və) Magma that flows out onto Earth's surface from a volcano. (B86) Flaming *lava* poured down the sides of the volcanic mountain.

law of conservation of mass The principle that states that matter can neither be created nor destroyed by a chemical or physical change. (C75) According to the *law of conservation of mass*, burning a log will not destroy any of the log's original mass.

law of conservation of momentum The principle that states that momentum can be transferred but cannot be lost. (F86) The *law of conservation of momentum* explains why the momentum resulting from the collision of two objects equals the total momentum of the objects before they collided.

learned trait (lurnd trāt) A trait that is acquired through learning or experience. (D36) The ability to speak Spanish is a *learned trait*.

lift The upward force, resulting from differences in air pressure above and below an airplane's wings, that causes the airplane to rise. (F111) Increasing the size of an airplane's wings increases *lift*.

lithosphere (lith'ō sfir) The solid, rocky layer of Earth, including the crust and top part of the mantle. (B38) The *lithosphere* is about 100 km thick.

magma (mag'mə) The hot, molten rock deep inside Earth. (B86) The *magma* rose through the volcano.

magnetic field (mag net'ik fēld) The space around a magnet within which the force of the magnet is exerted. (B28) The magnet attracted all the iron filings within its *magnetic field*.

magnetic reversal (mag net'ik ri-vur'səl) The switching or changing of Earth's magnetic poles such that the north magnetic pole becomes located at the south magnetic pole's position and vice versa. (B28) Scientists have found evidence of *magnetic reversals* in layers of rock along the ocean floor.

magnitude (mag'nə tōōd) The force or strength of an earthquake. (B59) *Magnitude* is a measure of the amount of energy released by an earthquake.

mantle The middle layer of Earth. (B19) The *mantle* is the thick layer of rock between the crust and the core.

mass The amount of matter in an object. (C10, F33) A large rock has more *mass* than a pebble.

matter Anything that has mass and takes up space. (C10) Rocks, water, and air are three kinds of *matter*.

meiosis (mī ō'sis) The process of cell division by which the number of chromosomes in sex cells is reduced to half the number in body cells. (D22) Because of *meiosis*, a sex cell in a human has only 23 chromosomes instead of 46.

melting The change of state from a solid to a liquid. (C27) The *melting* of the icicles began after sunrise.

menstrual cycle (men′strəl sī′kəl) A cycle of approximately 28 days during which an egg is released by the ovary and, if not fertilized, leaves the body with other tissue and blood. (G24) The *menstrual cycle* begins when a girl reaches puberty.

metric system A system of measurement based on a few defined units (such as the meter) and in which larger and smaller units are related by powers of 10. (F11) In the *metric system*, a centimeter is 10 times longer than a millimeter.

microorganism (mī krō ôr′gən iz-əm) An organism too small to be seen except with the aid of a microscope. (G40) Bacteria are *microorganisms*.

mid-ocean ridge A chain of mountains under the ocean. (B22, E34) The *mid-ocean ridge* extends almost 60,000 km.

mitochondria (mīt ō kän′drē ə) Cell organelles in which energy is released from food. (A11) The more *mitochondria* a cell has, the more energy it can release from food.

mitosis (mī tō′sis) The process in which one cell divides to form two identical new cells. (A23) The new cells formed by *mitosis* have the same number of chromosomes as the parent cell.

mixture A combination of two or more substances that can be separated by physical means. (C34) This jar contains a *mixture* of colored beads.

model Something used or made to represent an object or an idea. (C71) The plastic *model* showed the structure of the heart.

mold fossil (mōld fäs′əl) A fossil consisting of a hollowed space in the shape of an organism or one of its parts. (D56) Sediments collecting around a dead organism may lead to the formation of a *mold fossil* of the organism.

molecule (mäl′i kyōōl) A particle made up of a group of atoms that are chemically bonded. (C39) A *molecule* of water contains three atoms.

momentum (mō men′təm) A property of a moving object, calculated by multiplying the object's mass by its velocity. (F85) The train gathered *momentum* as its speed increased.

moneran (män′ər an) Any of mostly one-celled organisms in which the cell does not have a nucleus. (A50) Bacteria are *monerans*.

mucus (myōō′kəs) A thick, sticky fluid that lines the membranes of the respiratory system. (G33) *Mucus* helps trap particles that you breathe in.

multicellular (mul ti sel′yōō lər) Made up of more than one cell. (A33) Some protists are *multicellular*.

mutation (myōō tā′shən) A change in a gene that can result in a new characteristic, or trait. (D76) Certain *mutations* have helped species survive in their environment.

natural selection (nach′ər əl sə-lek′shən) The process by which those living things that have characteristics adapting them to their environment tend to live longest and produce the most offspring, passing on these favorable characteristics to their offspring. (D75) *Natural selection* helps explain why certain characteristics become common while others die out.

neap tide (nēp tīd) The tide occurring at the first and third quarters of the Moon, when the difference in level between high and low tide is smallest. (E71) *Neap tides* occur at two times during a month.

nekton (nek′tän) All the free-swimming animals that live in the ocean. (E25) *Nekton* include such animals as fish, octopuses, and whales.

neutralization (nōō trəl ī zā′shən) The reaction between an acid and a base. (C83) *Neutralization* produces water and a salt.

neutron (nōō′trän) A particle in the nucleus of an atom that has no electric charge. (C71) The mass of a *neutron* is about equal to that of a proton.

newton (nōō′tən) A unit used to measure force. (F66) A *newton* is the force needed to accelerate a one-kilogram object by one meter per second every second.

nuclear fission (nōō′klē ər fish′ən) The splitting of the nucleus of an atom, releasing great amounts of energy. (C77) Bombarding a nucleus with a neutron can cause *nuclear fission*.

nuclear membrane The structure that surrounds and encloses the nucleus and controls what substances move into and out of the nucleus. (A11) The *nuclear membrane* appears to be solid, but it actually has tiny holes through which materials can pass.

nucleus (nōō′klē əs) 1. The dense, central part of an atom. (C71) The *nucleus* contains nearly all of an atom's mass. 2. The control center of a cell. (A11) The *nucleus* contains the cell's genetic information.

obese (ō bēs′) More than 20 percent over normal body weight. (G60) *Obese* people have more health problems than people of normal weight.

organ A part of an multicellular organism made up of a group of tissues that work together to perform a certain function. (A26) The heart and the lungs are *organs* of the human body.

organ system A group of organs that work together to perform one or more functions. (A26) The stomach and the intestines are part of the *organ system* that digests food.

osmosis (äs mō'sis) The diffusion of water through a membrane. (A16) *Osmosis* maintains the balance of water inside and outside a cell.

paleontologist) (pā lē ən täl'ə jist) A scientist who studies fossils. (D58) A team of *paleontologists* discovered the remains of a dinosaur.

Pangaea (pan jē'ə) A supercontinent that existed about 200 million years ago. (B9) *Pangaea* broke apart into several continents.

pathogen (path'ə jən) A microorganism that can cause a disease. (G40) A virus is a *pathogen*.

period 1. A division of geologic time that is a subdivision of an era. (D59) The Jurassic *Period* is part of the Mesozoic Era. 2. The interval of time between two successive wave crests. (E65) The *period* for the ocean waves was about ten seconds.

petrification (pe tri fi kā'shən) The changing of the hard parts of a dead organism to stone. (D57) Fossils of trees have been preserved by *petrification*.

photosynthesis (fōt ō sin'thə sis) The process by which green plants and other producers use light energy to make food. (A18, E24) In *photosynthesis*, plant cells use light energy to make glucose from carbon dioxide and water.

physical change A change in size, shape, or state of matter, with no new kind of matter being formed. (C68) The freezing of water into ice cubes is an example of a *physical change*.

physical properties (fiz'i kəl präp'ər tēz) Characteristics of matter that can be measured or detected by the senses. (C34) Color is a *physical property* of minerals.

phytoplankton (fīt ō plaŋk'tən) Any of the usually microscopic plantlike protists that live near the surface of the ocean. (E11) *Phytoplankton* drift with the ocean currents.

plankton (plaŋk'tən) Organisms, generally microscopic in size, that float or drift in the ocean. (A35, E11) *Plankton* is a source of food for fish.

plate One of the slabs that make up Earth's crust and upper mantle; also called *tectonic plate*. (B19) Some of Earth's *plates* carry continents.

plate boundary A place where the plates that make up Earth's crust and upper mantle either move together or apart or else move past one another. (B20, B40) Earthquakes occur along *plate boundaries*.

pollution The contamination of the environment with waste materials or other unwanted substances. (E91) Dangerous chemicals dumped into the ocean are one source of *pollution*.

polymer (päl'ə mər) A compound consisting of large molecules formed from many smaller, linked molecules. (C92) Proteins are *polymers*.

protist (prōt'ist) Any of a large group of mostly single-celled, microscopic organisms. (A33) Amoebas and algae are *protists*.

proton (prō'tän) A positively charged particle found in the nucleus of an atom. (C71) The atomic number of an atom equals the number of *protons* in the atom's nucleus.

protozoan (prō tō zō'ən) Protists that have animal-like traits. (A34, G40) A paramecium is a *protozoan*.

puberty (pyoo'bər tē) The state of physical development when a person becomes capable of producing offspring. (G22) Girls generally reach *puberty* earlier than boys.

radioactive element (rā dē ō ak'tiv el'ə mənt) An element made up of atoms whose nuclei break down, or decay, into nuclei of other atoms. (C76) As the nucleus of a *radioactive element* decays, energy is released.

reaction force The force exerted in response to an action force. (F92) A *reaction force* is equal in strength to an action force but opposite in direction.

recessive gene (ri ses'iv jēn) A gene that is able to control how a trait is expressed only when paired with another recessive gene. (G14) A *recessive gene* will not be expressed when paired with a dominant gene.

recessive trait (ri ses'iv trāt) A trait that will be hidden if paired with a dominant trait. (D45) In his experiments with pea plants, Gregor Mendel learned that shortness was a *recessive trait*.

reproduction The process by which organisms produce more of their own kind. (D10) *Reproduction* ensures the survival of the species.

Richter scale (rik'tər skāl) A scale of numbers by which the magnitude of earthquakes is measured. (B59) Each increase of 1.0 on the *Richter scale* represents an increase of 30 times in the energy released by an earthquake.

rifting (rift'iŋ) The process by which magma rises to fill the gap between two plates that are moving apart. (B108) *Rifting* in eastern Africa may split the continent into two parts.

salinity (sə lin'ə tē) The total amount of dissolved salts in ocean water. (E9) The *salinity* of the ocean varies in different parts of the world.

salt A compound that can be formed when an acid reacts with a base. (C83) When vinegar and baking soda interact, they produce a *salt*.

saprophyte (sap'rə fīt) An organism that lives on dead or decaying matter. (A44) Molds are *saprophytes*.

sea-floor spreading The process by which new ocean floor is continually being formed as magma rises to the surface and hardens into rock. (B30) *Sea-floor spreading* occurs as magma fills the space between separating plates.

seamount (sē'mount) An underwater mountain that formed from a volcano. (E34) Thousands of *seamounts* rise from the floor of the Pacific.

second law of motion The concept that an object's acceleration is related to the strength of the force acting on it and on the object's mass. (F65) A gust of wind blowing an open umbrella out of your hands illustrates the *second law of motion*.

seismograph (sīz'mə graf) An instrument that records the intensity, duration, and nature of earthquake waves. (B74) Scientists use information from *seismographs* to determine the location of earthquakes.

seismometer (sīz mäm'ə tər) An instrument that detects and records Earth's movements. (B98) Data from the *seismometer* suggested that a volcanic eruption might soon occur.

selective breeding Breeding of living things to produce offspring with certain desired characteristics. (D70) People have used *selective breeding* to produce domesticated animals.

sex cell A female or male reproductive cell; an egg cell or sperm cell. (D22) Reproduction can occur when *sex cells* unite.

sexual reproduction Reproduction that involves the joining of a male sex cell and a female sex cell. (D22, G9) Most animals and plants produce offspring through *sexual reproduction*.

shield volcano A kind of volcano that is large and gently sloped and that is formed when lava flows quietly from a crack in the Earth's crust. (B89) Mauna Loa, a *shield volcano* in Hawaii, is the largest volcano on Earth.

solute (säl'yoot) The material present in the smaller amount in a solution; the substance dissolved in a solution. (C57) If you dissolve sugar in water, sugar is the *solute*.

solution A mixture in which the different particles are spread evenly throughout the mixture. (C57) Dissolving salt in water makes a *solution*.

solvent (säl'vənt) The material present in the greater amount in a solution; the substance in a solution, usually a liquid, that dissolves another substance. (C57) If you mix sugar and water, water is the *solvent*.

speed The distance traveled in a certain amount of time; rate of movement. (F16) The truck was moving at a *speed* of 40 mph.

sperm (spurm) A male sex cell. (G9) A *sperm* combines with an egg during fertilization.

spore A reproductive cell that can develop into a new organism. (A43) Ferns and mushrooms produce *spores*.

spring tide A tide occurring at or just after the new moon and full moon; usually the highest tide of the month. (E71) At the time of a *spring tide*, both the Sun and the Moon are in line with Earth.

state of matter Any of the three forms that matter may take: solid, liquid, or gas. (C20) Water's *state of matter* depends on its temperature.

substance Matter of a particular kind, or chemical makeup. (C34) Elements and compounds are *substances*.

symbiosis (sim bī ō'sis) A relationship between two organisms in which at least one organism benefits. (A61) Some fungi and algae grow together in *symbiosis*.

tectonic plate *See* plate.

temperature A measure of the average kinetic energy of the particles in matter. (C26) Water *temperature* rises as the motion of water molecules increases.

theory of continental drift A theory that states that the continents formed a single land mass at one time in the past and have drifted over time to their present positions. (B10) The idea of *continental drift* was first suggested by Alfred Wegener.

theory of plate tectonics The theory that Earth's lithosphere is broken into enormous slabs, or plates, that are in motion. (B19, B41) Scientists use the *theory of plate tectonics* to explain how Earth's continents drift.

third law of motion The concept that for every action force there is an equal and opposite reaction force. (F92) When you watch someone's feet bouncing off a trampoline, you see the *third law of motion* at work.

thrust (thrust) The push or driving force that causes an airplane, rocket, or other object to move forward. (F110) *Thrust* can be produced by a spinning propeller or by a jet engine.

tide The daily rise and fall of the surface of the ocean or other large body of water, caused by the gravitational attraction of the Moon and the Sun. (E70) As the *tide* came in, we moved our blanket back from the water's edge.

tissue A group of similar, specialized cells working together to carry out the same function. (A25) Muscle *tissue* contains cells that contract.

toxin (täks'in) A poison produced by an organism. (A58) *Toxins* produced by bacteria can cause serious illness.

trade wind A prevailing wind that blows from east to west on either side of the equator. (E56) South of the equator, the *trade wind* comes from the southeast.

transform-fault boundary (transfôrm' fôlt' boun'də rē) A place where the plates that make up Earth's crust and upper mantle move past one another. (B41) Movement occurring at a *transform-fault boundary* may cause cracks to form in Earth's rocks.

tsunami (tsoo nä'mē) A large and powerful ocean wave usually caused by an underwater earthquake. (B76) A *tsunami* can cause great destruction if it strikes a land area.

turbidity current (tur bid'i tē kur'ənt) A current of water carrying large amounts of sediment. (E38, E61) *Turbidity currents* may cause sediment to build up in some places.

upper mantle (up'ər man'təl) The outermost part of the mantle. (B20) Earth's plates consist of a thin layer of crust lying over the *upper mantle*.

upwelling The rising of deep water to the surface that occurs when winds move surface water. (E60) *Upwelling* brings pieces of shells and dead organisms up from the ocean floor.

vaccine (vak sēn') A preparation of dead or weakened bacteria or viruses that produces immunity to a disease. (A59, G35) The *vaccine* for smallpox has eliminated that disease.

vacuole (vak'yoo ōl) A structure in the cytoplasm in which food and other substances are stored. (A11) A *vacuole* in a plant cell is often quite large.

vegetative propagation (vej ə tāt'iv präp ə gā'shən) A form of asexual reproduction in which a new plant develops from a part of a parent plant. (D15) Using a cutting taken from a houseplant to grow a new plant is a method of *vegetative propagation*.

velocity (və läs'ə tē) The rate of motion in a particular direction. (F21) The *velocity* was northwest at 880 km/h.

virus (vī'rəs) A tiny disease-causing life form consisting of genetic material wrapped inside a capsule of protein. (A52, G40) *Viruses* cause such diseases as AIDS, chickenpox, and rabies.

volcano An opening in Earth's crust through which hot gases, rock fragments, and molten rock erupt. (B48, B86) Lava flowed out of the *volcano*.

volume (väl'yoom) The amount of space that matter takes up. (C11) A large fuel tank holds a greater *volume* of gasoline than a small tank.

wave The up-and-down movement of the surface of water, caused by the wind. (E65) Ocean *waves* crashed against the shoreline.

wavelength The distance between the crests of two successive waves. (E65) At the height of the storm, the waves had a *wavelength* of 10 m.

weight A measure of the force of gravity on an object. (F33) The *weight* of this package is five pounds.

westerly (wes'tər lē) A prevailing wind that blows from west to east. (E56) Ships that sailed from North America to Europe were aided by the power of the *westerlies*.

zooplankton (zō ō plaŋk'tən) Any of the tiny animal-like organisms that live near the surface of the ocean. (E11) Zooplankton float in the sea.

zygote (zī'gōt) A fertilized egg cell. (D24, G10) A *zygote* develops into an embryo by means of cell division.

INDEX

*Activity
Blue entries indicate Teaching Guide material.

Bioprospector, C62
Demolition expert, F78
Geological oceanographer, B4
Geophysicist, B34
Glaciologist, C4
Humor educator, G4
Immunologist, G28
Marine biologist, E4
Marine engineer, E28
Mycologist, A28
Obstetrician, D4
Paleontologist, D50
Pharmacist, G48
Phlebotomist, A4
Pilot, F28
Plant geneticist, D28
Research biologist, A46
Safety engineer, F52
Seismologist, B52, E50
Volcanologist, B82
Water treatment technician,
  C30
Cell(s), A6–A25, D8–D9*, D11,
  D18–D19*, D20–D21*,
  D22–D24, D34–D35, D39*,
  D40–D41*, D45, D47, G8*,
  G9, G23
  animal, A8*, A9–A10, A12,
    A18–A19
  blood, D22, D24
  bone, D22, D24
  differentiation of, A25–A26
  division of, A20–A21*, A23,
    A25
  egg, D18–D19*, D20–D21*,
    D22, D24, D34–D35, D39*,
    D40–D41*, D44, G8*, G9
  membranes of, A6–A7*, A8*,
    A10–A11, A14–A15*, A16,
    A22, D11
  nuclei of, A7*, A9–A10, D22
  plant, A6–A7*, A8*, A9–A11,
    A12, A18–A19
  reproductive, D18–D19*,
    D21*, D22–D24
  skin, D22, D24
  sperm, D18–D19*,
    D20–D21*, D22, D24,
    D34–D35, D39*, D40–D41*,
    D44, G8*, G9, G23
  transport in, A16
  walls of, A2, A6
  wastes, A18, A22, A25

Centimeter, F11. See also
  Metric units.
Changes, C68–C69
  chemical, C69–C71
  physical, C68
Chemical(s), C20–C21, C34,
  C36, C40, C46*, C64–C65*,
  C66*, C67*, C69–C71, C74,
  C86–C87*, C88–C89*, C90*,
  D10, D19*, D22, E80–E81,
  E93
  analysis of, C93
  bonding of, C74, C91
  changes in, C64–C65*, C66*,
    C67*, C69–C71
  coding of cells by, D10,
    D19*, D22
  equations for, C70
  forces, C20–C21
  formulas for, C40, C70
  mixtures of, C46*, C47*,
    C54*, C55*, C58,
    C64–C65*, C66*, C67*,
    C90*
  properties of, C34,
    C86–C87*, C88–C89*
  reactions, C70
  symbols for, C36
  synthesis of, C93–C94
Chemical reactions, C70,
  C93–C94
Chemistry, C93
Chemists, C93
Childhood, G20
Chlorella, A35
Chlorine, C40, C73
Chlorophyll, A18, A34–A35,
  A37
Chloroplast, A6, A9, A18,
  A32. See also Cells.
Cholesterol, C41, G60
Chromosomes, A10, A23,
  D18–D19*, D20–D21*,
  D22–D24, D35, D44, D47,
  D76, G12–G14
Cilia, A36–A37, G33
Climate, B9, B11
  zones, B11
Coal, B10–B11
Cohesion, C58
Cold, A59

Collaborative Strategies
  A6, A14, A20, A30, A48,
  A57, B6, B16, B18, B22,
  B23, B36, B42, B44, B54,
  B62, B70, B72, B94, C6,
  C9, C16, C18, C22, C32,
  C33, C44, C46, C47, C54,
  C55, C64, C66, C80, C86,
  C88, C90, D6, D8, D30,
  D38, D40, D64, E6, E14,
  E16, E22, E30, E31, E40,
  E42, E52, E54, E62, E64,
  E68, E77, E78, E88, E90,
  F6, F12, F18, F20, F30,
  F37, F42, F44, F54, F62,
  F64, F72, F80, F82, F90,
  F96, F106, F108, F116,
  F120, F122, G8, G31, G58
Collisions, F80–F81*,
  F82–F83*, F84–F85
Comets, E37
Compass, B28–B29
Compounds, C34, C39–C41,
  C49, C78–C79*, C80*,
  C81–C83, C91, C94
Condensation, C28
Conifers, B13
Conservation of mass, law of,
  C75
Conservation of momentum,
  law of, F86–F87
Continent, B6–B7*, B8,
  B11–B12, B14–B15, B19
Continental drift, B6*, B8–B12
Continental rise, E34
Continental shelf, B8, B10,
  E32–E33
Continental slope, E33
Convection, B39–B40
Convection current, B39–B40
Copper, E81
Coriolis effect, E56
Critical Thinking Processes
  Analyzing, A1h, B1h, C1h,
    D1h, E1h, F1h, G1h
  Applying, A1h, B1h, C1h,
    D1h, E1h, F1h, G1h
  Evaluating, A1h, B1h, C1h,
    D1h, E1h, F1h, G1h
  Expressing Ideas, A1h, B1h,
    C1h, D1h, E1h, F1h, G1h
  Generating Ideas, A1h, B1h,
    C1h, D1h, E1h, F1h, G1h

*Activity
Blue entries indicate Teaching Guide material.

*Activity
Blue entries indicate Teaching Guide material.

health, G52
hereditary, G52
Rivers, E91, E93
Rock, D56, E81, E86
Rockets, F112
Rust, C69

Salinity, E9
Salt, C83, E8–E10, E80
San Andreas Fault, B41, B58–B60
Sandstone, B10
Saprophytes, A44
Sargasso Sea, E53
Sargassum, A35
Science in Literature
A17, A36, B30, B46, B66, B91, C7, C38, C70, D12, D43, D67, E15, E35, E66, E92, F10, F34, F74, F92, F112, G24, G34, G60
Science Process Skills
Classifying, A1g, B1g, C1g, D1g, E1g, F1g, G1g
Collecting, Recording, and Interpreting Data, A1g, B1g, C1g, D1g, E1g, F1g, G1g
Communicating, A1g, B1g, C1g, D1g, E1g, F1g, G1g
Defining Operationally, A1g, B1g, C1g, D1g, E1g, F1g, G1g
Experimenting, A1g, B1g, C1g, D1g, E1g, F1g, G1g
Identifying and Controlling Variables, A1g, B1g, C1g, D1g, E1g, F1g, G1g
Inferring, A1g, B1g, C1g, D1g, E1g, F1g, G1g
Making and Using Models, A1g, B1g, C1g, D1g, E1g, F1g, G1g
Making Hypotheses, A1g, B1g, C1g, D1g, E1g, F1g, G1g
Measuring/Using Numbers, A1g, B1g, C1g, D1g, E1g, F1g, G1g
Observing, A1g, B1g, C1g, D1g, E1g, F1g, G1g

Predicting, A1g, B1g, C1g, D1g, E1g, F1g, G1g
Science, Technology & Society
A16, A23, A42, A50, B13, B46, B66, B78, B79, B98, B104, B106, C39, C74 , C91, D15, D22, D34, D70, E10, E24, E33, E43, E47, E57, E79, E83, E93, F24, F48, F60, F92, F100, G16, G22, G45
Scientific Reasoning Skills
Consideration of Consequences, A1h, B1h, C1h, D1h, E1h, F1h, G1h
Consideration of Premises, A1h, B1h, C1h, D1h, E1h, F1h, G1h
Demand for Verification, A1h, B1h, C1h, D1h, E1h, F1h, G1h
Longing to Know and Understand, A1h, B1h, C1h, D1h, E1h, F1h, G1h
Questioning of Scientific Assumptions, A1h, B1h, C1h, D1h, E1h, F1h, G1h
Respect for Historical Contributions, A1h, B1h, C1h, D1h, E1h, F1h, G1h
Respect for Logic, A1h, B1h, C1h, D1h, E1h, F1h, G1h
Search for Data and Its Meaning, A1h, B1h, C1h, D1h, E1h, F1h, G1h
Scuba, E17, F126
Sea, E76*, E91. See also Ocean(s).
Sea floor. See Ocean(s), floor of.
Sea rockets, B90
Seafood, E79
Seamounts, E33–E34
Seat belts, F60–F61
Seaweed, A34–A35, E81, E86
Secchi disk, E12–E13*
Sediments, E31*, E36–E37, E61, E81, E86
Selective breeding, D70–D71
Self-pollination, D45
Seismograph, B68–B69*, B74–B75

Seismologists, B60, E50
Seismometer, B98
Sewage, A62
Sexual characteristics, secondary, G23–G24
Sexual reproduction, D10, D18*, D22, D24, G9
Sharks, E15, E35
Sierra Nevada range, B43
Sloths, D50
Sodium, C40, C73
Sodium chloride, C40, C73
Soil, B27
Solids, C20, C25, C27, C33*
    converted from liquids, C67*
    converting to liquids, C33*
Solute, C57
Solutions, C52–C53*, C57–C60
Solvent, C57
Sonar, B24–B25*, B26–B27, E42*, E43, E74, E79
Sound, B26–B27
South America, B10–B11, B13–B15
Space shuttle, F118–F119
Species, D10, D25
    endangered, D25
    survival of, D25
Speed, F12–F13, F15–F19, F20*
    averaging, F16
    calculating, F12–F13
    definition of, F16
    measuring, F12–F13
    of pendulum, F20*
    predicting, F12–F13
    racing, F15
    recording, F12–F13
    and stress, F17
Spirogyra, A32, A35
Spores, A43
Spring tides, E71
Stages of growth, G18*, G19*, G20–G21
Standards and Benchmarks
See National Science Education Standards and Project 2061 Benchmarks
Sterilization, A54
Stolons, A43
Students Acquiring English
A6, A10, A12, A18, A20,